Experimental Design and Methods

Experimental Design and Methods

Michael S. Lewis-Beck
editor

International Handbooks of Quantitative Applications in the Social Sciences
Volume 3

SAGE Publications
Toppan Publishing

Published by Toppan Company, with the cooperation of Sage Publications, Inc.

This volume is an updated version of previously published volumes of
SAGE **UNIVERSITY** PAPERS: Quantitative Applications in the Social Sciences series.

For information address:

SAGE Publications Ltd
6 Bonhill Street
London EC2A 4PU
United Kingdom

SAGE Publications, Inc.
2455 Teller Road
Thousand Oaks, California 91320
United States

SAGE Publications India Pvt. Ltd.
M-32 Market
Greater Kailash I
New Delhi 110 048 India

Printed in Singapore

British Library Cataloguing in Publication Data

Main entry under title:

Experimental Design and Methods.—(International
Handbooks of Quantitative Applications in
the Social Sciences; Vol. 3)
I. Lewis-Beck, Michael S. II. Series
300.72
ISBN 0-8039-5429-8

93 94 95 96 97 10 9 8 7 6 5 4 3 2 1

Sage Production Editor: Astrid Virding

CONTENTS

EDITOR'S INTRODUCTION

In the social sciences, there are two broad traditions of research: experimental and nonexperimental. While both seek to explain human behavior, they differ critically in the amount of control they have over the data. Simply put, experimentalists manipulate variables suspected of producing an effect, while nonexperimentalists observe them. (For nonexperimentalists, regression analysis is the leading method; see **International Handbooks**, Volume 2.) Experiments have the advantage, at least in principle, of permitting causal inferences to be made with more confidence. The argument seems compelling: actual alteration of the values on independent variable *X* is followed by systematic change in dependent variable *Y*; therefore, *X* must somehow "cause" *Y*. Of course, things are not that easy. The experimental design and analysis must be properly conducted, before strong inference is feasible. The chapters in this volume, each written by an established expert, give the reader thorough instruction in experimental method.

In order to establish the effect of *X* on *Y*, early experimenters often sought physical control of extraneous factors. A primary difficulty with this strategy was that one could never be sure all the confounding factors had been controlled. Thus, any positive result might still be attributable to a relevant omitted variable that was not "held constant." Modern experimentalists have solved this problem by *randomization*. That is, subjects are randomly assigned to treatment. In this way, the confounding effects of the many possible other factors statistically cancel out. Hence, the analyst can, with a known degree of certainty, attribute an effect to the manipulation. Experimental designs, from the simple to the complex, are ably evaluated in the first chapter, by Spector.

The most elementary—the *two-group design*—illustrates well the general logic. In a two-group design, there is an independent variable with two categories (representing two different treatment groups), and a metric dependent variable (taking on response values along an interval). Subjects are randomly assigned to one group or the other, then their scores on the dependent variable are measured. To gain an appreciation of the method, I develop a practical example.

Suppose Professor Janet Green, an educational psychologist, hypothesizes that Mathematics Achievement (*Y*) among 5th grade students is influenced by Student Work Style (*X*). The independent variable, *X* has two categories: experimental and control. For the experimental, labelled the Cooperative group, students receive specific instructions encouraging them to help each other with in-class learning exercises. For the control, labelled the Independent group, students receive the instructions they always have, which is to work strictly on their own during in-class learning exercises. The 100 students in the study are assigned randomly to one group or the other, with 50 in each. After the treatment period, a standard math test (with a theoretical score range of 0-100) is administered to them, in order to measure dependent variable *Y*. Professor Green computes the mean math scores for the Cooperative group and the Independent group, and observes that the Independent group score is higher. She goes on to apply a *t*-test to this *difference of means,* and finds the difference is statistically significant at .05. The clear implication is that the Cooperative Student Work Style fails to improve Mathematics Achievement.

The second chapter, by Brown and Melamed, moves the discussion of experimentation from design to data analysis, beginning the latter with the *t*-test for the two-group design. They then rewrite the presentation in *analysis of variance (ANOVA)* terms. As Iversen and Norpoth note, in the third chapter, the *t*-test for difference of means is really just a special case of ANOVA. This is an important generalization, strengthening the role of ANOVA as the baseline methodology in experimental research. Whenever the experimenter has a single, metric dependent variable and a nominal independent variable (two or more categories), then ANOVA is the standard procedure.

In the above example, Professor Green had only two categories for the independent variable. But suppose, in a follow-up study, she expands to three categories, adding another treatment group labelled Competitive (i.e., students receive explicit instructions to work to obtain the top marks on math exams). After properly gathering the experimental data, she could carry out ANOVA to analyze the differences in mean scores across the groups. This would be called a *one-way ANOVA,* since there is one independent variable (Student Work Style). However, it may be that Professor Green is also interested in the effects of a second independent variable, labelled Homework (students either are assigned special math work to be done at home, or are not). Thus, she might turn to a *factorial design,* to be analyzed in a *two-way ANOVA.*

As versatile as ANOVA is, it is not the last word in the analysis of experimental data. The fourth chapter, by Wildt and Ahtola, offers an extension to the *analysis of covariance (ANCOVA).* Whereas ANOVA handles only categorical independent variables, ANCOVA can handle categorical independent variables plus a metric variable, a *covariate.* In an experiment, there may exist a metric variable that influences the dependent variable, thus making it more difficult to tease out the effect of the treatment. For such a case, ANCOVA would adjust the values of the dependent variable according to different values on the covariate, and examine the remaining, independent effect of the categorical variable. For example, suppose Professor Green is concerned that Math Achievement is influenced by Student Motivation (measured by number of days absent last term). By stretching her original analysis to include this covariate, she could improve the precision of her results.

So far, the assumption has been that we are dealing with experiments that have one dependent variable. The last chapter, by Bray and Maxwell, relaxes this assumption with multiple analysis of variance (MANOVA), extending analysis to two or more dependent variables. Imagine, for example, that Professor Green, in addition to the dependent variable of Math Achievement (Y_1), is also interested in explaining Verbal Achievement (Y_2). Then, MANOVA would be an appropriate methodology to consider. Moving beyond explication of the basics, Bray and Maxwell consider the advanced questions of the relationship of path analysis and LISREL to MANOVA, and look at such demanding issues as higher-order MANOVA.

The chapters of this volume cover all aspects of experimental methods, from design through analysis. Their order is logical, beginning with the simple and ending with the sophisticated. Investigators at any career stage should benefit from them. Even for the seasoned, the welcoming pedagogical style of the chapters will be a reward. Experimentation is perhaps the research tool of choice in psychology, education and, to some extent, sociology. However, even in economics and political science, it is gaining ground. Today, to be well-trained, social scientists must be conversant in the experimental approach, even if they do not actually follow it themselves. Careful reading of this volume will provide that necessary training.

—Michael S. Lewis-Beck
Series Editor

PART I

RESEARCH DESIGNS

PAUL E. SPECTOR

1.0 INTRODUCTION

Any scientific investigation, be it in the social or natural sciences, must begin with some structure or plan. This structure defines the number and type of entities or *variables* to be studied and their relationship to one another. Such a structure is termed a design, the topic of this monograph, which will be limited to two varieties — experimental and nonexperimental.

A scientific investigation or study in the social sciences is undertaken to answer some specific question or hypothesis concerning the behavior of animals, humans, or social systems. Such questions may concern whether certain conditions, events, or situations cause particular behaviors or events or if certain conditions, events, situations, and behaviors occur together in time. For example, a social scientist might ask if unemployment causes crime, if inflation affects voter turnout for presidential elections, or if college students learn better with lecture or seminar course formats. Such questions lend themselves quite well to being answered with methods of scientific inquiry based on principles to be discussed in this monograph.

Of course it is not necessary to use scientific methods to answer questions. One might rely on intuition or educated opinion concerning how the social world operates. In fact, commonsense beliefs about behavior often are correct. Unfortunately, as has been shown through the scientific study of behavior, human judgment is not always accurate. Scientific methods are not infallible either, but they are designed to minimize the biases that affect subjective opinion. The way in which this is accomplished will be explained in the following chapters.

In this monograph I divide designs into experimental and nonexperimental. The difference between the two concerns the degree to which the experimenter or investigator controls that which he or she studies. The experimental design occurs when the *subjects* (people or social systems) and *conditions* (events or situations) to be studied are manipulated by the investigator. That is, the investigator does something to affect the subjects studied and then determines the effects of those manipulations. Such studies involve a comparison of subject behaviors or characteristics under the various conditions being investigated. The key to experimental design is that the investigator assigns subjects to conditions rather than observing them in naturally occurring situations.

For example, one might design an experimental study to determine if personal tutoring improves student learning. A number or *sample* of students would be located, half being placed into one *treatment group* and half into another. The first treatment group would be given regular instruction while the second would be given regular instruction plus additional personal tutoring. After a period of time, perhaps half the school year, the progress of both groups would be assessed, possibly by comparing school grades. Differences would be attributed to the tutoring, provided that the only difference between the groups in the treatment they received was the tutoring.

The nonexperimental design differs in the degree to which the investigator manipulates subjects and conditions. The investigator may identify conditions, but subjects of the study are not assigned to them. Rather, various observations are made of the subjects who may naturally fall into conditions. In the nonexperimental study of tutoring the investigator would again identify a number of students, but they would only be observed and would not be assigned to conditions. Half the students would be chosen because they were receiving tutoring despite the study, and half would be chosen because they were not. After a reasonable period of time, the progress of the two groups would be compared, perhaps on the same grades as the experimental design subjects. In addition the investigator might administer an achievement test for purposes of the study or collect other data from existing records.

It should be clear from these examples that the nonexperimental study differs from the experimental in the amount of manipulation of subjects and conditions and not in the research question asked or even in the conditions and characteristics studied. Perhaps another example will help illustrate the contrasts.

Experimental designs are perhaps best illustrated by the laboratory experiment. The scientist wishes to determine which of two procedures, products, or treatments results in more of something than the other. For example, he or she might wish to determine if organic fertilizer is superior to inorganic in producing tomatoes. The scientist raises half the subject tomatoes with organic and half with inorganic fertilizer, being careful that the only difference in the treatment of the two groups of plants is the fertilizer. Sunlight, water, type of seed, and spacing are all held constant. He or she raises the plants and determines which had the highest yield of fruit.

This example contains all the elements of the experimental design. The investigator created the two conditions, in this case the fertilization schedule. Subjects were assigned so that half were in one condition and half in the other. All other factors that might differ between the two groups were held constant or controlled. Finally, the subjects were compared on a criterion or characteristic about which the study was conducted.

In contrast, nonexperimental designs utilize observational methods and involve the collection of data with far less direct manipulation of conditions or subjects. In the tomato study one could conduct the same investigation with a nonexperimental design by observing fertilization practices and tomato yields of actual farmers. One might identify two groups of farmers, one that used organic and one that used inorganic fertilizer. One would then gather data, perhaps by asking the farmers directly about yield. Fertilizer use could then be related to tomato yield and conclusions drawn about the efficacy of the two types of fertilizer. Of course there are problems with this study due to the lack of control over extraneous factors. The two types of farmers might differ in more ways than preference for fertilizer. One type might water more, allow less space between plants, or practice a different style of crop rotation. Also one type of farmer might tend to exaggerate reported yields more than the other, thus biasing the data.

It should be apparent that the lack of direct manipulation or control in the nonexperimental design can cause problems in the interpretation of results because the investigator is often unable to assure that extraneous factors, not of concern in the present study, are properly handled. Of course these problems also occur in experimental studies when proper procedures are not or cannot be followed. It should also be noted that the experimental/nonexperimental distinction represents two ends of a continuum rather than two distinct types. There are designs that fall somewhere in between when only partial manipulation is attained. Finally, it is sometimes said that experimental studies establish causal relationships, and nonexperimental studies only establish that two things are related. Although in practice experimental studies are more powerful in their ability to determine that one thing causes another, not all experimental studies establish causation, and not all nonexperimental studies fail to establish it. As mentioned previously, an experimental study can fail to hold constant or control all extraneous factors and would therefore have difficulty in establishing causality. On the other hand, systematic observation, especially over time, can allow powerful causal conclusions, and one should respect the efficacy of these designs. Practically all modern knowledge of astronomy comes from nonexperimental observation.

The beginning student of design might wonder why entire books are devoted to its study. Although the basic principles of design are relatively straightforward, the design of real studies can be extremely complex and difficult. There are many pitfalls and potential biases that may contaminate a study and make it less than conclusive. Considerable knowledge and experience are essential if one plans to conduct good research. Even the nonresearcher who only reads results of studies would do well to understand basic design principles so that he or she can evaluate conclusions drawn from a study. Many times we see in published articles conclusions that seem not to follow from the study described. The reader who is unaware of design principles is at the mercy of an author who might well have overlooked a problem with the design of a study. The individual who wishes to become an accomplished researcher must become an expert in design. The individual who reads results of others' research should learn design principles to be able to form reasonable judgments based on that research.

Plan of the Monograph

The remainder of this monograph will consist of five chapters that present a detailed discussion of experimental and nonexperimental design. Both general concepts and specific applications will be covered. The second chapter presents basic concepts and language for discussions to follow. Some readers may be quite familiar with these concepts and may skip this chapter with no loss in understanding subsequent material. Chapter 3 will be a discussion of design principles in general, pulling together several concepts defined in Chapter 2. In addition this chapter will present pitfalls to the design of good studies. Chapters 4 to 6 cover details of specific designs. Chapter 4 is a discussion of nonexperimental, single-group designs. Chapter 5 presents the multigroup designs, most of which are experimental. Finally, Chapter 6 covers the more complex factorial designs. In each of these three chapters, the advantages and disadvantages of each design are covered, as well as particular pitfalls. Suggestions are offered for minimizing problems with each design, and in many places appropriate statistical procedures for analysis are mentioned. Details of the statistics are beyond the scope of this presentation, and alternative sources are suggested. Several illustrative examples from published studies are included in Chapters 4 to 6 to demonstrate the points made about the specific designs.

2.0 BASIC CONCEPTS

This chapter is concerned with the establishment of basic concepts essential for an understanding of design. In a sense this chapter will provide a language through which later discussions can communicate about design. Included are the concepts of independent and dependent variables, measurement and measurement error, reliability, validity, randomization, control, and generalizability. A thorough understanding of these concepts is essential for achieveing mastery over the remaining material.

Variables

A variable is a qualitative or quantitative entity that can vary or take on different values. In research, variables are the things that are measured and represent the concepts studied. For convenience, variables are often classified as independent or dependent. In most experimental and many nonexperimental designs that deal with determination of causal relationships, it is useful to refer to the causes as independent and the effects as dependent. Sometimes data are collected on several variables, none of which is manipulated and which cannot be classified as cause or effect. In such cases the independent-dependent classification has little meaning, even though the same statistical analyses might be employed as in causal studies.

Perhaps the best example of the independent-dependent dichotomy is illustrated by the laboratory experiment, such as the organic-inorganic fertilizer example of the previous chapter. In this experiment the type of fertilizer (organic and inorganic) was the independent variable because it was directly manipulated by the experimenter and, more important, because it was the putative cause of yield, which was the dependent variable. This independent-dependent categorization would be maintained even if the study were nonexperimental, such as the study of organic using and inorganic using farmers. Again, it is the supposed relationship among the variables that determines variable type and not the experimental nature of the study.

As will be discussed at length in the following chapters, there can be more than two variables in a design, and in fact most studies published today involve multiple variables. The multiple independent variable study is most common, although multiple dependent variable designs have become quite popular in recent years.

Measurement

With any study, variables must be measured in order for analyses to be conducted and conclusions drawn. Measurement is simply the process of assigning numbers to variables that represent attributes or properties of subjects or treatments. The numbers derived through the measurement process can represent convenient labels for discrete categories, such as sex or race, or can represent an underlying measurement continuum for a continuous variable, such as time, length, or scores on an attitude scale. With a discrete variable such as sex, one would arbitrarily assign a number to each possible category, for example, one for males and two for females. The quantification of the discrete variable is a convenience that allows analysis to be conducted. With continuous variables, such as time, the numbers assigned represent amount with smaller numbers generally indicating less of the characteristic than larger numbers. There are actually four types or levels of measurement commonly discussed. For details the interested reader might consult Guilford (1954) or Torgerson (1958).

Measurement Error

Measurement is always accomplished with a specified device or procedure which will be referred to as an instrument. For example, one might measure response latency with a stopwatch, intelligence with a paper-and-pencil test, or education level by asking people how many years of school they completed. No matter what instrument is used, there is always some degree of error associated with it. Error comes from several sources including: the limits of precision of an instrument (a ruler might only be lined in 16ths of an inch), idiosyncratic tendencies of the person using the instrument (the person using the ruler might view it from the side), bias in the design of an instrument (one end of the ruler might be cut off too short), and simple errors in the way a person uses the instrument (a person might erroneously record length).

There are two types of error to be discussed here — random error and bias. Random error occurs when errors are nonsystematic and are as frequently in one direction as the other around the real or true score on the variable. If the theoretical true value is 10, random errors of +1 are as likely as −1 so that in the long run there should be as many values of 9 as 11. Bias occurs when the errors tend to be in one direction more than the other. Thus the measurement might always tend to be high. When the true value is 10, most observed values are 11 or 12, with few 10's and fewer 9's. Bias often occurs due to distortions in procedures and characteristics of instruments, observers, and investigators. While bias can occur due to intentional acts on the part of researchers, of particular concern here is bias that is unintentional, arising from instruments and procedures.

Random error causes data collected in a study to be less than precise. However, if one can make certain assumptions about the error component of measurement, one can use statistical procedures to circumvent this problem. Random error implies that deviations from true scores are as likely in either direction. Therefore, if one takes several measurements of a characteristic, the errors of measurement should average out. This is exactly what is done when multiple items are included in a questionnaire or psychological test. While each item itself may be subject to considerable error, averaging scores from several items, each designed to measure the same variable, results in a score in which the random error component averages out to be quite small. I have several times witnessed a class of students estimate the temperature of the classroom. While individual estimates were often off by as much as 10 degrees, the average for the entire class was not off by more than 1 degree, and in fact was probably as accurate as the thermometer against which it was compared.

Bias is far more problematic than random error. Since bias tends to be in one direction, there is no simple process to average out its effects. There may be instances in which it is possible to estimate the magnitude and direction of bias and to adjust for it. Most often investigators attempt to uncover its sources and design instruments or methods to avoid it, and in fact much effort in designing studies involves the avoidance of bias.

Reliability

Reliability is a crucial characteristic of measurement and refers to the consistency of a measuring device. In other words, does the instrument always come up with the same score or number when the true value is the same? For example, if one were to use a ruler to measure the length of a table, reliability would refer to one's ability to always find the same length.

As discussed earlier, measurement is associated with error, and it is the relative magnitude of error to the true or real score that is reliability. Error that is quite small in relationship to true score results in reliable measurement. When errors become large relative to measured characteristics, reliability declines, eventually to the point at which the instrument is worthless. Reliability can be increased by the use of multiple measurements or multiple measures, a strategy frequently adopted in the social sciences. As discussed in the previous section, several measures can be combined, averaging out random error.

Of the several types of reliability, the two most common are discussed here. *Test-retest* involves the continued use of the same instrument to make multiple measurements. Thus one might ask a respondent the same question several times in an interview. *Equivalent forms* refers to the use of different, but equivalent instruments. An example would be asking the same question phrased in different ways. These terms are derived from psychological testing where reliability of tests is established by these as well as other methods.

Validity

Validity of an instrument means that it measures what it is designed to measure. A valid ruler measures length, a valid stopwatch measures time, and a valid intelligence test measures intelligence. Of course validity is not quite this simple because researchers are not always precise in their meanings of concepts and rarely have standards for comparison. For example, a valid measure of socioeconomic status would consist of a composite of income, education level, occupation, and perhaps other variables, as well; but how should they be combined? Should one multiply annual income by education in years or should one add education in years to the hourly rate of pay? How should one quantify occupation — by job level in the organization, by time span of discretion, or by a survey of occupational status?

Validity itself is a simple concept, but the determination of the validity of a measure is elusive. Generally a variable is taken as part of a theoretical framework and establishes that certain hypothesized relationships exist between the instrument and other variables. Thus one might validate a measure of socioeconomic status by showing that the measure is related to certain types of attitudes and behaviors. As one finds that hypothesized relationships are supported, evidence for validity accumulates. When hypotheses are not upheld, either the instrument is invalid or the theories are wrong. Through the collection of evidence over time, a case is built for the validity of measures, which is dependent upon the theoretical models and hypotheses.

Validity and reliability go hand in hand and are two crucial properties of instruments. Their relationship can best be shown with an example. Suppose one has three baseball pitchers and wishes to determine if their pitching is reliable and valid. Reliability is defined as consistency in pitching the ball to the same place each time. Validity is defined as being able to pitch strikes rather than balls. An investigation is set up in which data are collected on each pitcher's performance in several games. The first pitcher always pitches low and outside and walks every batter. In fact, the catcher can predict exactly where the ball will be thrown. This pitcher is perfectly reliable but perfectly invalid. The second pitcher throws a collection of balls and strikes, some high, some low, some inside, and some outside. He is not very reliable, and not very valid either, although he sometimes pitches strikes. The last pitcher throws all strikes — he is both valid and reliable. The principle is this — an instrument can be reliable but not valid, but to be valid an instrument must be reliable. Furthermore, the level of reliability sets a limit to how valid an instrument can be. (See Carmines and Zeller, 1979, for a more thorough treatment of reliability and validity.)

Control

The cornerstone of experimental design is control. It involves holding constant or varying systematically variables so their effects can be removed from a study or compared to other conditions. Control can involve the active manipulation by an investigator of subjects or conditions, or it can involve merely the structuring of an investigation and the manipulation of data. In an experimental design, control usually refers to holding constant the level of a particular variable. Thus one might hold constant or control for sex or intelligence of subjects or time of day in which an experiment is run. This type of control involves the selection of subjects or conditions so their characteristics remain at a constant level or value.

In a nonexperimental study, control can occur by selectively deleting cases that do not have the characteristics of present interest. Suppose one does a study by collecting data from census records. Area of the country, sex of the respondent, type of dwelling, and a host of other variables can be controlled by selecting all cases that are at a certain value for the variables to be controlled. However, there are limits to what can be controlled because there may be crucial variables not collected or available for observation. For example, with census data time of day of the interview or race of the interviewer may not be available and thus could not be controlled. Also, there may be a relationship between the control variables and experimental variables in such a way that one cannot be held constant without the other. In such cases the variables are said to be totally confounded.

Control, then, is holding constant variables not of direct interest in the current investigation so they do not contaminate results. However, once a study is limited to certain values of a control variable, one may not be able to generalize the results to other values. Studies conducted only on women may not yield similar results for men.

One other use of the term *control* is in reference to the control group. Literally, a control group is a group in which values of the independent variable are held at a base or comparison level. When one is comparing a new procedure or process to an old one, the old one represents the control, and the group of subjects in the group comprise the control group. Often the control group is untouched or untreated in an investigation, although they may receive some standard or currently existing treatment or condition. For example, suppose one wished to determine if a particular program was effective in reducing recidivism of convicted felons. One might select two groups of newly released felons, an experimental group that receives the program and a control group that does not. The study would involve a comparison of the two groups.

Randomization

The concept of randomization has already been discussed in the sense of random errors of measurement. With measurement this referred to the fact that positive errors were as likely as negative. With experimental design, randomization refers to the assignment of subjects to conditions or levels of an independent variable — either by the investigator or by a natural process in the field.

If there are several levels of an independent variable, which might be represented by several treatment groups (one or more of which might be a control group), randomization means that each subject in the study had an equal chance or probability of falling into each group.

Randomization in a sense is a process opposite from control. Where controlling means holding the value of certain variables constant, randomization means letting the value run freely. The intent is that, through random assignment of subjects to groups, the effects of uncontrolled subject variables will cancel out. With the convicted felon example, one might suspect that the reaction of younger felons will be different from older felons but not wish to include age as a variable for study. If the age distribution of the two groups differed, it would be difficult to determine if age alone accounted for the results. To control for age one might hold it constant by choosing as subjects only those felons between certain age limits. Alternately, all felons could be randomly assigned to the program and control group, assuming that the two groups will be about equivalent on age. Of course, one could test this assumption by comparing ages between the groups.

Confounding

The best way to describe confounding is with an example. Suppose an investigator is interested in determining the relationship between achievement test scores and average family income among Mexican-Americans. The problem is that achievement scores are probably related to or confounded with education level. It would be difficult to determine whether achievement or education was the crucial variable if a relationship was found. That is, suppose people with high school diplomas tended to get better jobs and also tended to have higher scores. It would not follow necessarily that achievement was the causal factor. Perhaps it was just the diploma, independent of achievement, that resulted in better employment and more income.

Often in studies, both experimental and nonexperimental, there are variables related to variables of interest which distort or confound the results. With experiments they might be related to the independent variable so that both are actually manipulated. In such cases one does not know which of the two was responsible for the observed levels of the dependent variable. Well-designed studies are able to handle this confounding, as will be shown throughout this monograph.

Generalizability of Results

At the end of any study or investigation there arises the question of generalizability of results. That is, do the results found in the present study hold as well for other samples of subjects at other locations? Studies in the social sciences are rarely, if ever, universal, and one must keep in mind the limitations. A particular study may be limited only to males, certain areas of the country, certain cultures, or the subjects chosen. The variables included, the particular controls used, and the way in which subjects are assigned to treatments all determine the limits to generalizability.

Campbell and Stanley (1963) discuss at great length factors which limit the internal and external validity of studies. Internal validity refers to the generalization of conclusions within a given study itself. That is, given the structure of a particular investigation, can valid conclusions be drawn? In other words can one state that the independent variable caused the dependent variable or are there confounding factors that prevent conclusions? External validity is generalization beyond the current study and sample. Given that there is internal validity, do the results generalize to other samples?

It is both confounding and the design structure of an investigation that determine whether it is internally valid. Campbell and Stanley (1963) discuss many sources of invalidity including: (1) instrument reactivity — the effects instruments have on the subjects in a study; (2) history — things that may happen to subjects over time that have nothing to do with the study; (3) unreliability of instruments; (4) differential subject loss over time in various groups; (5) bias in the assignment of subjects to treatment groups; and (6) instrument changes over time.

External validity is compromised when conditions in the investigation differ from those in the generalization. Examples of factors leading to external invalidity include: (1) reactivity of instrumentation — effects caused by use of instruments; (2) Hawthorne effects — effect on subjects of knowing they are in an experiment; (3) invalidity of instruments; and (4) confounding characteristics of the particular samples, that is, the samples chosen might not adequately represent the population to which results are to be generalized. The best example is the use of college students for studies generalized to the U.S. population as a whole.

In this chapter we have established some basic concepts essential for the understanding of design. The reader at this point should have a general feel for the major design principles. One should be aware that a design involves structuring the measurement of variables in such a way that their relationships can be determined. When the study is conducted, data are collected on the variables and are analyzed with statistical methods. At many places in the following chapters specific statistical techniques will be suggested for particular designs, and references will be provided for the reader interested in more detail. Statistics is a topic essential for study by the serious researcher, and it goes hand in hand with a study of design. While design involves the structure of a study, statistics deals with analysis of the data generated and the drawing of conclusions from that data.

3.0 BASIC LOGIC OF DESIGN

The major purpose of any design is to answer some specific research question utilizing well-developed principles of scientific inquiry. The basic ideas of design are reasonably simple and straightforward, but the design of actual social science investigations is often quite complex and difficult due to several factors including: limitations on the degree of control an investigator can exert over human beings and social systems, poorly formulated concepts, instruments of limited validity, complex interrelationships among large numbers of variables, and lack of well-developed and validated theoretical models. Research questions are often imprecise, instruments to measure variables are often unavailable, and simple relationships among variables seem quite elusive.

Any investigation requires several steps to complete. First, the investigator must formulate a researchable question. This question may be in the form of a hypothesis that certain relationships exist among variables, or it may be of an exploratory nature, essentially asking what is the relationship among variables. A research question may begin in a loosely formulated form, but must eventually be stated such that a testable hypothesis or model is generated. The more precise the question, the easier it will be to answer, and if asked precisely enough, the remaining steps will fall more easily into place. Of course, one must certainly avoid formulating questions that are so narrow as to be of no practical or scientific significance, but to formulate meaningful questions requires experience and considerable knowledge of a content area.

The second step is to plan the design of the investigation. This step involves choice of variables, procedures, controls, and randomization plans. At this point one must decide whether the design will be experimental or nonexperimental and whether the study will take place in a laboratory or field setting. Decisions must be made about where and how to collect the data, and which variables are to be controlled, at what level, and with what methods? If subjects are assigned to levels of the independent variable, some procedure must be chosen for assignment. Once the basic design is laid out, careful consideration should be given to possible confounding variables. If variables are identified as possible confounds, a strategy should be chosen to deal with them. General procedures will be discussed at a later point in this chapter.

The third step, which may occur at the same time as the second, involves selection of instruments for dependent variables, and *operationalization* of independent variables, which is essentially the statement of procedures used to create their levels. Choice of instruments is as important as any step in an investigation, but too often little attention is given to instrumentation. This is especially true in experimental laboratory studies where considerable effort might be put into operationalizing levels of the independent variable, but little is given to measuring the dependent variable. Too often an investigator spends much time and energy developing a complex manipulation for the independent variable, but only spends a few moments creating self-report items of unknown reliability and untested validity to measure the dependent variable.

The fourth and final step of any study is simply to conduct it. It is always best to carefully design a study and then to carry it out as planned, but often unforeseen problems arise and modifications are made to the original plan. Instruments are sometimes revised until they are sensitive to manipulations of independent variables, and sometimes procedures are modified when conditions change. If these things occur, it is always best to replicate the study so that more confidence can be placed in the results and the conclusions.

Much has been written about all four of these steps. The present topic is research design, which is step 2. The remainder of this chapter will limit itself to the design aspect.

Experimental Studies

For the most part, experimental studies are considered to be more powerful than nonexperimental designs in uncovering causal relationships among variables. This is due to the fact that through control and randomization, potential confounding effects can be removed from a study. A nonexperimental study merely establishes that relationships exist among variables. However, through systematic observation over time, and collection of data on several variables, it is indeed possible to determine cause and effect. Experimental studies which involve direct manipulation are more frequently conclusive because they involve principles of control, randomization, and comparison.

In a sense an experimental design can be viewed as a trade-off among comparison, randomization, and control. Some variables are set at different levels and compared, others are held at a constant level and controlled, and still others may be free to vary with the hope that randomization will average out confounds. In the perfect experiment the independent variables are manipulated, subjects are randomly assigned, and all other variables are held constant. The investigator identifies a set of variables and makes a decision whether he wishes to manipulate (treat as independent) or hold constant (control) each variable. Of course when he controls a variable by holding it constant, he limits generalizability to only the chosen level. If he treats a variable as independent, he determines its effects on the dependent variable, as well as its relationship to other independent variables in the study.

If one had unlimited time, subjects, and resources, one could include any number of independent variables in a study. However, the more independent variables included in a study, the more subjects needed to fill conditions, the more data collected on those subjects, and the more complex the analysis and interpretation. Thus there are practical limits to the number of independent variables that can be included in a study. Hence, control by holding variables constant is essential.

Of course, rather than holding values of a variable constant, one can let them vary and randomly assign those values to the different levels of the independent variables. This method is most often used by assigning subjects at random to conditions. However, it is not always practical or appropriate to randomly assign values to variables, especially when the variables in question are related to the experimental conditions. These situations undoubtedly call for some sort of control, and sometimes this can be accomplished systematically. For example, in a laboratory experiment it is common practice to mix up the order in which conditions are run. Sometimes this is done by alternating, or *counterbalancing,* a procedure to be discussed later in this monograph.

As discussed previously, confounding occurs when a variable not of immediate interest in a study is related to variables in the study. These confounding variables can be related to experimental conditions or treatments or to subject characteristics when these are the independent variables in the study. An example of the latter situation is the failure to definitively answer the controversial and highly explosive question about racial differences in abilities. The race variable is so confounded with social and economic variables that racial comparisons of intelligence test scores are inconclusive.

Confounding of subject characteristics can be handled by randomly assigning subjects to groups or by choosing subjects at the same level of the confounding variable. This latter approach is often difficult because it may be hard to find enough subjects with the necessary characteristics, because the confounding variable itself may be related to a host of other variables, and because there might be prohibitions against such choices.

Confounding of treatment variables can be handled through careful design and planning of a study. However, there are instances when two variables are confounded in such a way that it is impossible to completely separate them in a single study. For example, suppose one wished to compare two interactive teaching methods on learning. Students would be randomly assigned to the two methods and would be subsequently tested for knowledge of the subject with a standard achievement test. Now suppose one method produces more student responses in a unit of time than the other. Method 1 might require two responses per minute while method 2 requires four. Number of subject responses would be confounded with treatment and may alone account for learning differentials. One could equate number of responses by making the sessions with method 1 twice as long as with method 2. Unfortunately, now duration of training is confounded with treatment. One would have to make a choice about which confound is the most damaging and control it at the expense of the other. The only way out would be to somehow redesign the teaching methods so they produce the same frequency of response. Otherwise, interpretations of the efficacy of the two methods could only be made in terms of the confounding variable. More research would have to be conducted with the frequency variable to determine its role in learning.

Nonexperimental Studies

Perhaps the most important difference between the experimental and nonexperimental study is subject assignment. In the experimental design, the researcher assigns subjects (optimally at random) to conditions or levels of the independent variable, but in the nonexperimental study there is no assignment. Often creation of the levels of independent variables is another difference, but an experimental design does not require that the investigator create the levels of the independent variable — he or she merely assigns subjects and observes results. When subject assignment does not occur, the study is nonexperimental even if a treatment is created.

For example, one might ask the question whether compensatory education improves college grades for low-income students. One might identify a group of low-income students and assign half of them to an existing program and half to a no-treatment control group. College grades would be the dependent variable, and the design would be experimental. On the other hand, one might be active in designing a compensatory education program which a number of students would attend. One could collect data on college grades of these students as well as a group who did not attend. However, without assignment, the study is nonexperimental. The fact that the investigator created the program is irrelevant. The design itself is not concerned with who created the independent variable. Rather it is concerned with the structure of the investigation, and from this structure, inferences can be drawn.

Although in a nonexperimental study there is no assignment of subjects, many of the other principles of research design still apply. Control over levels of certain variables can be exerted, but control does not involve active manipulation of conditions. Rather control can be exercised in the selection of cases to include in the observational study. Cases can be chosen to meet certain specified criteria, such as selecting only males, only people below a certain annual income, or organizations in the nonprofit sector. Control is achieved by selecting only certain values of control variables and observing the variables of interest.

Statistical procedures are also available to help control the effects of certain variables. Although these procedures are based on certain assumptions which may not always be true, it is possible to statistically adjust for or control the effects of certain variables. If one is interested in studying the relationship between income and political party preference, one might simply correlate income level with party membership. However, education is related to income and education alone might be related to preference, independent of income. Education level can be controlled by selecting only those subjects who are at a certain level, perhaps high school graduates. The correlation between income and membership can also be statistically adjusted for education using partial correlation. This would indicate whether there is a relationship remaining between income and membership after removing the common relationship among all three variables.

It is often taught that only experiments can establish causal relationships among variables and that observational or correlational studies can only establish that relationships exist without specifying causal direction. While in practice this is often true, one should be cautious in assuming that experimental designs always establish causality and observational studies do not. Many experimental designs are so fraught with confounding variables that causal inferences cannot be made with reasonable confidence, and there are nonexperimental, observational designs that can establish causal chains of events.

Going back to the income-party preference example, suppose one hypothesized that income causes party preference through some theoretical process. Merely showing that Republicans have higher incomes than Democrats would not convince any social scientist that the hypothesis was correct. However, one could make systematic observations over time and compile quite convincing evidence. One could identify a large sample of young high school graduates and track their income and party membership for the following 20 years. If those individuals with higher initial incomes became Republicans and those with lower initial incomes became Democrats, and if party membership shifted with income, one would have strong evidence for the hypothesis. Observing the close correspondence of the two variables over time with income change almost always preceding party change would be convincing and indicate a causal connection. Of course other variables would certainly be involved, but these could be observed as well, and a theory of party preference might be validated.

Problems with Internal and External Validity

In the previous chapter there was brief mention of internal and external validity and design problems that threaten each. Such problems, which arise from confounding variables within a design, have been extensively covered by Campbell and his colleagues (e.g., Campbell and Stanley, 1963; Cook and Campbell, 1979). Variables that are related to the independent variables may account for observed differences in the dependent variable, giving the false appearance of a valid answer to a research question. The astute researcher is aware of the possible sources of these invalidating influences on results and guards against them in planning designs. Specific sources are covered below.

History. There are events that may affect subjects in addition to the independent variables or conditions of interest. For example, one might design a study to see if the 55 mile per hour speed limit reduced traffic fatalities. Data on traffic deaths before and after the limit was introduced could be collected and might show that deaths declined. However, it might also be discovered that due to higher gasoline prices, people drove fewer miles. If differences in fatality rates were found, it would be difficult to separate the effects of speed limit from the effects of mileage.

Instrument Reactivity. It is an established principle of measurement that instruments react with the things they measure. In some cases the reactivity is small relative to the variable measured and is inconsequential, but in other cases it may totally distort measurement. In nuclear physics the principle of uncertainty is a statement of the fact that measurement of subatomic particles is never exact because instruments disturb the particles being measured. In the social sciences it is often difficult to know when reactivity is severe enough to be problematic. It may affect someone's attitudes to fill out an attitude questionnaire, and it may change behavior when a person knows he is being observed. Furthermore, there is a vast literature on the effects an experimenter can have on the behavior of subjects, many of which would be considered instrument reactions.

Instrument reactivity occurs in two ways. First, instruments directly affect subjects so that true measurements are distorted. In other words the instrument disturbs that which is measured. Second, instruments may interact with treatments so that subject responses to various treatments are changed and differ from treatment to treatment. As long as the former distorition is constant, comparisons among variables can be made, although with increased error. The latter situation may totally distort results and confound a study.

Perhaps the best way to deal with instrument reactivity is to test for its effects within a design. That is, the design would be structured to include a test for instrument reactivity. The best example is the Solomon four-group design where a dependent variable is measured after application of the independent variable, and half the subjects receive an additional preindependent variable measurement while half do not. A comparison of these two groups on the measurement after intervention would be a test for reactivity of the pretest and its possible interaction with the independent variable.

Unreliability of Instruments. This problem was discussed previously in the section on reliability. When instruments are unreliable, it becomes difficult to draw firm conclusions from a study because the variance among subjects becomes too large. The best solution for unreliability is to improve the instrument, find another, or take multiple measurements with the same or equivalent instruments. Using large samples can also help as the large errors of measurement may average out. However, if an instrument is too unreliable, it will lack any validity and be totally worthless.

Invalidity of Instruments. This is an obvious problem since an invalid instrument does not measure the variable of interest. However, it is not always easy to determine when an instrument is invalid. If one can define precisely what is to be measured and can derive hypotheses concerning the behavior of the measured characteristic, one can validate an instrument against those hypotheses. For example, if one were to develop an instrument to measure mathematical ability, one could validate it against the hypotheses that individuals high on this characteristic, in comparison to low scorers, would receive better grades in mathematics courses, score higher on standardized mathematics achievement tests, and make more successful statisticians. If these hypotheses were not supported empirically, one would question whether the instrument could really measure the characteristic in question. The only solution to invalidity is to develop or find an instrument that is valid.

Instrument Change Over Time. This problem refers to an instrument's changing validity over time, termed temporal invalidity by Chubb (1978), who demonstrated the phenomenon with a political cynicism questionnaire. In this case subjects changed their perceptions of the questions over an eight-year period. Instrument changes are not limited to shifts in subject characteristics. For example, in interview studies, interviewers may improve their technique with practice and later interviews might be more valid than earlier interviews due to improved interviewer skills. The best way to handle this problem is to be certain that collection of data among levels of the independent variable is not systematic. That is, data should not be collected first for one level and then for another. Also, checks should be made on the instrument periodically to be sure its characteristics have not changed.

Differential Subject Loss. In many studies that take place over time, subjects may be lost due to refusal to continue or to events that preclude continuation, such as injury or death. This problem is of concern for two reasons. First, attrition may not be random and completers might be different from noncompleters, a situation that would limit generalizability of results. Second, if attrition differs among treatment groups, it may be difficult to know if attrition alone accounted for results.

Solutions to this problem go beyond design considerations and involve selecting procedures that assure continued subject participation, such as payment, preliminary commitment, and selecting elapsed time to be as short as possible between the beginning and end of a study.

Bias in Assignment of Subjects to Treatments. This problem has already been discussed; it represents a breakdown in random assignment. It is always best to randomly assign subjects to levels of the independent variable, but when this is not possible, one should attempt to control as much as possible all differences among groups. This could be done by selecting matched subjects for each group. Matching variables might include personal characteristics, demographic characteristics, scores on pretests, and specific behaviors such as arrest records or school grades. One can also use statistical methods to control for differences, but these procedures are not attractive alternatives to matching or random assignment.

Hawthorne Effects. Hawthorne effects, named from the well-known Western Electric studies in industry (Roethlisberger and Dickson, 1939), refer to the distortion in behavior that occurs when people know they are subjects of a study. This effect is somewhat akin to instrument reactivity, but it does not have to involve the instrument itself. That is, the mere knowledge that one is in a study may affect behavior even if observations are not being made. Procedures to control this problem are: unobtrusive studies in which subjects are unaware they are being studied, telling control subjects they are also in an experiment even if they are to receive no manipulation, and allowing an adaptation period during which no observations are made.

Nonrepresentative Samples. This problem is mainly one of generalization when the samples chosen are so specialized that conclusions can only be made to a limited population, in some cases not beyond the original sample itself. For example, much research in psychology has been criticized for its generalization from male subjects to humans in general in light of frequent findings of sex differences in behavior. In addition, most psychological studies have been done in the United States, and since most subjects are college students, many findings may well be limited to an American college student population. Solutions to this problem are to choose samples that represent the population to which generalizations are to be made. This may require replication of studies using various samples in different areas of the United States, as well as other countries.

Design Notation

The remainder of this monograph will be concerned with specific designs and the application of the principles discussed to this point. The various designs are best explained diagrammatically. Hence, for all but the most complex designs, a notation system will be used that is based on Campbell and Stanley (1963). In this system, observations or measurements of variables are represented by O's. Applications of the independent variables or treatments are X's. The time sequence of O's and X's in the design run from left to right. For example, three observations, each immediately following one of three sequential treatments for a single group of subjects would be diagramed as:

$$X_1\ O_1\ X_2\ O_2\ X_3\ O_3.$$

For two groups each receiving the same treatments but in a different order the structure would be:

$$X_1\ O_1\ X_2\ O_2\ X_3\ O_3.$$

$$X_2\ O_1\ X_3\ O_2\ X_1\ O_3.$$

Each row represents a separate treatment group, but not necessarily a separate condition. The subscripts on the treatments are labels to distinguish among them. The subscripts on the observations indicate the order in which they are made.

4.0 ONE-GROUP DESIGNS

One-group designs are all considered nonexperimental since they do not involve assignment of subjects to conditions. Rather a single group of subjects is observed, although the investigator may create a treatment condition. There are three designs that will be covered in this chapter, although these three can be expanded to more complex designs involving a single group. These are the most basic designs involving a single group, and they are popular throughout the social sciences because of their simplicity and ease of application.

Pretest-Posttest Design

The pretest-posttest design involves two measurements of the dependent variable surrounding, in time, the administration or occurrence of a single treatment or level of the independent variable. Its structure in the notation of the previous chapter is:

$$O_1\ X\ O_2.$$

In this design subjects serve as their own control, and comparisons are made before and after treatment. An assumption is made that differences between pretest and posttest are due to the effects of the treatment that occurred in the middle.

The most obvious shortcoming of this design is that one cannot be certain that some factor or event other than the treatment was responsible for posttest change. This problem is especially acute where the time period between pretest and posttest is long and when the researcher has limited control over events occurring to the subjects. For example, suppose one were to conduct a study to determine if a media campaign would increase the frequency of voter registrations in a particular city. A pretest could be taken of the number of registrations one month prior to the campaign, and a posttest one month after the campaign. However, a host of other events might transpire in the middle, such as emergence of a heated issue in the community or the intensification of a campaign. With this design it would be impossible to determine which factor or factors were responsible for increased registrations. A colleague of mine was involved in an evaluation of a state police crackdown on drunk driving. Accident records were gathered before and after implementation of the crackdown. Unfortunately, the crackdown occurred just as the state adopted a 55 mile per hour speed limit, destroying the possibility of drawing definitive conclusions.

This design is also sensitive to instrument reactivity and Hawthorne effects. Since there are no comparison groups, it is difficult to separate the effects of treatment from the effects of measurement or knowledge of being in an experiment. Hawthorne effects are especially problematic when the pretest is taken before the subjects know about the study. Conditions then change from pretest to posttest beyond the treatment of interest. Instrument reactivity is a special problem when it involves treatment-instrument interaction. In many cases the pretest might sensitize subjects to aspects of the treatment to which they might not otherwise react. In other words the pretest cues subjects about the treatment and enables them to guess what the investigator is expecting. These problems can be minimized by careful selection of instruments to be minimally reactive and by assuring that any reactivity is constant from pretest to posttest. For Hawthorne effects this would involve informing subjects before the pretest about the study, thus holding that knowledge constant.

The structure of this design is simple, and simple procedures can handle the data this design generates. Most commonly, dependent t tests are used to test for statistical significance from pretest to posttest (Winer, 1971).

The one-group pretest-posttest is not one of the better designs available due to the rather severe limitations already described. It is a rather simple design to use, but it is strongly advised that a more conclusive design be used whenever possible. This design is often utilized for program evaluations where the goal is to determine the effectiveness of a particular program. Many times with such activities, control or comparison groups are unavailable, requiring the use of this design or no design.

Interrupted Time Series

This design is similar to the pretest-posttest except that there are more than two measurements. Ideally, there are an equal number of measurement periods before and after treatment, and the period between measurements is constant. These designs can range from several to hundreds of measurements, with the number determining what types of analyses can be conducted.

This design is found in two applications. First, it is a direct extention of the pretest-posttest with more than two measurements. The second use is when periodic data exist over a considerable length of time, and the purpose of the investigation is to determine whether the variables of interest changed at a specified point in the series. This second use is generally considered to be a time series, although a broader use of the term is taken here. Several examples of time series are:

$$O_1\ O_2\ O_3\ X\ O_4\ O_5\ O_6$$

$$O_1\ X\ O_2\ O_3\ O_4$$

$$O_1\ O_2\ .\ .\ .\ O_{50}\ X\ O_{51}\ O_{52}\ .\ .\ .\ O_{100}$$

The multiple pretest-posttest designs are an improvement over the single pretest-posttest. The advantage with this design is that it allows determination of trends over time, that is, the slope of the graph of the dependent variable over time. This trend estimate is important because it might well be that the posttest level of a dependent variable is at exactly the place one would expect, based on previous observations over time. The dependent variable might show an increase, decrease, or cyclical change over time without treatment or intervention. This is especially true with aggregate data based on naturally occurring social units. Traffic accident rates, crime rates, and unemployment rates all show trends over time having causes that lie outside of most studies. Techniques have been developed to determine trends in data and estimate whether a discontinuity occurred at a specified location in the series.

Procedures to analyze time series data can become quite complex and most social scientists receive little exposure to them in graduate school. For long series with 50 measurements or more, complex mathematical modeling procedures have been developed that can well describe the form of the series and uncover any changes that may have occurred. Perhaps the most powerful technique is the autoregressive integrated moving average (ARIMA), which indicates complex trends in a time series (see Mc Dowall, McCleary, Meidinger and Hay, 1980, for details).

For a smaller number of measurements, other less complex and powerful procedures must be used. Certainly the analysis of variance is available when there are a few retestings. However, there would be too many group means to compare as the number of retestings becomes large. Swaminathan and Algina (1977) have developed multiple regression procedures which allow a comparison of regression lines before and after treatment.

While the multiple testing designs are certainly more powerful than the single pretest-posttest, they do suffer from most of the same shortcomings. Again the major problem is lack of control for history. One can never be certain that some event other than the treatment in question caused the change in dependent variable. The advantage of the time series is that one can see the direction in which trends were heading at the time of intervention or treatment. A treatment might inhibit or stop a trend which would not be reflected in a single pretest-posttest comparison. Therefore, the multiple-measurement design provides somewhat stronger evidence for treatment effects.

Instrument reactivity and Hawthorne effects are in some ways attenuated and in some ways compounded. Many instruments, if administered several times, might show declining validity and reliability due to boredom and fatigue on the part of subjects. Distortions may occur because subjects attempt to be consistent over time when they know they are being studied. On the other hand subjects may adapt to being part of an investigation and give more natural responses after an initial adjustment period.

Time series studies may be especially subject to instrument change over time since measurements may take place over many months or years. In fact it is not unusual to find historical studies utilizing data from previous centuries. However, with such data, procedures for collection may change over time. Once I attempted to gather time series data on the number of admissions to state psychiatric hospitals between 1978 and 1980 in one of the southern states. Due to changes in definition of admissions, it was impossible to acquire equivalent data for the entire period from the records. So much more severe are the problems in acquiring good data over longer periods of time. ARIMA requires a minimum of 50 measurement periods, which would require half a century of data if annual rates are of interest. Such studies that cannot utilize previously collected data are quite time consuming and are not often undertaken.

Correlational Designs

Included with the other one-group studies are correlational designs which are purely observational. That is, the investigator does not intervene in any way or expose subjects to a manipulation. Rather measurements are taken on a group of individuals or social entities, and relationships are determined among the measures. These measurements can be taken through direct observation, questionnaires, or existing records. They may be repeated over time, a procedure that makes this approach quite powerful. In this section both the one-measurement cross-sectional design and the multiple-measurement longitudinal design will be covered.

Cross-sectional Design. The simplest of the correlational designs is the cross-sectional in which all measurements are taken at one point in time. The structure of the design would be simply:

O

where O represents all observations on all variables. This design is extremely popular due to its simplicity and ease of administration. It requires nothing more than the collection of two or more measures on a set of subjects or social entities at one point in time and requires no treatments or manipulations. A well-conducted study can involve time-consuming development of instruments, but many use existing measures or collect data from available records. Such studies can sometimes be completed in a single day.

Cross-sectional designs are especially attractive in field studies where control over subjects is quite difficult to acquire. In fact, probably most field studies utilize this design because of its simplicity and ease of conducting.

The cross-sectional approach is quite useful in determining if two or more variables are related, and often establishment of relationships is the extent of a research question. When there are more than two variables in a study, it may become difficult to tease out complex interrelationships. For two variables one can calculate the correlation coefficient as an index of strength of relationship and test it for statistical significance. With three or more variables, more complex data-analytic procedures are possible.

When one has several variables, the interest might be in determining whether one can construct a smaller number of dimensions or factors which does an adequate job of explaining the original, larger set. Procedures such as factor analysis are dimension-reduction techniques developed to determine the underlying theoretical factors among a set of variables. The interested reader is referred to any of a number of sources on the topic including Kim and Mueller (1978) and Rummel (1970).

If one can assume that certain variables are caused or preceded by others, one can use multiple regression to derive a functional relationship between the two sets. With multiple regression one predicts a criterion or dependent variable from a set of predictor or independent variables. Equations are generated of the form:

$$y = b_0 + b_1x_1 + \ldots + b_nx_n$$

where y is the dependent variable, the x's are independent variables, and the b's are constants. The x's and y are observed; the b's are calculated from the data (see Lewis-Beck, 1980, for a more complete treatment of multiple regression).

Multiple regression can be used for theory testing and can provide weak support for causal models. Such regression procedures fall under the rubric of path analysis, which is a means of using cross-sectional, correlational data to examine likely causal connections among variables. Using correlations and regression coefficients, one compares observed results to those predicted by a model. Finding that set of results is evidence in support of the model, but is consistent with other possible models as well. For details on path analysis, see Asher (1976).

One way to improve the ability of cross-sectional studies to yield causal data would be to take some measurement at a later point in time. Such a design would be represented as:

O O′

where O and O′ represent observations of different variables. Such designs fall somewhat between the truly cross-sectional and the longitudinal — they take place over time, but only a single measurement is made on each variable. In such designs variables predicted to be causes are measured first, followed in time by variables expected to be effects. For example, I conducted a study of employee turnover to test a causal model hypothesizing that certain organizational and personal employee characteristics would lead to job dissatisfaction, which would lead to intentions of quitting, which would lead to actual turnover. Although the ideal design would have been to lag all four steps in the causal chain, the final variable, turnover, was collected after the other variables. This procedure made it difficult to argue that turnover could have caused the variables measured before it. Of course this study, while supporting the causal model, in no way provided proof that it was correct.

Perhaps the major shortcoming of the cross-sectional design is that it only establishes relationships, although path analysis can be used to provide a weak test of causal relationships. For the purely cross-sectional study with all measures taken at the same time, history is of little consequence. That is, there is probably little that can happen within the short time span of data collection that can distort results. However, when some of the variables are measured at a later time, it is possible that intervening events caused spurious relationships. For example, suppose in the turnover study, those employees who were dissatisfied and intending to quit all expressed their feelings and were given raises and concessions to get them to stay. It might well have happened that the concessions changed the normal sequence of events, and no support would have been found for the model.

A more serious problem in the correlational design is instrument reactivity. Of particular concern is *common method variance* in studies that make use of one procedure for collecting data, most commonly the self-report questionnaire or interview. Subject response tendencies and bias when responding to requests for self-report may account for false relationships that are found. People may report attitudes and behaviors in a manner that is more consistent than they are in reality. This tendency toward consistency can enhance correlation coefficients. The component of the correlation due to bias common to the method of data collection would be the *common method variance*. Studies that utilize several modes of data collection, or collect data in a way that assures noninteraction of measures, are more powerful.

Hawthorne effects can also be a problem with the cross-sectional study for much the same reason as instrument reactivity. People who know they are in a study may distort their responses for a number of reasons including a desire to look good or provide good data for the investigator. Some procedures are available to help identify certain biases such as faking and social desirability bias. Subjects found to exhibit biases might be eliminated from the sample. Of course elimination of subjects may limit generalizability to only subjects who do not distort results.

Longitudinal Designs. A variation of the correlational study is the longitudinal or panel design which involves two or more measurements of variables in a study taken on the same group of subjects. Its structure is:

$$O_1 \; O_2 \ldots O_n$$

where the O's represent measurements on all variables. This approach is more powerful than the cross-sectional due to the lagging procedure explained above. That is, it is possible to observe over time if certain values of a variable at one point are associated with certain values of another variable at a different point.

The simplest example of a longitudinal design is the cross-lagged panel design with two variables, each measured twice (see Kenny and Harackiewicz, 1979, for details). Such a design is shown in Figure 4.1, where variables income and education are each measured at age 25 and age 50 for a group of subjects. There are six possible correlations: the correlation of each variable with itself across time and the correlations of income with education within the same time period and across time periods. Of particular interest are these last four coefficients. If one hypothesizes that education is a strong cause of income, but income is at best a weak cause of education, one would expect that income at age 25 would show a weak correlation with education at 50, but education at 25 would show a relatively strong relationship to income at age 50. Furthermore, one would expect little correlation between income and education at 25, but a strong relationship at age 50. This pattern provides support for causal hypotheses, somewhat stronger than a cross-sectional study using path analysis. However, with no control over these variables, the support is weak as there are many alternative explanations for these results.

Longitudinal designs can involve far more than two variables and measurement periods can be quite long. Of course with many variables and measurements, the data analysis becomes complex and difficult. Such studies are not frequent in the social sciences, perhaps due to their complexity and the difficulty of studying individuals over a long time span.

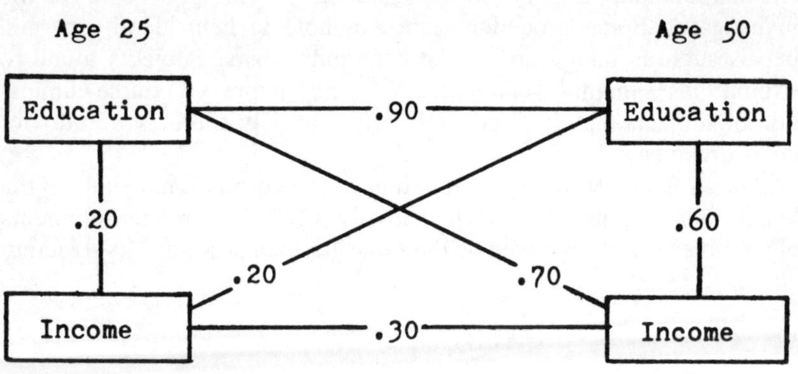

Figure 4.1 Cross-Lagged Panel Design

Note: Hypothetical correlations are indicated, illustrating that education at age 25 might cause income at age 50.

History can become quite a problem for longitudinal designs since there are no controls for outside events, although often it might be just those events that are of interest. That is, the goal of a study might be to ascertain if the relationship between variables changes over time as a function of historical events. Unfortunately, with this type of design, one would never be certain what events caused changes in relationships.

Instrument reactivity and Hawthorne effects may also pose problems for the same reasons as with other one-group designs. Again, multiple testings may attenuate or accentuate these problems.

Examples

Pretest-Posttest Design. The one-group pretest-posttest design is well-illustrated by an organizational study reported by Frederiksen (1978). This was an applied study intended to evaluate the effectiveness of behavioral problem solving and participation in reorganization. The study was undertaken at a Veterans Administration outpatient clinic in response to recognized problems with patient dropout, long waiting lists, and long time periods between appointments.

A pretest-posttest design was chosen with data collected on several important variables including proportion of new patients seen, dropout rate, and interappointment interval. The reorganization was designed by the professional staff utilizing a behavioral problem-solving approach. Results showed significant decreases in dropout (52 vs. 26%), time on waiting list (22 vs. 8 days), and interappointment interval (25 vs. 11 days). These results were taken for support of the effectiveness of the intervention.

While this study is certainly clear in showing that changes occurred, the lack of control makes results difficult to interpret. Of particular concern is that the expressed goal of the study was to evaluate the particular intervention strategy. Unfortunately, while one can state that the intended effects occurred, one cannot be certain specifically what caused them. That is, the same effects might have occurred through use of other techniques for reorganization. Furthermore, there may well have been factors occurring at the time of intervention that in fact accounted for the change. Finally, the application of this procedure to only one organization makes generalization to other sites difficult. Overall, the results of this study are quite suggestive of the efficacy of the behavioral problem-solving approach in organizations. However, the results are merely suggestive and are quite limited. They need to be replicated in other organizations and under more controlled conditions. A comparison of this approach with others, including reorganization with no staff involvement, would provide a more meaningful evaluation. However, as a first step, this study was useful and provided interesting data at relatively little investment of resources.

Interrupted Time Series. There are many examples of time series studies in the program evaluation literature. The one chosen here was conducted by Mazur-Hart and Berman (1977) to determine if no-fault divorce laws tend to increase the number of divorces. This study asked a simple question and used a simple design. Its concern was whether the divorce rate for a particular state increased after implementation of no-fault divorce. The design was an interrupted time series.

This study was conducted in Nebraska about four years after implementation of a new no-fault law. Public divorce records provided the data which consisted of monthly total divorces for the state. Data were analyzed for 41 months before and 29 months after the law went into effect.

The data were first analyzed to determine if autocorrelation existed among the observations. Since it did not, it was felt that multiple regression would be preferable to the more complex ARIMA. The purpose of the regression analysis was to determine if there were any changes in the divorce rate trend from the period before to the period after implementation of the new law. The data showed an upward trend during the entire period; that is, the divorce rate drifted upward for the entire series. There was no discontinuity or change in trend around the time of intervention. Thus the conclusion was that the new law had no effect on divorce rate, a conclusion that failed to support the contentions of the law's critics who felt that it would encourage divorce.

Of course there are obvious limitations to this study since it was nonexperimental and failed to control for invalidating factors. First, there was no control for history, and many other events might have occurred at the time of the law's implementation that would have suppressed the divorce rate. Of course, in defense of the design it seems unlikely that such effects would have occurred at exactly the same time as the new law and would have exactly canceled out its effects. This problem would have been more severe had the series shown a change which might have had several causes.

Perhaps a bigger limitation of this study was that it was conducted only in a single state. The one-sample nature of the study makes premature generalization risky until replication can confirm these results in other settings.

However, overall this study was a well-conducted time series in that the research question was clearly formulated, appropriate data were located, and sufficient observations were taken on either side of the intervention. Thus it provided useful data about the likely effects, or lack thereof, of no-fault divorce laws on divorce rates.

Correlational Design. An example of a correlational design has been conducted by O'Malley (1975). The interesting feature, making it an obvious example of this design, is that it was a retrospective study of suicide in Australia during World War II. Its purpose was to validate a theory relating suicide to war. Specifically, it was proposed that the more severe the threat to a population, the more social integration within the population, and the less the suicide rate. Thus the closer the war's threat to Australia and the more closely it was related to territorial invasion, the lower would be the suicide rate.

Data were collected from two sources — suicide rates *(apparently)* from official records and threat from content analyses of two Australian newspapers. Threat was broken down into two variables — aspect (territorial, logistic, and predictions) and theater (Pacific, North African, and European).

The data for the study were intercorrelated separately for each of the variable combinations above. Results showed negative correlations between threat and suicide for each of the nine possible variable combinations. Overall the correlation was −.52, which provided considerable support for the main hypothesis. In addition the correlations were stronger the nearer and more territorial the threat. Unfortunately, although the trends were in the predicted direction, O'Malley did not report statistical comparisons of the coefficients. Statements about comparative magnitudes of correlations must be made with care.

The results of this study are intriguing, considering the rather large correlations between newspaper article content and suicide. Unfortunately, these data are quite weak as a test of the causal hypothesis. There are a host of other variables that may have caused the relationship which have nothing to do with the theory. In fact, O'Malley discussed at great length the possibility that these results may simply have reflected changes in reporting of suicide rather than suicide itself. That is, during war when medical personnel were in short supply, the reporting of suicide might have become imprecise. Times of unusual threat may have been accompanied by increased casualties, increased military need for medical personnel, decreased supply of medical personnel for autopsies, and decreased reporting of suicide.

This study illustrates well the problems of drawing causal inferences from correlational data. All this study established was the existence of a relationship between two variables. More data would be necessary to establish causality. A next logical step would be to measure social integration and, using appropriate procedures such as path analysis, test whether threat seems to lead to integration which leads to suicide reduction.

5.0 MULTIPLE-GROUP DESIGNS

This chapter is concerned with the simplest of the experimental designs — the multiple group. These designs can involve comparison of two or more treatment groups that differ along a single independent variable. Included in this chapter are designs involving both single and multiple observations. Multiple-group time series designs are covered, as are ex post facto designs. The single characteristic that was used to assign designs to this particular chapter was the existence of a single independent variable in the design, exclusive of time or measurement period. These designs may include any number of measurements.

Two-Group Design

The simplest experimental design is the two group, which involves two variables — one independent and one dependent. The independent variable represents group membership and has two values or levels although, as will be seen in the next section, there is no reason why independent variables are limited to two values. The dependent variable is the measured characteristic of subjects that is free to take on any value possible. The structure is:

$$X_1\ O_1$$

$$X_2\ O_1$$

where the X's represent the two treatment groups and the O's are observations of the dependent variable. The levels of the independent variable might be treatments or conditions created or observed by the experimenter in a laboratory or field setting. In either event the investigator assigns subjects to conditions, ideally at random, and observes or measures levels of the dependent variable.

The major advantage of the two-group design over the nonexperimental designs is the control achieved by randomly assigning subjects to groups. If one can be certain that random assignment was achieved and that the two subject groups were truly equivalent, and if one can be assured that the only common difference in experience by the two groups was the treatment, one can be quite confident that differences in the dependent variable were due to the independent variable. The trick is to be sure that control was exercised over all factors irrelevant to the study. These conditions are not always easy to meet, and many times reinterpretations of studies are made based on the hypothesis that certain confounding variables explained results.

Of particular concern in this design is bias in assignment of subjects to groups since it is not always possible to use a truly random procedure. In some instances subjects must volunteer for treatment, or subjects are members of larger social units which must be assigned intact. This last case often occurs in educational research where treatments are assigned to entire classes. When assignment is made in this way, the true subject of the study is the class and not the individual student. In other words students are nested or contained in classes, and there may well be idiosyncratic class characteristics that produce nonequivalent assignment of students to treatments. Also, with social groups, treatments may affect the groups as a whole and may interact with group dynamics. Thus effects found for one group of people may not generalize to another, and the response of a particular person may vary depending upon other people in the group. Procedures are available for handling this problem and will be discussed later.

When subjects are not randomly assigned, it is often difficult to draw definitive conclusions from a study. When random assignment is impossible, there are two approaches, admittedly patchwork, that may add some confidence to the conclusions. The first involves checking for initial equivalence of groups, and the second involves selecting matched cases from all those available. With both approaches the variables used for matching are characteristics of the subjects or, ideally, a pretest on the dependent variable. The testing for pretest equivalence is a common procedure even with random assignment. When pretest differences are found, conclusions must be made with extreme care. The matching procedure, or ex post facto design, will be discussed in a later section of this monograph.

Nonrandom subject loss is another potential problem with the two-group design. Bias in subject loss can be as damaging as in subject assignment, as it destroys the entire concept of randomness. Subject loss is especially problematic in studies where the time between subject assignment to conditions and measurement of the dependent variable is long, or where treatments are of such a nature that subjects do not complete them. Studies involving some treatments that are unpleasant or painful may result in systematic subject attrition. In the psychotherapy research area, sometimes treatment groups consist of those individuals who completed treatment, compared with control subjects. There is an obvious bias in such studies since dropout or noncompletion of treatment is not a random event.

Other sources of invalidity are of no more concern to the two-group study than to other studies, and points made previously about them are relevant here. Overall, the advantage of the two-group study is its ability to control treatments so that only levels of the independent variable of interest are compared. However, independent variables are often complex situations which can differ along many dimensions. A well-designed study is based on a careful and thorough analysis of these dimensions and assures that the treatment conditions created truly reflect the underlying theory or hypothesis.

The analysis of data in the two-group study usually involves comparing group means on the dependent variables of interest. This can be done with a simple t test or with the analysis of variance (ANOVA). The results are equivalent with either approach. The analysis of variance will be discussed in greater detail in the next section.

There is one distinction that needs to be made here and that concerns the level of measurement of the independent variable. The underlying characteristic upon which the group membership variable is based may be discrete, such as sex or race, or it may be continuous, such as dosage of drug or amount of time spent in an activity. With the discrete variable, the numbers represent convenient labels, and intermediate values are meaningless, except, perhaps, as additional labels. Thus with the sex variable if males are considered to have a value of 1, and females a value of 2, a value for sex of 1.5 has no meaning in relationship to males and females. However, with continuous variables, such as time, 1.5 minutes has meaning in relationship to 1 and 2 minutes; it is the midpoint between them. With a continuous independent variable, one can state a functional relationship between it and the dependent variable, and one can interpolate to values between those chosen for study. For example, if one were to find that a student can learn twice as much material in 4 hours than 2 hours, one might interpolate that one and one-half as much material is learned in 3 hours than in 2 hours.

If the independent variable is discrete or if one is not going to extend conclusions to values of the independent variable that were not included in the study, the independent variable is said to be a *fixed effect*. On the other hand if the underlying continuum of the independent variable is continuous, and if conclusions are made to values not in the design, the independent variable is said to be a *random effect*. One should note that when an independent variable is truly discrete, one cannot extend conclusions to other values of the variable and in fact intermediate values might not exist. Therefore, the effect must be fixed. When the independent variable is continuous, one can choose whether to treat the effect as fixed or random. For example, suppose one designs a study to determine the effects on voter preference for a particular condidate of two media presentations, one lasting for one minute and the other lasting for five minutes. If one were to find that the five-minute spot was more effective than the one-minute spot at inducing a favorable response toward the candidate, one could treat the effect as fixed or random. If fixed, one would conclude that the five-minute presentation was more effective than the shorter one, but one would make no statements about the effects of presentation length in general. That is, one would not conclude that a two-minute presentation would be more effective than a one, or a three-minute one better than a two. If this were done, the effect would be random, as one would be interpolating results to intermediate values not chosen for study.

In the social sciences, independent variables are usually considered fixed, especially when there are only two levels. It is not particularly good practice to choose only two levels for a random variable since only two of many possible points are included along the measurement continuum, and the actual form of the relationship between independent and dependent variables will be based on too little information.

With fixed variables or effects, one can select levels to compare two procedures, treatments, or conditions or to compare one treatment to a control of no treatment. In many cases this distinction is somewhat arbitrary as control conditions may actually involve treatment, but perhaps not conducted by the researcher. A good example is in the area of psychotherapy research where a particular treatment approach might be compared to no treatment. The most common practice is to compare individuals who receive treatment, for example systematic desensitization, to individuals who spend an equivalent amount of time on a waiting list. However, it is difficult to say that the control subjects receive no treatment — only that they receive no professional treatment. They may in fact receive help from family and friends, which is indeed a treatment. What is compared in these studies is professional treatment and naturally occurring treatment in the community.

Laboratory research certainly provides more control over alternative treatments for control group subjects. However, even in highly controlled settings, the control subjects experience something during the time they are in the control condition. This control treatment is carefully chosen to be neutral and may involve giving the subjects some task or activity to occupy their time. Elements of this control activity are designed carefully to control various aspects of actual treatment. In verbal learning experiments it is common to give control subjects a mental task to prevent them from mentally rehearsing material, and in studies involving manual or perceptual tasks, control tasks might hold fatigue constant.

Although with fixed effects one does not extend conclusions to intermediate values of the independent variable, there is always some interpretation or generalization beyond the exact conditions of the study. That is, one interprets how far the experimental conditions can be extended. In a psychotherapy study, one decides whether results can generalize to the particular treatment approach applied by different therapists, at different institutions, and with different orientations. Unfortunately, treatments sharing the same label are not necessarily equivalent. Generalization is a difficult task requiring much judgment and knowledge of a content area. Replication is important for testing the same hypothesis utilizing somewhat different operationalizations of the independent variable and instruments for the dependent variable.

Multiple-Group Posttest Design

An expansion of the two-group design is the multiple-group design, with a single dependent variable measured once and an independent variable that can have any number of values or levels. This design has the structure:

$$
\begin{array}{cc}
X_1 & O_1 \\
X_2 & O_1 \\
. & . \\
. & . \\
. & . \\
X_n & O_1
\end{array}
$$

For the most part all of the discussion related to the advantages and problems of the two group study applies to the multiple group. The multiple group has the additional advantage that more levels of the independent variable can be compared, and more control groups can be included. For example, if one were to try out a new procedure of some sort, one might compare the new procedure or treatment against both no treatment and a commonly used treatment. This would represent a double control in that one would establish that the conventional procedure worked better than no procedure in a particular setting and that the new procedure was better or worse than the conventional.

In the previous section I made the distinction between fixed and random effects. One can have fixed effects with any number of groups, as some variables may be represented by many possible discrete values. Occupation, for example, may be categorized into hundreds of levels, although this would not be practical in a real design. Random effects become useful when there are several values of the independent variable. For example, one might conduct a study to ascertain the effects of varying doses of a particular drug on memory. The effects of five doses of the drug could be measured on the number of items remembered after a single presentation of a word list. Since the independent variable would be random, one could determine a mathematical function relating dosage to memory.

The major data-analytic tool for such multiple-group studies is the analysis of variance. This procedure is designed to statistically compare two or more treatment groups on the dependent variable. The mechanics involve a comparison of two variances derived from the data. The first is the between-group variance, that is, the variance of the treatment means between or among groups. The second is the within-group variance or the variance among subjects within each treatment group. If there are no group differences other than those resulting by chance, variance between groups should be equivalent to variance within groups. That is, the two variances would be equivalent statistically or there would be no significant group differences. If there are group differences, there should be more between-group variance than within-group variance, and the comparison should become statistically significant. This discussion is admittedly an oversimplification of ANOVA; the interested reader should consult a text on statistics for computational details (e.g., Iversen and Norpoth, 1976; Myers, 1972; Winer, 1971).

Multiple-Group Pretest-Posttest Design

By adding pretest observations of the dependent variable to the first two designs of this chapter, one will create a pretest-posttest design as diagramed below:

$$
\begin{array}{ccc}
O_1 & X_1 & O_2 \\
O_1 & X_2 & O_2 \\
\cdot & \cdot & \cdot \\
\cdot & \cdot & \cdot \\
\cdot & \cdot & \cdot \\
O_1 & X_n & O_2
\end{array}
$$

The advantage of this design lies in being able to demonstrate the level of the dependent variable before as well as after treatment. This can be useful information for establishing that groups were initially equivalent and for providing a baseline against which to compare treatment effects, of particular value when a control group is not available.

Pretest-posttest designs are especially popular in program evaluation studies where the research question concerns the efficacy of programs or specific interventions for producing change in participants. Many of these studies may not have available an untreated control, as all people available as subjects may receive some treatment or intervention. This is especially true in educational, mental health, and social service program research.

It is always preferable to have proper control groups, and, as with the one-group pretest-posttest, the existence of change with the current design does not indicate the factors that caused it. If a nontreated control group is unavailable in a study which compared two types of interventions, one would never be certain what might have happened to subjects in either treatment group had they received no treatment. The use of pretests is not a good substitute for proper control groups.

The addition of pretests to a design creates the potential for instrument reactivity with treatments. As discussed in the previous chapter, subjects may be affected by pretests in such a manner as to influence their reactions to the treatments. Perhaps the best control for this possibility is that used in the Solomon four-group design, described in the next chapter.

Other problems with this design are similar to those of the previous two in this chapter. However, there does exist a particular problem in the analysis and interpretation of change data generated in pretest-posttest studies. One possible means of analyzing these data would be to compare groups on average changes from pre- to posttesting, subtracting posttest from pretest scores, but there is a significant problem with the use of change scores and that involves measurement error.

It is widely known that the reliability of the difference between two imperfect measures is worse than the reliability of either measure itself. Suppose one were to administer an attitude questionnaire to a group of subjects before and after an attitude change treatment. Furthermore, suppose the instrument had a reliability of .90, a very good reliability coefficient for such a measure. Unless scores on the pretest were uncorrelated with scores on the posttest, a very unlikely phenomenon, the reliability of the difference scores would be less than .90. In fact if the correlation between scores at the two times was .70, the reliability of the difference would be only .67, based on the formula provided by Guilford (1954: 394). Difference scores based on less reliable instruments would have considerably worse reliability.

A second problem with pretest-posttest data involves a statistical artifact, regression toward the mean. This artifact is an outcome of measurement error that accompanies imperfectly reliable instruments. It is a statistical fact that scores on an instrument for subjects extreme in value relative to all people who might be measured tend to become less extreme upon retesting. If an individual has a score that is unusually high, it probably is associated with a large error component. It is unlikely that, upon retesting, that individual will score as high again. Thus scores of individuals tend to become closer to the average score upon retesting. This tendency is greater the further away from the mean the initial score.

When a group of subjects produces scores that are extreme, chances are that part of that extreme score was due to random error; and upon retesting, even with no intervention, the scores will fall toward the mean, and the gorup will seem to demonstrate change. If two groups were each tested twice on the same instrument and one happened to be more extreme than the other, one would expect the more extreme group to show more change than the less extreme group merely as a function of regression toward the mean. If different treatments were applied to the groups, it might be difficult to separate real treatment effects from regression toward the mean.

These problems have led some to question whether change scores are at all valuable in research studies (Cronbach and Furby, 1970). In fact if random assignment occurs and subjects are initially equivalent, comparison of posttest scores alone will indicate if the dependent variable differed among levels of the independent variable. If random assignment did not occur, statistical procedures are at best a weak means of patching the design. (For a discussion of the problems and procedures for the measurement of change see Harris, 1963.)

Two procedures for analyzing data from pretest-posttest designs have already been discussed. The analysis of change scores directly is relatively simple and easy to interpret. Unfortunately, it suffers from the problems of low reliability and statistical artifacts. The second procedure that has been suggested is to use the pretest scores merely to verify that the groups were initially equivalent and then to test for posttest differences. That is, if all groups show pretest equivalence, differential scores upon posttesting would indicate differential change. Of course if pretest differences were found, posttests would not indicate change. A problem with this approach is best illustrated with an example. Suppose one were to collect both pretest and posttest data for two groups. Considering the sample sizes and variance of both groups, suppose it would take a mean difference between groups of exactly 5.00 to achieve significance. If one were to find for pretests that the difference between means was 4.99, one would conclude no pretest differences. Now suppose for posttest the difference was 5.00. It would be quite difficult to argue that there was differential change between groups because the pretest was not significant but the posttest was. One must be quite cautious in drawing conclusions with such procedures.

Other procedures for analyzing these data have been developed. ANOVA can be used for this design and is quite reasonable if there has been random assignment to treatment conditions. Analysis of covariance has been suggested where posttests are compared after being statistically adjusted for pretest scores. This procedure can provide a more sensitive test than analysis of posttests alone, but it is a poor substitute for random assignment.

Ex Post Facto Design

The expost facto design is a patchwork procedure intended to make a pseudo-experimental design out of a nonexperimental one. This is done in observational studies where one variable can be identified as independent or in experimental designs where it was not possible to randomly assign subjects. The logic of the design, as mentioned previously, is to match on several critical variables subjects in two or more groups and then to analyze data from the matched subjects only. The design is diagramed as:

$$\begin{matrix} X_1\ O_1 & \text{Match} \\ X_2\ O_1 & \end{matrix}$$

where the two groups are matched after treatment.

For example, suppose a study is designed to ascertain if job enlargement leads to less absenteeism than traditional work design. One might find a factory whose management agrees to participate in an enlargement experiment. However, management might insist that employees be given a choice whether they want to try the new system or stick with the old, traditional assembly line process. One could assign the volunteers to enlargement and nonvolunteers to the control group and then check absenteeism for the two groups. Since random assignment would not occur, one would not be certain that enlargement was the cause of absenteeism differences. One could therefore select samples for analysis that would be matched on variables considered to be relevant. In this example one might match on salary, tenure, age, sex, marital status, history of serious medical problems, and job performance. One would then have two samples that were equivalent on at least these seven variables.

Unfortunately, the two groups would still differ on one important variable — volunteering. It may well be that those who volunteered would respond favorably and show absenteeism improvement. The nonvolunteers might well react in the opposite way, and if enlargement were instituted throughout the company, the net result might be no difference in average absenteeism, although some employees might improve and some become worse. In the final analysis one cannot match for every possible variable, and one can never know for certain which variables are most crucial.

Another major problem with matching is shrinkage in sample size with multiple matching variables. Campbell and Stanley (1963; 70) illustrate well this problem citing a study conducted by Chapin (1955). They point out that Chapin's original sample of 1194 shrunk to only 46 after matching. This shrinkage alone caused severe problems for generalization. Also, they note that the original effects found with the entire sample shrunk considerably after matching and question whether they might have totally disappeared had other matching variables been added.

Nevertheless, the ex post facto design may be an improvement over the two-group design with no random assignment, although without random assignment the design is hardly experimental. Perhaps the most crucial variable for matching would be a pretest on the dependent variable itself. This at least would enable the investigator to state that the groups were equivalent initially on this variable. Conclusions could then be drawn about differntial change, although its cause still might be the selection process interacting with treatment. In the enlargement example, even if employees were matched for prior absenteeism, the only firm conclusion would be that job enlargement may reduce absenteeism for employees willing to volunteer for it. Its efficacy with non-volunteers would be a question for empirical verification.

Multiple-Group Time Series Design

The final design to be covered in this chapter is the multiple-group time series. This design involves multiple measurements of the dependent variable on two or more groups representing levels of the independent variable. It is an extension of the pretest-posttest design where there are more than two measurement periods and an extension of the interrupted time series to multiple groups. It is represented as:

$$O_1\ O_2\ O_3\ X_1\ O_4\ O_5\ O_6$$

$$O_1\ O_2\ O_3\ X_2\ O_4\ O_5\ O_6$$

for a two-group, six-measurement design.

As with the time series design for one group, the multiple-group time series can involve a few measurements over a relatively brief duration or many measurements taken over considerable time. The number of measurements determines the type of analysis to be used, as some analyses are not feasible for many testings, while others cannot be used if there are not a sufficient number of time periods selected. Some of these procedures assume that time periods between measurements are constant, although designs for which ANOVA would be appropriate can have unequal periods.

The simplest time series design is one where there are two or more levels of an independent variable, and these treatments are applied in the middle of a series of observations of the dependent variable. The advantages and problems with this design are similar to the pretest-posttest discussed earlier in this chapter. This particular design is potentially more sensitive to instrument reactivity due to the repeated application of the instrument, although subjects may tend to adapt to being measured. An advantage of this design is that it allows determination of trends on the dependent variable before and after treatment. Before treatment this would indicate whether the dependent variable was stable over time for all treatment groups. This is especially important when subjects are not randomly assigned. After treatment the multiple measurements indicate whether treatment effects occur immediately or last for an extended period of time. Program evaluations often take relatively long-range measurements on subjects to see if gains made as the result of a program or intervention sustain themselves over time. Such follow-up studies are frequent in mental health and criminal justice.

With time series involving several measurement periods, the analysis of variance can be used to test for differential change or trends among treatment groups. However, with several measurements, the analysis of variance suffers the problem of autocorrelation. That is, with repeated measurements, those measurements occurring more closely to one another in time tend to be more highly correlated than those occurring more distally. This results in biased statistical tests and may indicate false statistical significance. Adjustments are possible, although they may not be totally satisfactory. An alternative approach would be to use the multivariate analysis of variance (MANOVA), which does not suffer from autocorrelation. Discussion of this procedure would be beyond the present scope. The interested reader is referred to Cole and Grizzle (1966) or Poor (1973).

For many measurements, neither ANOVA nor MANOVA would be possible. If there are 50 or more measurements, ARIMA can be used. These applications are discussed by Glass, Willson, and Gottman (1975: Chapter 8) and by Chatfield (1975).

Examples

Two-Group Design. Experimental designs in field settings are rather rare due to problems involved in gaining control over subject assignment and confounding factors. An exception is a study by Waldo and Chiricos (1977), who were able to randomly assign prison inmates to one of two treatments which they did not create. Since there was in fact random assignment, this design is experimental.

The question of interest in this study was whether work release is effective in reducing recidivism among prison inmates. The investigators were able to assign at random prisoners to either work release or traditional treatment. As a check on random assignment, the two groups were compared on several characteristics, particularly those related to prior arrest record. No significant differences were found, which gave the investigators greater confidence in their results.

Measures of recidivism were taken for each subject in the study. Since the investigators were unable to select a single measure, they included 18, each of which was analyzed separately. There were no statistically significant differences found between the two groups on any of the recidivism measures. Thus work release, which is widely assumed to be effective in reducing recidivism, was found to be no better than more traditional treatment.

It is difficult to find fault with the design of this study since subjects were randomly assigned to both the experimental and control groups. One might wish to investigate further what the control subjects received in the way of treatment, as other possible control treatments might yield different results. The question here is whether the control treatment used can generalize to other prison systems. This question can also be raised concerning the generalizability of the sample. That is, would these results be found in other facilities with different inmate populations or different operating environments? Such questions suggest the need for replication of studies, especially by other investigators in other geographic areas. Replication is an essential element in verifying hypotheses.

Multigroup Design. Reilly, Tenopyr, and Sperling (1979) conducted a study to determine the effects of job previews on job acceptance and survival of applicants to a telephone company. A total of 325 job applicants were randomly assigned to one of three conditions which varied only on the type of preview given. In the first or realistic condition, applicants were given balanced information, some favorable and some unfavorable, about working for the company. The second was the favorable condition in which only favorable information was given. The third condition was a control that was given no additional information. There were four separate dependent variables separately analyzed in the study by means of chi-square statistics appropriate for frequency data. Only the results of the job acceptance variable will be summarized here.

Job acceptance rates were found to differ significantly among the treatment groups (acceptance rate = 56.1%, 68.6%, and 71.6% for realistic, favorable, and control, respectively). Subsequent analysis indicated that this difference was accounted for solely by the lower acceptance rate for the realistic preview group.

These data suggest that the realistic preview reduced the frequency of acceptance for those job applicants receiving it. Since the design was experimental, one would assume that the only systematic difference among groups was the independent variable. This yielded conclusions quite strongly that the preview led to decreased acceptance. That is, this study can be considered internally valid. However, external validity or generalization to other samples might be more problematic. This particular study was done with telephone operator candidates at one particular compnay. It is an empirical question whether these results would be found in another organization with different personnel procedures and with another population applying for different types of jobs. For definitive conclusions that could be widely generalized, this study would have to be replicated at additional organizations and for additional job categories.

Two-Group Multiple-Measures Design. Stephens and Burroughs (1978) conducted a study to ascertain whether different operant conditioning procedures would be effective in reducing employee absenteeism in a hospital. They created two treatment conditions as the independent variable and measured absenteeism three times. The two treatment conditions were slight variations of a lottery in which employees who met the criteria of good attendance would be eligible for a cash prize in a drawing. One condition required no absenteeism during a three-week period while the other required attendance on eight secret, random days during the same three weeks. Data on absenteeism were collected for both treatment groups during three time periods — before, during, and after treatment.

The results of this study are depicted in Figure 5.1. As can be seen, there were small and nonsignificant differences between the two treatment groups. Likewise, there was a nonsignificant interaction between treatments and repeated measures, indicating similar effects for both groups. However, there was a strong retesting effect with absenteeism declining during the lottery period and increasing after its termination to a level higher than before treatment.

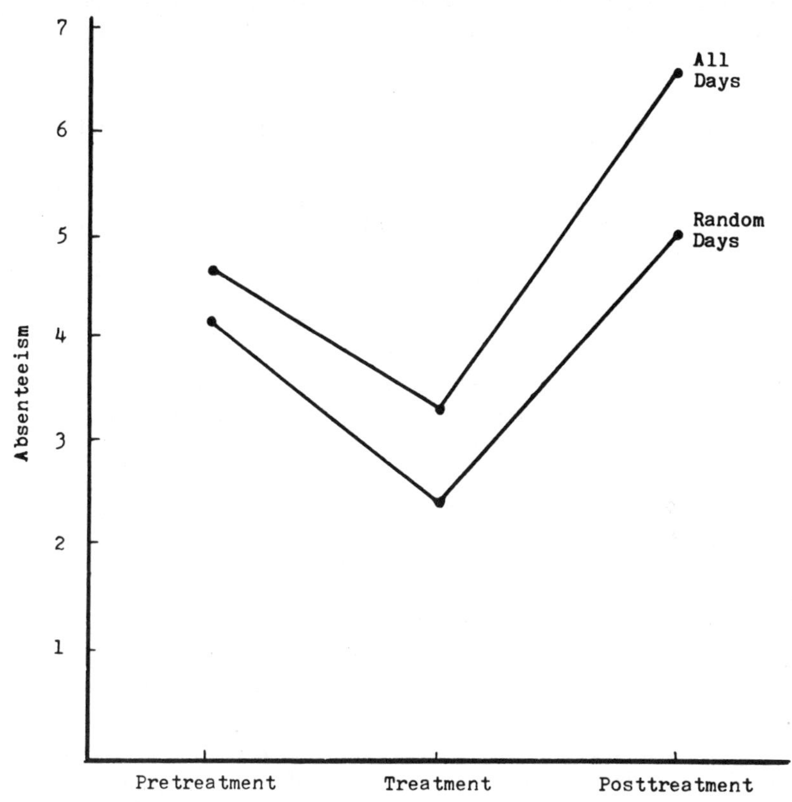

Figure 5.1 Absenteeism as a Function of Experimental Condition

Although this study is experimental, it is inconclusive due to the investigators' choice of independent variable levels. While it provides strong evidence that both treatments were equal in their effects, there was no control group that received neither procedure. In effect each treatment group served as its own control through the repeated measurement, but there was no control for history apparently because the investigators felt that there were no other events that occurred which might have confounded the results.

Perhaps more important, considering that this was an organizational field study, is the potential for Hawthorne effects. That is, the effectiveness of these procedures might have been due to the subjects' knowledge that they were in an experiment. What suggests that there might be a transitory effect was the absenteeism increase during the final phase of the study after treatment was discontinued. This might have reflected the employees' putting off discretionary absences until after the lottery. These results certainly suggest the need for a longer term study to determine if the absenteeism reduction would continue over an extended period.

This study points out the limitations of even an experimental design, especially in field settings. Despite that fact that it was rather well-designed and implemented, it was still not conclusive. This is because it allowed only comparison of the two treatment conditions, which do not necessarily represent all reasonable treatment conditions possible. Furthermore, there is the possibility of Hawthorne effects which were not controlled. Finally, as with most studies, there is the generalizability problem, and one cannot be certain that the same results would be found with a different organization or other employees.

6.0 FACTORIAL DESIGNS

To this point the designs discussed involved only a single independent plus a retesting variable. However, most experimental designs encountered in practice have several independent variables and are meant to determine their combined effects on the dependent variable in question. Usually the independent variables are placed into a factorial structure for ease of analysis. These structures can be simple or complex, depending upon the number and nature of variables chosen. It is the purpose of this chapter to review factorial designs, from the most simple involving two independent variables to the complex involving several.

Two × Two Factorial Design

By far the simplest factorial design is the 2 × 2, which consists of two independent variables, each taking on two levels or values. The design is structured so that every level of one independent variable is crossed or associated with every level of the other. For example if the independent variables are sex (male vs. female) and treatment (A vs. B), the design would consist of four treatment combinations or cells — males receiving treatment A, males receiving treatment B, females receiving A, and

TABLE 6.1 Example of a 2 × 2 Factorial Design

Treatment	*Sex*	
	Male	Female
A	Subject 1 Subject 2 Subject 3 Subject 4 Subject 5	Subject 11 Subject 12 Subject 13 Subject 14 Subject 15
B	Subject 6 Subject 7 Subject 8 Subject 9 Subject 10	Subject 16 Subject 17 Subject 18 Subject 19 Subject 20

females receiving B. The design structure is outlined in Table 6.1 for a study with 20 subjects, 5 per cell. As can be seen, every possible combination of independent variable levels is represented, and each cell contains the same number of subjects who are different individuals or social entities. These last two conditions are not necessary, but they greatly simplify the analysis.

For the most part the advantages and problems with the factorial design are similar to those of the multigroup. However, the factorial design allows the addition of variables which may be used as controls for confounding factors or as additional aspects to be studied. An example of additional control is the Solomon four-group design, discussed in the following section, which has as one independent variable whether the subject receives a pretest. This design allows a determination of instrument reactivity.

Most factorial studies contain independent variables that are factors of interest rather than possible confounds such as instrument reactivity. These designs have the advantage that they allow determination of joint effects of independent variables in addition to their independent effects. These are represented as interactions and main effects, respectively.

A main effect in a factorial design is the independent (in a conceptual rather than mathematical sense) effect of a particular variable. In the previous example there would be a main effect for sex and a main effect for treatment. Each would involve a comparison of all subjects at each of its two levels. One would compare all males with all females on the dependent measure, regardless of their level of treatment. Likewise, the treatment main effect would involve a comparison of all A subjects with all B subjects, regardless of their sex. This is done by ignoring the other variable and *collapsing* across it. Means would be calculated for all males and all females by collapsing across the levels of the treatment variable. The same would be done with sex for the treatment variable.

The interaction is the joint or qualified effect taking into account both variables. The interaction in the example would be concerned with whether differences between treatment A and B were the same for males and females, whether there were main effects. In other words, if females are higher on the dependent measure for B than A, do males show the same pattern? The same pattern can exist even though the means for males may be higher or lower than for females.

Interaction can best be understood by illustration. Figure 6.1 indicates graphically several possible combinations of main effects and interactions. For each graph the x-axis represents the independent variable, treatment, which takes on its two values, A and B. The y-axis represents the dependent variable, and the sex variable is represented by the two lines, labelled male and female.

Figure 6.1a indicates two main effects and no interaction. Females are higher than males for both treatments, and treatment B is higher than treatment A for both sexes. There is no interaction since the pattern of results is the same for both sexes. This is reflected by the fact that the two lines are parallel.

Figure 6.1b indicates a case of interaction with no main effects. The pattern for males and females is exactly opposite. Males are higher on A than B, and females are higher on B than A. Overall neither treatment is higher than the other, and neither sex is higher than the other. The interaction is indicated by the 'x' pattern formed by the two lines.

Figures 6.1c and 6.1d illustrate two other possible interactions. In c there is no difference on the treatment variable for males, but there is for females. Furthermore, females and males do not differ on A, only on B. In 6.1d females are higher than males on both treatments but show an opposite pattern. Where females are higher on B than A, males are higher on A than B. This pattern is similar to 6.1b except that there is now a sex main effect.

Interactions are more precise statements of the results than main effects and usually once an interaction is found, the main effects should be discarded. This is especially true with patterns like 6.1c where a difference is only found for females. To say there is a treatment main effect, though technically correct, implies that all subjects, on the average, are different at one treatment than the other, a situation that is not true since only females show the effect.

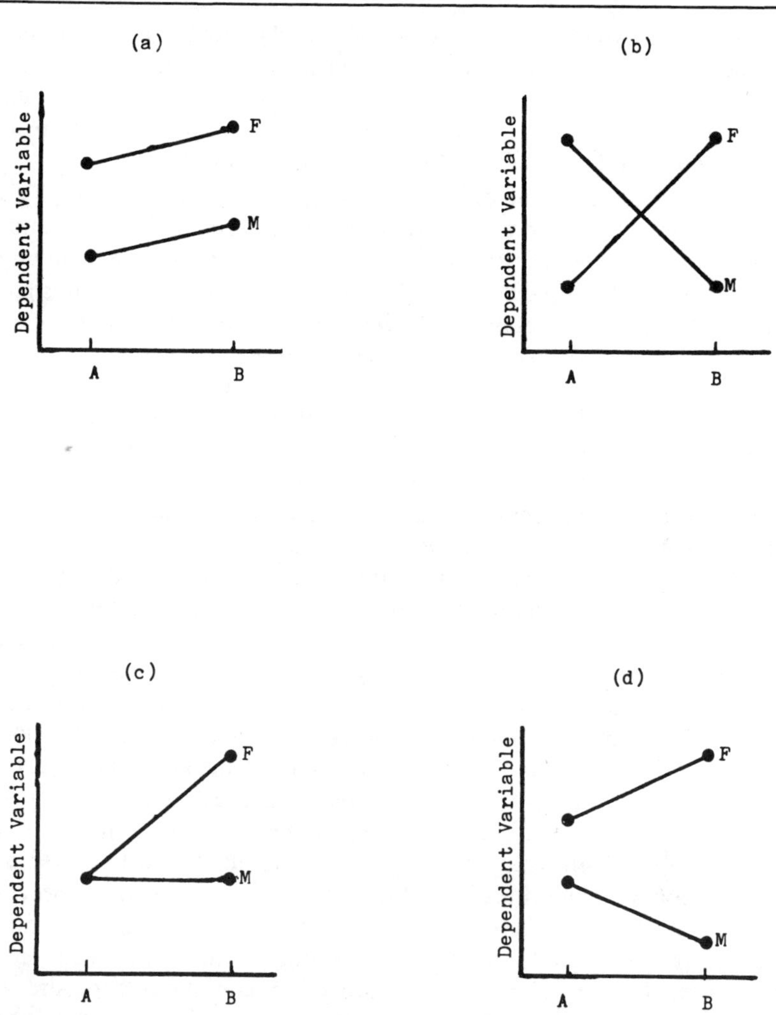

Figure 6.1 Examples of Possible Interactions for a 2 × 2 Design

The analysis of factorial data is conducted with the analysis of variance. As mentioned in the last chapter, ANOVA involves calculating two variance estimates and testing them for statistical significance. With the more complex 2 × 2 design, however, there are three effects to test, not one. Therefore, in addition to an estimate of within-group or error variance, one must devise an estimate for all three between-group effects — the two mains and interaction. Total between group variance can be partitioned into components for each of the effects to be tested. Each is compared to error variance using the same statistical logic discussed in the previous chapter. Thus there would be three tests conducted with the possibility that any or all are significant.

Earlier mention was made of two limiting assumptions that simplified ANOVA; first, that different subjects were in each cell of the design and, second, that there were the same number of subjects in each cell. Having different subjects in each cell makes this a *between-subjects* design, which is the easiest to analyze. However, it is not necessary to have all between-subjects effects, and the same subjects can be found in more than one cell making the effect *within subject*. The most common circumstance in which this occurs is with the pretest-posttest design. One of the independent variables is the time of measurement which is included as a within-subject effect in the ANOVA. With such a design the treatment main effect indicates that ignoring or combining retestings, one treatment is higher on the dependent variable than the other. The main effect for retesting indicates that average posttests differ from average pretests. The interaction indicates that the two treatments differed in the pattern of scores from pretest to posttest. This is the effect that indicates group differences, usually the question of primary interest.

The within-subject variable is not limited to retesting, and in fact multiple levels of a treatment variable can be applied to the same subjects. In the Sex × Treatment example, both treatments could be given to each subject. The advantage is that this tends to reduce error variance due to idiosyncratic differences among subjects. At the same time it creates the problem that treatments are confounded with order of presentation and with retesting. Order can be controlled with a procedure termed *counterbalancing*. That is, half the subjects receive A first and half receive B first, allowing one to compare the same treatments given at each order. However, this procedure confounds exposure to prior treatments with number of measurements, making it difficult to separate instrument reactivity from treatment carryover. Procedures to control for reactivity are discussed below and could be incorporated with counterbalancing. It is always hoped that there will not be order effects, because such effects complicate interpretation of results.

Another complication arises in a factorial design when cell sizes are not equal. With equal sample sizes or *orthogonal designs,* the independent variables are totally independent or uncorrelated. As sample sizes become unequal, the independent variables become dependent and correlated (nonorthogonal). Hence it is difficult to determine the inde-

TABLE 6.2 Examples of Equal and Nonequal Sample Size Factorial Designs

(a)

	A		
B	a_1	a_2	*Total*
b_1	M = 100 n = 50	M = 150 n = 50	M = 125 n = 100
b_2	M = 200 n = 50	M = 250 n = 50	M = 225 n = 100
Total	M = 150 n = 100	M = 200 n = 100	

(b)

	A		
B	a_1	a_2	*Total*
b_1	M = 100 n = 10	M = 150 n = 90	M = 145 n = 100
b_2	M = 200 n = 90	M = 250 n = 10	M = 205 n = 100
Total	M = 190 n = 100	M = 160 n = 100	

pendent effects of each independent variable since they are confounded with one another. Table 6.2 shows what inequality of cell sizes does to main effect means. In both designs shown, the individual cell means and total number of subjects are identical. However, the main effect or marginal means are different due to the unequal sample sizes. In fact the means for treatment A completely reversed from a_2 being larger than a_1 to a_2 being smaller. Statistical tests for significant differences between these means will be distorted in the same way. Hence, straightforward ANOVA might not yield correct conclusions. The solution to this problem is complex and certainly beyond the scope of this discussion. Proper procedures for analyzing such data are discussed in other sources (Spector, 1980; Spector, Voissem, and Cone, forthcoming).

Solomon Four-Group Design

The Solomon four-group design is a combination of the 2 × 2 factorial and the pretest-posttest, used to control for instrument reactivity. This design is similar to factorial designs because subjects are placed into a 2 × 2 structure and similar to the pretest-posttest because subjects receive two measurements, but in this case only half the subjects receive the pretest. It is represented as:

$$O_1 \; X_1 \; O_2$$

$$X_1 \; O_2$$

$$O_1 \; X_2 \; O_2$$

$$X_2 \; O_2$$

The Solomon four-group design offers all the advantages of the factorial with the additional feature that it tests for instrument reactivity. That is, for both groups one is able to compare subjects who differ only in that they received the pretest. Furthermore, one is able to assess the degree of change that occurred between pretesting and posttesting for each treatment. This design is quite powerful and sees too little application in the social sciences — surprising since it would require little additional effort in many situations.

The basic logic of the Solomon four group could be extended to both larger and smaller designs. For the single-group pretest-posttest, this procedure could be used to control for instrument reactivity by omitting pretests for half the subjects. It could also be used in studies involving more than two groups, using the same idea of adding pretests for half the subjects. The only limitation would be that a sufficient number of subjects must be available for each of the groups in the study.

The analysis of four-group design data is somewhat more complex than analyses discussed earlier. Since only half the subjects receive pretests, the design is incomplete from a statistical perspective. That is, if one were to set all data into an ANOVA design, there would be missing data for half the subjects. Perhaps the best procedure would be to conduct the analysis in stages. The first stage might be to compare the two treatment groups on pretests to verify that there were no pretest differences. This would be a check on random assignment to conditions. If differences exist, it would be difficult to draw definitive conclusions from the study. The second stage would involve an analysis of all posttest scores. These data would fit a 2 × 2 factorial design with treatment level as one factor and pretest (present or absent) as the other. One could then test for treatment differences, the major hypothesis of interest, and instrument reactivity in two ways. First, one would see whether there were significant differences overall between subjects receiving pretests and subjects not receiving pretests. If this test was significant, pretests would be affecting either posttest measurement or treatments. The interaction term would yield a test for a differential effect of pretesting on the two treatments. That is, pretests might affect one treatment more than another, especially if one is a control group that receives no manipulation.

Finally, if there are no pretest differences and no instrument reactivity effects, one might wish either to analyze change scores or to conduct an analysis of posttests adjusted for pretests for those subjects who received pretests. Of course one must take appropriate care in analyzing such data in light of the problems, discussed previously, with change score analysis.

M × N Factorial Design

The 2 × 2 factorial design can be expanded where the independent variables have any number of levels within practical limits. Such designs are an extension of the 2 × 2 and share the same advantages and problems. However, they enable the researcher to investigate more than two levels of the independent variables at one time, often a useful feature.

In designing factorial studies, one must decide how many levels of the independent variable to construct. For some variables, such as sex, there are a limited and fixed number of levels possible. For others the number of possible levels might be unlimited. This is especially true when an independent variable can be represented on a continuous scale, such as time, number of trials, or scores on a test. Such variables are usually treated as fixed, although they could be treated as random. In the social sciences it is rare to find analyses of variance conducted with other than fixed effects.

When independent variables are continuous, and the investigator is not faced with choosing several from all possible levels, it is better to retain the variable's continuous nature than force it into a limited number of categories. This is a procedure often overlooked when the independent variables are characteristics of subjects such as age, income, or scores on psychological tests. In the latter case it is common to dichotomize scores into upper and lower halves, assigning all subjects above the median to one level of the independent variable and subjects with scores below the median to the other. This practice is wasteful in that it ignores the fact that the independent variable was measured with far greater precision than reflected by a two-value variable. The reason for the popularity of such practices can be found in the common preference for certain experimental designs and the analysis of variance.

The same hypotheses can be tested utilizing all the precision in the variables by using multiple regression instead of ANOVA. As discussed previously, multiple regression is a procedure that allows one to specify a linear functional relationship between the dependent variable and the independent variables. An equation is generated of the form:

$$Y = b_O + b_1 x_1 + b_2 x_2 + \ldots + b_n x_n$$

where Y is the dependent variable, the x's are the independent variables, and the b's are constants derived from the data. The mathematical procedures to solve for the constants can be found in many sources including Cohen and Cohen (1975), Kerlinger and Pedhauzer (1973), and Lewis-Beck (1980).

The use of multiple regression for the factorial design enables one to ascertain which main effects and interactions are significantly related to the dependent variable. With continuous independent variables, main effects would be created by entering into the analysis, observations of the independent variables as x values. Interactions would be represented as products of the independent variables. For example, the interaction of variables A and B would be created by multiplying individual scores on A and B (Lewis-Beck, 1980). Since most variables are based on different underlying metrics, it is common to convert both variables to standard scores before multiplying them together.

One complication with using multiple regression in this way is that the effects in the equation may not be independent. That is, the independent variables might be correlated. When this occurs one must take care in interpreting the results. One method for analyzing correlated terms involves stepwise addition or deletion of effects in the analysis. For example, with the stepwise addition procedure, one would first calculate the regression of the dependent variable on the first independent variable. One would then see if adding the second independent variable to the analysis results in a significant increase in relationship between the dependent variable and the two independents. If it does, the next independent variable would be added, and so on until all independent variables are added or until a point is reached at which adding more variables adds nothing to the analysis. Of coures, the major problem with this procedure is specifying the order of entry of the variables, rendering it of maximum value when one has a hypothetical model that specifies order. See Cohen and Cohen (1975) or Kerlinger and Pedhauzer (1973) for details on stepwise procedures.

The interaction term in the m × n design is more difficult to handle than in the 2 × 2 since the graphs can represent more complex patterns. Figure 6.2 illustrates some possible patterns with a 3 × 4 design. Figure 6.2a is a situation in which there are main effects but no interaction. The A variable shows no differences between a_1 and a_2 or between a_3 and a_4, but a difference between each pair. The pattern remains identical for all levels of the B variable, but b_1 is greater than b_2 which is greater than b_3.

Figure 6.2b indicates no main effects but a significant interaction. For b_1 there is an upward trend from a_1 to a_4, while for b_3 the trend is exactly opposite. For b_2 there are no differences among levels of A. Figure 6.2c indicates a complex pattern with all three effects. One should note that the number of possible patterns is far greater than the three shown here, and explanations are more difficult and lengthy than with the 2 × 2 patterns.

Higher Order Factorial Design

Factorial designs are not limited to two independent variables, and higher order designs are frequently encountered. In theory one could include any number of independent variables in a design, provided one could collect data on a sufficient number of subjects. There are, however, practical limitations since the number of subjects is finite, and interpretation of large designs quickly becomes unwieldy.

The advantage of higher order factorials is obvious. One can investigate the combined effects of several independent variables simultaneously. Some variables could be included to control for confounding, such as in the Solomon four-group design. The major disadvantage is the complexity that comes with size. Even when the number of levels of each independent variable is kept small, the number of cells grows quickly as variables are added. For example, a 2 × 2 design has only 4 cells, but a 2 × 2 × 2 × 2 has 16, requiring four times as many subjects. The same four independent variable design with three levels per variable would have 81 cells needing hundreds of subjects to fill.

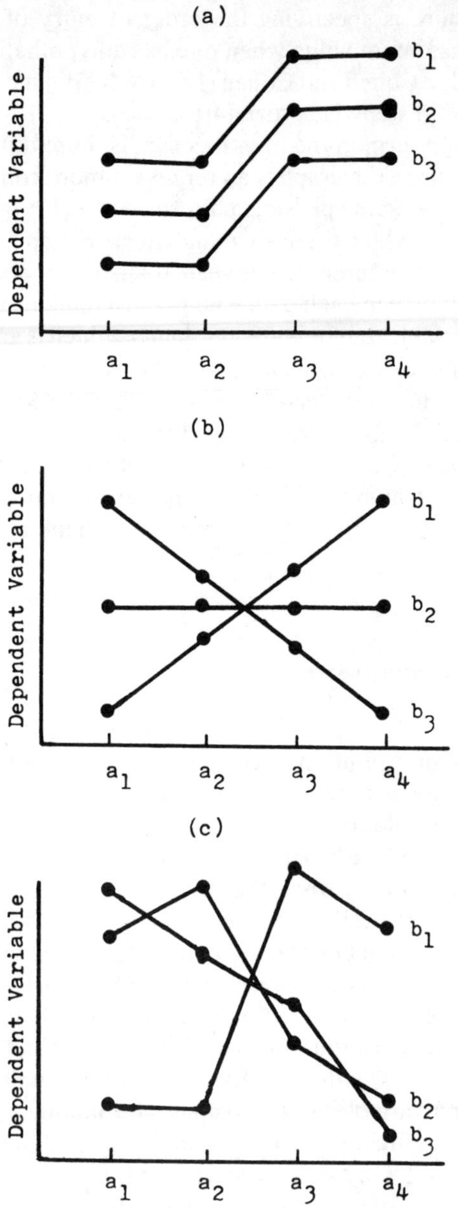

Figure 6.2 Examples of Interactions in m × n Designs

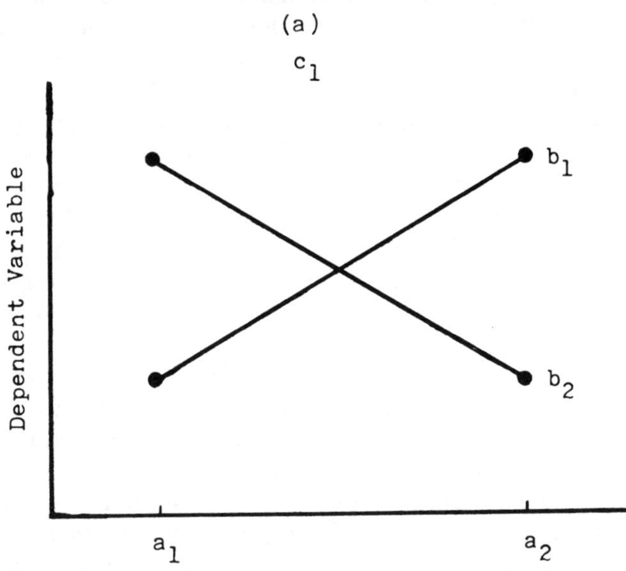

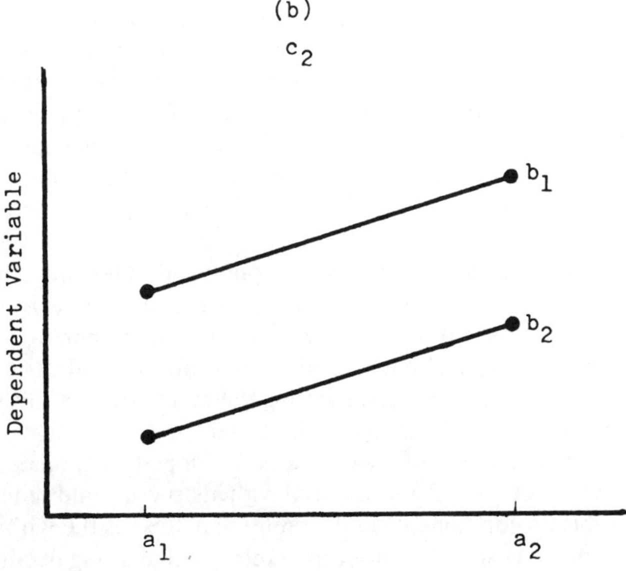

Figure 6.3 Example of a Three-Way Interaction in a 2 × 2 × 2 Factorial Design

The number of effects is also compounded with higher order designs. Each higher order introduces another level of interaction, and these higher order interactions are extremely difficult to interpret. A three-way interaction is illustrated for a three-variable design in Figure 6.3. Since a three-way interaction would take a three-dimensional graph to represent, the common practice is to illustrate it with multiple graphs, one for each level of one independent variable. A 2 × 2 × 2 design is illustrated where a three-way interaction exists. In this case the interaction is manifested by a different pattern within each two-variable graph. In Figure 6.3a there is a clear A × B interaction, while in Figure 6.3b there is no interaction. Thus the interaction between A and B is dependent upon the level of variable C.

Three-way interactions involving more levels become complex to interpret. More difficult is interpretation of still higher order interactions. In fact most researchers will ignore such interactions and consider their variance components to be error variance.

With the three-way design there are, of course, three main effects, one for each independent variable. There are also three two-way interactions, one for each possible combination of independent variables, that is, A × B, A × C, and B × C, and one three-way interaction. With higher order designs there are still more effects, and for each a variance component must be calculated to test for statistical significance.

Within the higher order designs, it is not necessary that all effects be between subject. That is, one can have any combination of between- and within-subject effects. They require some different computational procedures, but basically any combination is allowable. As with the m × n design, the most common use of this mixture of effect types is to add pretests to the posttests of a between-subjects factorial design. As with the smaller design, the interactions involving the within-subject factor would indicate change on the between-subjects variables or their interactions.

For example, suppose a study were conducted to test the effects on learning of two types of instruction (lecture and seminar) and two schedules (8 hours per week for 8 weeks and 4 hours per week for 16 weeks). Note that elapsed time is confounded with concentration, but in this case there is no interest in separating them. To conduct this study a pool of subjects is acquired and a dependent measure of knowledge appropriate to the content of the course is developed. A good design for this study would be a 2 × 2 × 2 factorial with instruction and schedule as between-subjects components and a pretest-posttest as the within. The retesting variable is added in order to determine if learning occurred, as reflected by change in performance on the dependent varible from before to after treatment. One could omit the retesting variable and focus only on level of knowledge after treatment, attributing posttest differences to the independent variable. However, it would be unknown whether any real change occurred because the posttest differences might merely have reflected pretest differences. Of course with random assignment to conditions and sufficient sample size, one would assume initial equivalence of groups. Unfortunately, random assignment still will not indicate change. It will only indicate after treatment differences. There might well be posttest differences because some conditions caused a performance decrement while others caused an increase, a possibility testable only with repeated measurements.

One should keep in mind that the purpose of this design is to determine both the separate and joint effects of schedule and instruction type on learning. Of the seven effects in this design, only four offer information relevant to this purpose. The interaction terms involving the between-subjects variables and the retesting variable reflect differential learning among subjects in the various treatment groups. The interaction of Retesting × Instruction Type indicates if subjects learned better with lecture or seminar. Likewise, the interaction of retesting by schedule concerns the differential learning of subjects on the 8-week versus the 16-week schedule. The three-way interaction or Retesting × Instruction Type × Schedule reflects the interactive effects on learning of schedule and instruction type. For example, it might be found that for lecture, the 8-week schedule results in better learning while for seminar neither schedule results in significantly more learning. Thus the effects of each variable are qualified by the other. Although it might be correct based on a significant main effect to conclude that seminar was superior to lecture in student learning, the more precise conclusion would be to refer to the interaction. It might well be that seminar under the 16-week schedule is the best procedure, but the other three do not differ from one another. Thus seminar with an 8-week schedule would be no better than lecture with either schedule and would only show superiority with the longer time span.

One final effect, of particular value when none of the three interaction terms is significant, is the main effect for retesting. This effect indicates change for all groups combined and would show if there was significant learning by all subjects regardless of condition and despite no treatment differences. All treatments might be equally effective or ineffective, a possibility tested with the retesting main effect.

It should be apparent at this point that higher order factorial designs are complex to interpret. Their advantage in allowing joint effects of independent variables to be studied is partially offset by their complexity of analysis and interpretation. These designs remain powerful tools for research when used properly by skilled investigators.

Hierarchical Design

To this point two types of independent variables in factorial designs, the between-subjects and within-subject, have been covered. There is a third, and that is the nested or hierarchical variable. A nested, in contrast to a between-subjects, variable is one in which all levels of the nested variable are not crossed or represented in all levels of other between-subjects variables.

The concept of nesting is not new; in between-subjects designs one can consider subjects to be nested in treatment groups. That is, there are different subjects in each group. This stands in contrast to the within-subject design where each subject is represented at each level of the independent variable. However, effects can also be nested when the levels of an independent variable are found only at some levels of another independent variable. Most often this occurs when subjects are members of preexisting groups or classifications, and entire groups are assigned to treatment conditions. If subjects are not randomly assigned to groups, or if treatments involve interaction among group members, it is the entire group that becomes the subject rather than each member. If many groups exist, one can assign them at random to conditions and still retain features of random assignment to conditions. In many cases conclusions must be made to the group rather than to the individual.

Probably the most common situation where individual subjects are in groups of some sort involves research on students who are nested in classes that are assigned to treatments. In such cases it would be a mistake to analyze the data as if the classes did not exist, because there is a confounding of the treatment with class membership. There might well be, and often is, an interaction between the characteristics of the classes and the treatments. When this is the case, the data are analyzed as if classes are the subjects, although the data from individual class members are still used. Thus in designs where subjects are nested in units which are assigned to treatments, one must have a sufficient number of units available for analysis.

The analysis of hierarchical variables within a factorial design is done with the analysis of variance, which has specific procedures for such situations. Such an analysis is a two-step process where first there is a test for significant differences among groups. If groups are equivalent within treatments, one can analyze the data as if subjects were not tested in them. If there are differences among groups, the group itself is the subject for analysis.

Often one does not purposely design a study to be hierarchical, but finds that subjects happen to be part of larger social units which cannot be split. When this is the case, the larger units should initially be considered as the units of analysis, and the design of the study should include enough of the larger units in case there happen to be group differences. In other cases one is interested in the large social unit, but collects data on individuals in the unit. This might occur in educational studies where units are classes, but measurements are taken on individual students. One should be cautious in such cases that one draws proper conclusions either to individual students or to the aggregate classes. If one were to take a class average and use that as the data for analysis, one could draw conclusions to other classes as a whole, but one may not be able to draw conclusions to individual students (see Langbein and Lichtman, 1978, for a discussion of the aggregate bias that occurs when scores are combined for social units). The hierarchical design deals with both the individual subject and the larger unit.

Hierarchical analyses are not often found in the social science literature, although many studies in which subjects are nested in groups ignore the hierarchical nature of the data. In such cases erroneous conclusions can be reached because it may be the interactive effects of the treatment with the group that was responsible for the significant effect rather than the treatment itself.

Designs with a Concomitant Variable

Social science studies tend to be plagued with large error variance due to the complex nature of social phenomena and the vast heterogeneity of individuals and social units. At least two procedures exist within factorial designs (as well as multigroup experimental designs) to remove or statistically control some of this variance. Both procedures accomplish a similar aim, although they use somewhat different procedures. The first is blocking and the second is analysis of covariance (ANCOVA). Both will be discussed, and some contrasts will be drawn.

In a study there are sometimes variables that can be identified as potentially related to the dependent variable, and which might account for error variance in the design. These additional or *concomitant vari-*

ables can be added to the design and handled in a special way that enables one to draw variance out of the error term in the ANOVA or to adjust the dependent variable for the effects of the additional variable.

The idea of blocking is to use a concomitant variable as an additional independent variable in the analysis. Such designs will often include subjects so that there are an equal number at each level of the concomitant variable and an equal number in each cell of the design. Blocked variables often include sex, intelligence, and scores on various psychological tests.

Blocking often increases the precision of a design by reducing the size of the error variance component in the AVOVA. When it is expected that a particular characteristic of subjects or treatments may affect the study, one can control the effect by assuring that an equal number of subjects will be at each level of the blocking variable. In animal research, for example, it is common to block on litter, so that an equal number of animals from each litter would be assigned to a different condition. Thus if one needs 10 animals for each of 3 conditions, one could acquire 10 litters of 3 animals each and assign at random 1 animal per litter to each condition. Litter would become an effect in the analysis, and could be tested to see if there were significant litter differences. Note that with this design there is only a single subject in each treatment by litter cell of the design, making a test for the interaction impossible.

In human research blocking variables often include sex, intelligence, socioeconomic status, and residence region of the country. With continuous variables such as test scores, one would dichotomize or trichotomize, placing subjects into their appropriate level. The blocking variable, if it is in fact related to the dependent variable, increases the likelihood of finding statistical significance on the independent variables of interest. They are treated the same as any independent variable in a factorial design, although one might not be particularly interested in the significance of the blocking variable.

Analysis of covariance accomplishes the same objective, but does so without compressing the continuous variable into several discrete categories. Thus with test scores one would treat the concomitant variable as a *covariate* in the analysis and adjust the dependent variable for it. Precisely how this is done is beyond the scope of this monograph, but ANCOVA is a statistical means of adjusting for the covariate in a design, and it is based on several assumptions which may or may not hold within a given set of data (Wildt and Ahtola, 1978; Winer, 1971).

The ANCOVA is also used as a means of controlling statistically for confounding factors that were not controlled by the experimental design. For example, suppose one designed a study to determine if one teaching method was superior to another. One might assign a class to each method and then compare knowledge gain of both calsses. Forgetting that this is a hierarchical design, it might be found that the average intelligence scores of students in one class tend to be higher than for students of the other. If these scores were available, the classes could be statistically adjusted to equate for intelligence before comparison. Such adjustments are quite sensitive to violations of assumptions underlying ANCOVA and are not always feasible. Unfortunately, there are no good statistical adjustments for poor designs. Conclusive results from this study would require random assignment of students and classes to teaching methods.

Feldt (1958) has compared the use of blocking and ANCOVA for handling concomitant variables. He contrasted the two by analyzing the same data with each. The concomitant variables were continuous, appropriate for ANCOVA. For blocking they were recoded into varying numbers of categories. His conclusions were that ANCOVA was somewhat more precise, not unexpectedly since it uses all the information in the data, but that its sensitivity to violations of assumptions was a major liability. Thus blocking was recommended as it is simpler to use and understand, and it is far less sensitive to violations of assumptions in actual application.

Multivariate Designs

All of the designs discussed thus far have involved a single dependent variable and are considered to be univariate designs despite the fact that they contain multiple variables. In recent years there has been growing popularity of multivariate designs — those involving multiple dependent variables. Two factors are primarily responsible for this trend toward more complex designs — the realization that social phenomena are complex and not easily reduced to single measures and the widespread availability of computers for data analysis.

Virtually any experimental design discussed in this monograph can be expanded to a multivariate version by collecting data on more than one dependent variable. The advantage of including multiple dependent variables in the same design is that it allows determination of complex relationships among the measures. This may be especially critical in areas where measurement is not well-developed, and the use of several different instruments may add much to the study. Multiple measures are also important in the study of complex and multidimensional phenomena. For example, task performance is not easily represented by a single variable. At the minimum performance includes elements of task speed and task accuracy. The rather basic task of typing involves typing speed, number of errors, and neatness of page layout.

The easiest way to handle multivariate data is with a series of univariate analyses, a procedure used in some of the previous univariate examples. Suppose one had data from a 2 × 2 factorial design with five dependent measures. One might perform a separate 2 × 2 ANOVA on each dependent variable and interpret each result separately. This procedure is rather simple computationally and conceptually, although interpretation could be difficult if there were differential patterns among the five variables. There is, however, one major problem with this approach and that has to do with the basic underlying probability theory upon which statistics are based. When a significance test is made, one calculates a probability that the particular findings occurred purely by chance. Normally the $p < .05$ convention is selected. For any single statistical comparison, or for all the comparisons within an ANOVA, the probability level remains at .05. However, when multiple comparisons are made with the same statistic, the probabilities do not remain at the chosen level. That is, if one were to conduct 100 comparisons at the .05 level, one would expect in the long run that 5 would be significant by chance alone. With the 2 × 2 design the probability of finding one or more significant effects across the five dependent variables is greater than the probability level set.

There are two ways to circumvent the probability problem with multivariate data. One could set the significance level for each comparison at a more stringent level so that overall the probability level would remain at .05. Unfortunately, this procedure is too conservative, especially with several dependent variables. If one set the level at .01, one would be forced to conclude that no significant differences were found, even if every dependent variable for every effect was significant at .02.

A better approach would be to use multivariate statistical procedures which analyze all dependent variables simultaneously. These procedures also have the advantage that they can uncover complex relationships among the dependent variables which are ignored by univariate approaches.

Most of the designs discussed in this monograph make use of ANOVA, and every one of them has a counterpart in the multivariate analysis of variance (MANOVA). Although it is more complex and requires somewhat different computational procedures, MANOVA results in a multivariate test for each effect in the design. This multivariate test indicates whether there is a significant effect for all dependent variables simultaneously. If there is an effect, additional analyses are conducted to ascertain which individual dependent variables are responsible for it and how the dependent variables are interrelated. Such analyses can become quite complex and necessitate use of computers. (For a nonmathematical introduction to MANOVA, see Spector, 1977. Tatsuoka's, 1975, monograph is a good introduction to the computational details.)

Although multivariate procedures offer a powerful way of analyzing complex data, they require considerable proficiency to utilize properly. Their use necessitates knowledge of statistical computer packages as well as the statistical procedures themselves. Their results are also considerably more difficult to interpret, and in some areas there are no clear-cut rules for interpretation. For many social scientists, use of multivariate designs would require assistance from individuals knowledgeable about multivariate methods and computers.

Examples

Factorial Design. A study by Mossholder (1980) is especially instructive because he used a 2 × 2 design with multiple dependent variables and a concomitant variable. This laboratory study was an attempt to investigate the interactive effects on intrinsic motivation of initial task interest and goal setting. Mossholder's hypothesis was that subjects who worked on an interesting task would show more intrinsic motivation when performing without a goal than with a goal, and with a boring task, intrinsic motivation would be higher for subjects with goals than without goals. The two tasks chosen, one boring and one interesting, involved putting together erector set pieces. Subjects worked under goal or no-goal conditions created by the experimenter. Three dependent variables were chosen: persistence, defined as amount of time the subject continued working on the task after the task period was concluded, task interest, and task satisfaction, each measured with two questionnaire items.

The results for each of the dependent measures are illustrated in Figure 6.4. A separate ANOVA was conducted for each dependent variable, and all three found a similar pattern of results. The interaction of goal and task was significant for all but task satisfaction which was marginal ($p < .07$), and all three main effects for task were significant.

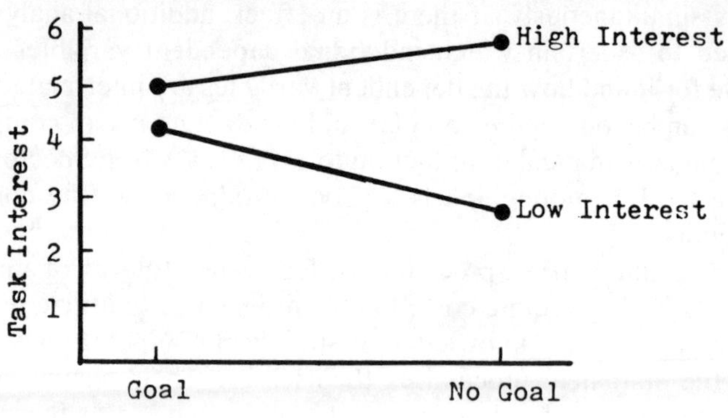

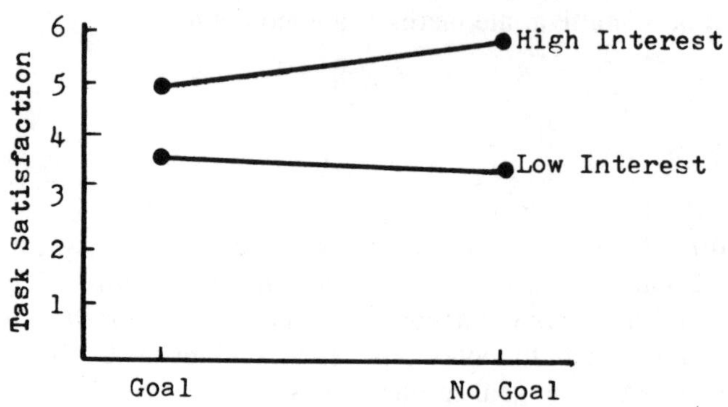

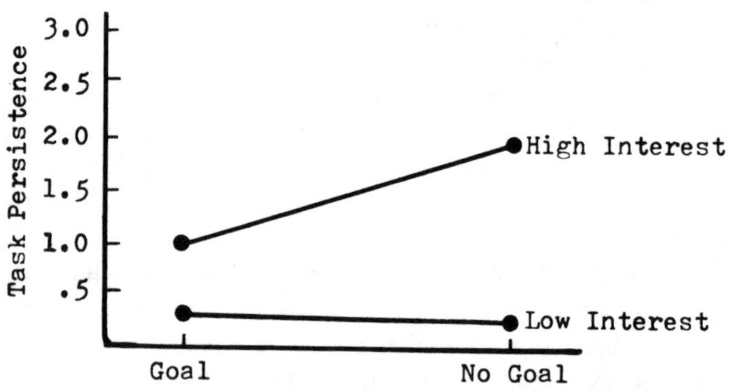

Figure 6.4 Intrinsic Motivation as a Function of Task Interest and Goals

These results can be seen in the figure, as all three graphs show the same pattern.

For additional precision, the investigator included a measure of finger dexterity as a concomitant variable. A comparison of the four treatment groups verified that there were no differences among the groups on dexterity. Thus the random assignment was successful in producing equivalent groups on at least this one important variable. However, Mossholder decided to conduct some additional analyses including finger dexterity as a covariate. He calculated an ANCOVA for each dependent variable, covarying on dexterity. He found no differences between the ANOVA and ANCOVA results.

Finally, a MANOVA was conducted on all three dependent variables simultaneously. In actuality this analysis would be conducted first, and if no differences were found for each effect, the ANOVA's would not be computed. The MANOVA's results were consistent with the ANOVA's in that the interaction was found to be significant. Mossholder failed to report the main effects which may or may not have been significant. However, his interest was only in the interaction.

Mossholder's study illustrates several points and represents the modern trend toward more complex designs and analyses. First, Mossholder recognized that intrinsic motivation can be measured several ways, so he included three measures. Of course, he might have done analyses to determine the interrelationships among these measures and whether they measured the same or different underlying variables. This would have required correlation and perhaps discriminant analysis (Spector, 1977).

Second, the use of the covariate in an attempt to increase precision was a good effort to reduce error variance in the analysis. In this particular instance, the randomization procedure was effective, and the dexterity measure did not increase sensitivity of the analyses.

This study involved a several step procedure of MANOVA, ANOVA, and ANCOVA, again showing the trend toward complexity and the use of statistical procedures in a series where the results of one analysis lead into another. Studies often involve long sequences of analyses which may check for effectiveness of independent variable manipulations, efficacy of controls, existence of confounding variables, and finally the hypotheses of interest. While such studies are complex, they can provide strong and convincing evidence for the verification or refutation of hypothesis and theory.

Higher Level Factorial Design. The higher order factorial design presented here is a 2 × 2 × 2 published by Perry, Abrami, Leventhal, and Check (1979). This study was an attempt to explore instructor-related factors that affect student evaluations of faculty. Three independent variables were manipulated: course content (high vs. low), instructor expressiveness (expressive vs. nonexpressive), and instructor reputation (positive vs. negative). The effects of these variables on overall student ratings was the focus of the study.

This study was conducted in the laboratory which allowed far greater control than would have been possible in the field. Content was manipulated by preparing the high-content lectures from actual class notes and then eliminating material for the low-content condition. Expressiveness was created by the lecturer changing style according to carefully defined roles. In the expressive condition the lecturer injected humor, physical movement, and enthusiasm into the presentation. These were excluded from the nonexpressive condition. The reputation of the instructor was manipulated by presenting subjects with either a positive or negative description of him. A series of videotaped lectures was prepared and presented to groups of students who were placed at random into one of the eight treatment groups.

The results of this study are summarized in Figure 6.5. Since this was a three-level design, two graphs were necessary to present the results. ANOVA was conducted and found significant interactions for reputation by expressiveness (Figure 6.5d) and expressiveness by content (Figure 6.5c), as well as significant main effects for reputation, expressiveness, and content.

The main effects indicated that instructors got better ratings overall if they were expressive, had positive reputations, and had high course content. The two interactions qualified these conclusions somewhat; that is, reputation affected ratings only for expressive instructors, and content was only a significant factor for nonexpressive instructors. Thus the interactions were more precise in their conclusions. It would be a mistake to conclude that content alone or reputation alone affected ratings when it was shown that they do so only under certain levels of expressiveness.

Perhaps the biggest limitation to this study is generalizability. That is, the laboratory results might not generalize to real college courses outside of the laboratory. It might well be that the subjects' knowledge of the experimental nature of the situation affected their ratings in an artificial way. However, this study indicated variables that might be critical in student ratings and suggested variables for further study in the field. In other words this study had reasonable internal validity; its external validity to field settings must be demonstrated with further research.

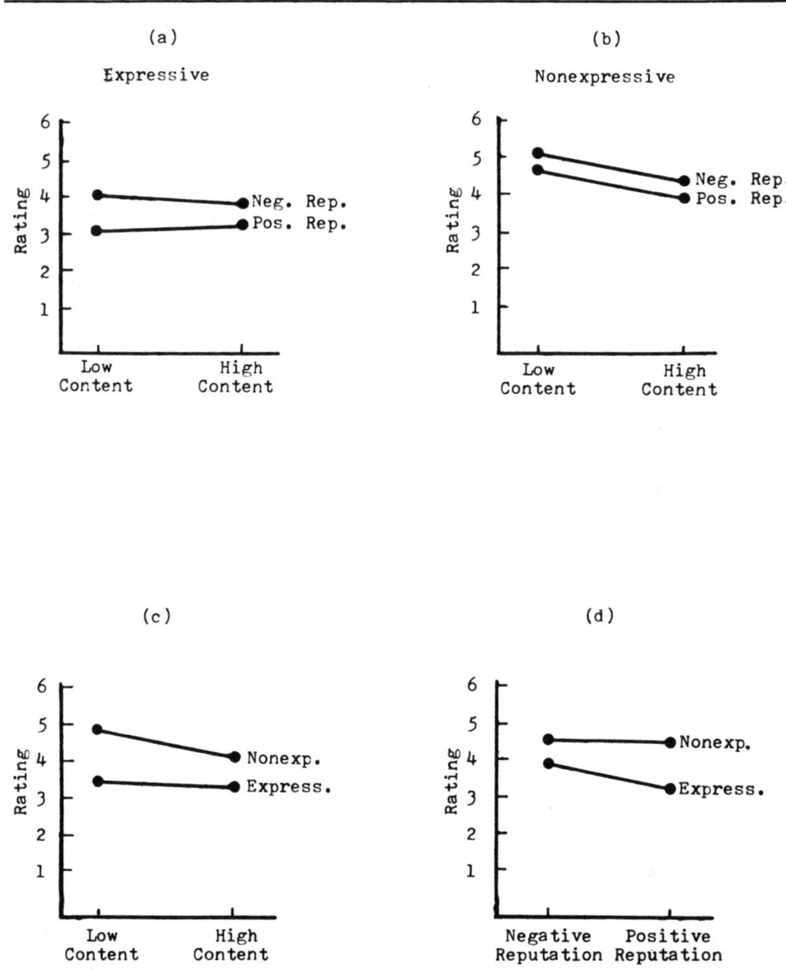

Figure 6.5 Instructor Ratings as a Function of Content, Expressiveness and Reputation

7.0 CONCLUDING REMARKS

This monograph has covered considerable material and has presented the major aspects of experimental and nonexperimental design. The reader who has understood this material now has a basic understanding of design and has at his or her fingertips many specific designs applicable to a myriad of research situations. The nonexperimental designs are extremely useful for field studies and program evaluations. Although they are often less than conclusive, they can provide much useful information which may be far superior to intuitive judgment. Furthermore, one should not overlook the value of systematic observation and assume that significant knowledge can only be gained with experimental designs. However, experimental designs are powerful tools for determining the affects that conditions or treatments have on specific behavior. Of course the astute researcher and student of design is aware of the limitations and pitfalls of even the most sophisticated experimental designs.

Design is an essential study for both the producer and consumer of research in the social sciences. Past trends that will undoubtedly continue have been toward greater sophistication in social science research methodology and the use of complex designs. The aspiring researcher would do well to consider this text as the beginning to a continuing study of design. Ancillary to that study should be a thorough treatment of statistical methods, which are essential in the analysis and interpretation of data generated by designs. There are far too many poorly designed studies that waste time, resources, and journal space, but it is difficult indeed to conduct good research or fully understand it without a strong background in design.

REFERENCES

ASHER, H. B. (1976) Causal Modeling. Beverly Hills, CA: Sage.

CAMPBELL, D. T. and J. C. STANLEY (1963) Experimental and Quasi-Experimental Designs for Research. Skokie, IL: Rand McNally.

CARMINES, E. G. and R. A. ZELLER (1979) "Reliability and Validity Assessment." Sage University Paper series on Quantitative Applications in the Social Sciences, 07-017. Beverly Hills, CA. Sage.

CHAPIN, F. S. (1955) Experimental Designs in Sociological Research. New York: Harper & Row. Cited in D. T. Campbell and J. C. Stanley (1963) Experimental and Quasi-Experimental Designs for Research. Skokie, IL: Rand McNally.

CHATFIELD, C. (1975) The Analysis of Time Series: Theory and Practice. New York: Wiley.

CHUBB, J. E. (1978) "Multiple indicators and measurement error in panel data: An evaluation of summated scales, path analysis, and confirmatory maximum liklihood factor analysis." Political Methodology 5: 413-444.

COHEN, J. and P. COHEN (1975) Applied Multiple Regression/Correlation Analysis for the Behavioral Sciences. New York: Wiley.

COLE, J. W. L. and J. E. GRIZZLE (1966) "Applications of multivariate analysis of variance to repeated measurements experiments." Biometrics 22: 810-828.

COOK, T. D. and D. T. CAMPBELL (1979) Quasi-Experimentation: Design & Analysis Issues for Field Settings. Skokie, IL: Rand McNally.

CRONBACH, L.J. and L. FURBY (1970) "How we should measure 'change' — or should we?" Psychological Bulletin 74: 68-80.

FELDT, L.S. (1958) "A comparison of the precision of three experimental designs employing a concomitant variable." Psychometrika 23: 335-353.

FREDERIKSEN, L.W. (1978) "Behavioral reorganization of a professional service system." Journal of Organizational Behavior Management 2: 1-9.

GLASS, G. V., V.L. WILLSON, and J. M. GOTTMAN (1975) Design and Analysis of Time-series Experiments. Boulder, CO: Associated University Press.

GUILFORD, J. P. (1954) Psychometric Methods. New York: McGraw-Hill.

HARRIS, C. W. [ed.] (1963) Problems in Measuring Change. Madison: University of Wisconsin Press.

IVERSEN, G. R. and H. NORPOTH (1976) "Analysis of Variance." Sage University Paper series on Quantitative Applications in the Social Sciences, 07-001. Beverly Hills, CA: Sage.

KENNY, D. A. and J. M. HARACKIEWICZ (1979) "Cross-lagged panel correlation: Practice and promise." Journal of Applied Psychology 64: 372-379.

KERLINGER, F. N. and E. J. PEDHAZUR (1973) Multiple Regression in Behavioral Research. New York: Holt, Rinehart — Winston.

KIM, J. and C. W. MUELLER (1978) "Introduction to Factor Analysis." Sage University Paper series on Quantitative Applications in the Social Sciences, 07-013. Beverly Hills, CA: Sage.

LANGBEIN, L. I. and A.J. LICHTMAN (1978) "Ecological Inference." Sage University Paper series on Quantitative Applications in the Social Sciences, 07-010. Beverly Hills, CA: Sage.

LEWIS-BECK, M. S. (1980) "Applied Regression: An Introduction." Sage University Paper series on Quantitative Applications in the Social Sciences, 07-022. Beverly Hills, CA: Sage.

MAZUR-HART, S. F. and J.J. BERMAN (1977) "Changing from fault to no-fault divorce: An interrupted time series analysis." Journal of Applied Social Psychology 7: 300-312.

McDOWALL, D., R. McCLEARY, E.E. MEIDINGER, and R. A. HAY, Jr. (1980) "Interrupted Time Series Analysis." Sage University Paper series on Quantitative Applications in the Social Sciences, 07-021. Beverly Hills, CA: Sage.

MOSSHOLDER, K. W. (1980) "Effects of externally mediated goal setting on intrinsic motivation: A laboratory experiment." Journal of Applied Psychology 65: 202-210.

MYERS, J. L. (1972) Fundamental of Experimental Design. Boston: Allyn — Bacon.

O'MALLEY, P. (1975) "Suicide and war: A case study and theoretical appraisal." British Journal of Criminology 15: 348-359.

PERRY, R. P., P. C. ABRAMI, L. LEVENTHAL, and J. CHECK (1979) "Instructor reputation: An expectancy relationship involving student ratings and achievement." Journal of Educational Psychology 71: 776-787.

POOR, D. D. S. (1973) "Analysis of variance for repeated measures designs: Two approaches." Psychological Bulletin 80: 204-209.

REILLY, R. R., M. L. TENOPYR, and S. M. SPERLING (1979) "Effects of job previews on job acceptance and survival of telephone operator candidates." Journal of Applied Psychology 64: 218-220.

ROETHLISBERGER, F.J. and M.J. DICKSON (1939) Management and the Worker. Cambridge, MA: Harvard University Press.

RUMMEL, R.J. (1970) Applied Factor Analysis. Evanston, IL: Northwestern University Press.

SPECTOR, P.E. (1980) "Techniques for handling nonorthogonal analysis of variance: A review." Evaluation Review 4: 843-855.

——— (1977) "What to do with significant multivariate effects in MANOVA." Journal of Applied Psychology 62: 158-163.

——— N. H. VOISSEM, and W. L. CONE (forthcoming) "A monte carlo study of three approaches to nonorthogonal analysis of variance." Journal of Applied Psychology.

STEPHENS, T. A. and W. A. BURROUGHS (1978) "An application of operant conditioning to absenteeism in a hospital setting." Journal of Applied Psychology 63: 518-521.

SWAMINATHAN, H. and J. ALGINA (1977) "Analysis of quasi-experimental time-series designs." Multivariate Behavioral Research 12: 111-131.

TATSUOKA, M. M. (1975) The General Linear Model: A "New" Trend in Analysis of Variance. Champaign, IL: Institute for Personality and Ability Testing.

TORGERSON, W.S. (1958) Theory and Methods of Scaling. New York: Wiley.

WALDO, G. P. and T. G. CHIRICOS (1977) "Work release and recidivism: An empirical evaluation of a social policy." Evaluation Quarterly 1: 87-108.

WILDT, A.R. and O. AHTOLA (1978) "Analysis of Covariance." Sage University Paper series on Quantitative Applications in the Social Sciences, 07-012. Beverly Hills, CA: Sage.

WINER, B.J. (1971) Statistical Principles in Experimental Design. New York: McGraw-Hill.

PART II

EXPERIMENTAL DESIGN AND ANALYSIS

STEVEN R. BROWN

LAWRENCE E. MELAMED

Until there are experiments, I take no notice of anything that's done. (William Stephenson, 1902–1989)

1. INTRODUCTION AND OVERVIEW

In a certain sense, experimentation can be viewed as an extension of inquisitiveness, and consequently is as old as curiosity itself. There is evidence that it was beginning to take root as an organized procedure as early as the thirteenth century when the received wisdom of the Greeks was being questioned. In a more formal sense, however, the experimental method received its greatest impetus from the scientific advances of the sixteenth and seventeenth centuries, and it was because of its success that Sir Isaac Newton could confidently state that "the qualities of bodies are only known to us by experiments."

By the twentieth century, "classical" experimentation—the practice of holding everything constant except the one variable under consideration—was widely accepted in the sciences, but "modern" experimentation dates from the publication in 1935 of Sir Ronald A. Fisher's *The Design of Experiments* (see Box, 1978). According to Fisher (1960), experimentation is "experience carefully planned in advance" (p. 8), and its advantage in this respect is often attributed to its active as opposed to passive nature. Specifically, this active method consists of manipulating levels or amounts of selected independent variables (causes) to examine their influence on dependent variables (effects).

For performance on the dependent variable to be traced unambiguously to manipulated changes in the independent variable, rival sources of influence must be rendered ineffective. Under classical conditions, as noted previously, possible sources of contamination were controlled so far as possible by holding everything constant save for the experimental variable (the so-called "rule of the single variable"), but the primary way in which these extraneous sources are controlled in modern experimentation is through randomization.

Suppose, for illustrative purposes, that we wished to test the comparative effectiveness of three textbooks, and so assigned one book to one class, a second to another class, and a third to yet another, as pictured in Table 1.1. If "grade on the final exam" is our performance criterion (dependent variable), then if at the end of the semester the average grade for group A is higher than those for B and C, we might be tempted to attribute that difference to the text. But if texts were assigned to preexistent groups (i.e., to groups which had been composed on a nonrandom basis), we would not really know whether the differences in final exam scores were due to the texts or to a priori group differences. Group A might have contained more seniors, for example, or greater numbers of majors than B or C, thereby biasing the outcome in favor of A: The textbook variable, in short, might be confounded with (i.e., causally inseparable from) class status, academic major, or some other variable occupying the same experimental space.

The classical solution to this uncertainty might have been to assign the texts to three groups each of which was composed of seniors and chemistry majors only, thereby neutralizing at least two important variables; for good measure, only students with average grades might be utilized in order to protect against the effect of academic achievement. Whatever the precautions, however, the classical experimenter could never wholly escape the worry that other uncontrolled contaminants might be undermining the outcome, nor could it be known whether the same results could be obtained from groups composed, say, of sophomore chemistry majors or senior mathematics majors.

But suppose that some control could be exercised over class composition, and that students could be assigned to classes on a purely random

TABLE 1.1

Text A	*Text B*	*Text C*
Student 1	Student 1	Student 1
2	2	2
3	3	3
.	.	.
.	.	.
.	.	.

basis. Each student would then have a probability of one-third of being in group A, B, or C. Assuming random assignment, Table 1.1 can be looked at anew with some confidence that class status is no longer confounded with the textbook variable; that is, under conditions of random assignment, there is no reason to expect seniors (any more than juniors, sophomores, or freshmen) to be disproportionately exposed to text A (any more than to B or C). Nor would we expect academic major or academic achievement to enter systematically into the picture.

And when one thinks about it, any and all possible variables associated with the students will be expected *in theory* to be found in roughly equal numbers across the groups: Left-handed persons should be distributed randomly among all groups, for example, and so left-handedness should in no way be in a position to bias the findings; prior education and academic achievement should have been nullified as potential contaminants; and metabolic rate, marital status of parents, number of hours of sleep the previous night, color of eyes, personality makeup, birth order, hair length—all such variables (and all others unnamed and not even conceived of) should have been neutralized through the process of randomization. What randomization succeeds in accomplishing, therefore, at least in theory, is the conversion of all irrelevant sources of possibly systematic variability into unsystematic variability, that is, into random error. The only thing that persons in group A should have in common—that is, the only source of systematic variability—is exposure to the same textbook.

Randomization procedures mark the dividing line between classical and modern experimentation and are of great practical benefit to the experimenter, as Fisher (1960: 44) noted, for they provide relief "from the anxiety of considering and estimating the magnitude of the innumerable causes by which . . . data may be disturbed," that is, from the classical difficulties of trying to hold everything constant without ever being certain that this has been achieved. Randomization has therefore been likened to life insurance inasmuch as "it is a precaution against disturbances that may or may not occur and that may or may not be serious if they do occur" (Cochran and Cox, 1957: 8). It provides no absolute guarantee, of course, but it has been judged superior to any alternative yet devised, and its possibility in experimental work is part of what distinguishes experiments, in the strict sense of the word, from quasi-experiments and surveys (see, e.g., Black, 1955; Deconchy, 1981; Martin and Sell, 1979; Selvin, 1957; Weir, 1985).

In the pages that follow, the elements of experimental design and analysis are introduced and illustrated with actual examples. It is assumed that the reader has been exposed to at least one course in basic statistics, and consequently has a nodding acquaintance with concepts such as central tendency, variability, hypothesis testing for differences between means (z and t tests), and correlation. For review purposes, and in order to establish notation to be used subsequently, the fundamental concept of variability is summarized in Chapter 2. Chapter 3 then demonstrates how variance enters into procedures for hypothesis testing, including a review of the logic of the t test for determining the statistical significance of differences between the means for two groups (experimental and control), which represents the most elementary of experimental designs. Chapter 4 shows how analysis of variance (ANOVA) is equivalent to the t test in the two-group situation, and how ANOVA can then be extended to the multigroup situation, thereby paving the way for a consideration of various experimental designs.

Experimental designs that involve the random assignment of subjects to different levels of the independent variable (i.e., to the various experimental conditions or groups) are called *completely randomized designs*. However complex these designs become, the control of extraneous influences on subjects' behavior is achieved only through randomization, and the validity of these designs in answering questions about the independent variable rests primarily on the success of the randomization procedure. These completely randomized designs are illustrated in Chapter 5.

Two potential problems with completely randomized designs concern their precision and efficiency. With regard to precision, it was noted previously that there is no absolute guarantee that randomization will keep extraneous influences in check. Were it suspected ahead of time that academic major, for example, might be an important factor in determining how a subject would perform using a particular textbook (see Table 1.1), then it might be judged wise to measure the influence of this factor directly rather than leave its control to the less certain randomization procedure. One bonus that often accrues when such extraneous factors are directly controlled is a more efficient, or powerful, statistical test of the independent variable—that is, a test more apt to detect the influence of the experimentally controlled variable—and experimental designs that control extraneous variables directly are the *treatments × blocks procedures* described in Chapter 7.

The problem with inefficiency arises because of the fact that completely randomized designs require the maximum number of subjects in examining questions about independent variables. From the standpoint of efficiency, it would be beneficial for a subject to participate in more than one experimental condition, thereby reducing the number of subjects required. In an examination of the influence of hours of sleep on some measure of motor performance, for example, each subject could be repeatedly tested at each level of the independent variable (hours of sleep). Such *repeated measures designs* are described in Chapter 10. It should be added that these designs also increase precision by removing extraneous variables associated with individual differences between the participants involved in the experiment. There are also designs that combine the conceptual simplicity of the completely randomized design for one or more independent variables with increasing precision and efficiency by employing a repeated measures design for one or more others. Examples of these *mixed designs* (or split-plot designs) are also given in Chapter 10.

In certain kinds of experiments it is sometimes necessary to involve several investigators in obtaining data. For example, several psychotherapists might be employed to treat clients in each segment of an experiment examining the relative efficacy of various types of psychotherapy. Any imprecisions arising from the individual characteristics of these multiple "experimenters" are as important to control as those contributed by the actual participants. Experimental designs that allow for such control are called *hierarchical designs* and are described in Chapter 9. Also described in Chapter 9 is the factorial design, which most often consists of combining two or more completely randomized designs into a single experiment.

Regardless of the experimental design selected, there are many statistical alternatives for determining the effectiveness of the manipulated variables. Not only can the overall effectiveness of a variable be examined, but an experimental design can be decomposed into a set of simpler ones, with analytical comparisons being performed between experimental groups in these simpler designs. This procedure—which is akin to placing the results of the original experimental design under a microscope, bit by bit—is introduced in Chapter 6 and applied to completely randomized designs, and subsequently reintroduced for use with other designs.

The question of how to select an experimental design can be answered only indirectly. A design must be structurally congruent with the research question and compatible with available resources. This monograph offers a series of plans to be judged in light of the following considerations: (1) The number of independent variables, (2) the sources and number of extraneous variables, (3) the number of subjects available for participation in the research, and (4) the questions about the independent variables that require answers. The last consideration presumes an immersion in research in one's field and knowledge of how questions are asked and what experimental designs have traditionally been used in providing answers.

In the pages that follow, unrealistically small numbers of cases are used for the sake of computational simplicity; the examples which are presented should therefore not be taken as guides beyond the principles being illustrated. Notation is likewise kept simple, with algorithms introduced in Chapter 8 to assist in conceptualizing and analyzing later and more advanced designs. Finally, treatment is restricted to experimental designs only, and the reader is referred to Spector (1981) for discussion of the broader research enterprise, field as well as experimental, of which experimentation is a part.

2. VARIABILITY

The language of science is, to a large extent, the language of variation, and experimentation is that method which seeks to explain variability by artificially effecting a change in the external world and observing the results: It is, as Machiavelli once said, the scientist's way of asking Nature a question.

By the term *variance*, statisticians are referring to the mean squared deviation around the arithmetic mean. Suppose, as an example, that four people are asked how many cups of coffee they drink per day, and that they report 3, 6, 2, and 5. The mean is therefore

$$\begin{aligned} \overline{X} &= \frac{\Sigma X}{n} \\ &= \frac{1}{n} \Sigma X \end{aligned} \qquad [2.1]$$

where n is the number of observations ($n = 4$ in this case), X stands for the scores that are to be summed, Σ represents the summing operation itself, $\overline{X}$ is the mean. In this particular case,

$$\overline{X} = \tfrac{1}{4}(3 + 6 + 2 + 5) = 4$$

It is around this mean score that variance (symbolized by S^2) is conventionally defined, according to the expression

$$S^2 = \frac{1}{n} \Sigma(X - \overline{X})^2 \qquad [2.2]$$

In this case,

$$S^2 = \tfrac{1}{4}[(3 - 4)^2 + \cdots + (5 - 4)^2] = 2.50$$

Variance is therefore an average (just like $\bar{X}$), that is, the average amount of squared deviation from the mean, hence its alternative name: mean squared deviation. In applications of the variance concept, the numerator of expression 2.2 is referred to as the sum of squares, or SS, and is the focus of mathematical development.

When a set of scores is selected from a larger universe of scores (i.e., when a sample is drawn from a population), the statistics which are calculated are estimates of population *parameters*: $\bar{X}$, for example, is an estimate of the parameter μ, which would be the mean number of cups of coffee consumed by all coffee drinkers, and not just those in the sample. With respect to the variance, it turns out mathematically that the best estimate of the population variance (symbolized by σ^2) is given by a modification of equation 2.2, as follows:

$$S^2 = \frac{1}{n - 1} \Sigma (X - \bar{X})^2 \qquad [2.3]$$

which, in the example of the coffee drinkers, yields

$$S^2 = (\tfrac{1}{3})(10) = 3.33$$

That the denominator in equation 2.3 is $n - 1$ rather than n reflects the fact that $\bar{X}$, which is necessary for the calculation of S^2, is itself an estimate (i.e., $\bar{X}$ is an estimate of μ); S^2 is therefore based on $n - 1$ *degrees of freedom* (df $= 3$), where the df represents the total number of observations minus 1 for each parameter (such as μ) that must be estimated in order to calculate the variance. Another way of expressing this is to note that with $\bar{X}$ given, as is required to calculate S^2, the sum total of all the n scores (ΣX) must also be fixed, because $\Sigma X = n\bar{X}$; therefore, if we know the value of all X scores except one, we can determine that one by subtracting the sum of all the other $n - 1$ scores from the total—that is, for any set of numbers for which the sum is known, one of those numbers is predetermined while the other $n - 1$ of them are free to vary (df $= n - 1$).

The *standard deviation* (S) is the square root of the variance, in this instance $S = \sqrt{3.33} = 1.83$. All of the squaring involved in calculating the variance is therefore compensated for by taking the square root. The standard deviation consequently expresses a kind of average deviation of all the raw scores from the mean score, that average having been weighted by the squaring operation, with the most deviant scores (when squared) carrying the greatest weight.

Equation 2.3 defines the sample variance, but for illustrative purposes below it will be convenient to employ an alternative but equivalent expression:

$$S^2 = \frac{1}{n-1}\left[\sum X^2 - \frac{1}{n}\left(\sum X\right)^2\right] \qquad [2.4]$$

In the coffee drinking example, this yields the same result as equation 2.3:

$$S^2 = \tfrac{1}{3}\left[(3^2 + \cdot\cdot\cdot + 5^2) - \tfrac{1}{4}(3 + 6 + 2 + 5)^2\right] = 3.33$$

In expressions 2.2 and 2.3, the mean score is subtracted from each raw score prior to squaring, whereas in equation 2.4 the raw scores are squared (ΣX^2) without $\bar{X}$ having first been subtracted. Expression 2.4 compensates for this by subtracting a correction factor: CF $= (1/n)(\Sigma X)^2 = 64$, which turns out to be equivalent to the mean squared n times, that is, $n\bar{X}^2 = (4)4^2 = 64$.

In the illustrations to follow, it will be convenient to simplify the statistical expressions in equation 2.4 as follows:

$\text{TSS} = \sum X^2$	uncorrected total sum of squares
$\text{CF} = \frac{1}{n}\left(\sum X\right)^2$	correction factor
$\text{SS}_\text{T} = \text{TSS} - \text{CF}$	corrected total sum of squares
$\text{df} = n - 1$	degrees of freedom

Hence, the variance can be expressed as

$$S^2 = \frac{\text{TSS} - \text{CF}}{\text{df}} = \frac{\text{SS}_\text{T}}{n-1}$$

The standard deviation is therefore

$$S = \sqrt{\frac{\text{SS}_\text{T}}{n-1}}$$

The concept of statistical variability can be summarized by thinking of it as a collective expression of individual uniqueness, that is, of the extent to which persons in the same group (e.g., coffee drinkers) are dissimilar from one another, as measured by their deviation from the group average.

As will be seen, this within-group variability provides a basis for evaluating the variability that exists between groups, for example, differences between control and experimental groups.

3. *t* TEST

Experimentation at its most basic involves two groups, experimental and control, the first group typically receiving some treatment (independent variable) designed to induce an effect (dependent variable), and the second not. For purposes of illustration, suppose that members of the above group of coffee drinkers (designated group B) were observed drinking the numbers of cups reported in Chapter 2 during an experiment in which cream and sugar were available, and that four other persons comprising group A were deprived of cream and sugar.

In this illustration, the availability (group B) or unavailability (group A) of cream and sugar represents the independent variable—in this case, availability and unavailability are *levels* of the independent variable—and the number of cups of coffee consumed is the dependent variable. It is to be noted that independent variables can be either qualitative or quantitative in nature, whereas dependent variables must always be quantitative. Had the experiment included a group C in which tea as well as coffee were available, for example, then the three groups would clearly have been qualitative in character; however, had the three groups been formed around the availability of different amounts of coffee (2, 4, or 6 pitchers available to each group, say) or on the basis of group members' prior sleep deprivation (e.g., 24, 36, and 48 hours), then the groupings would have been quantitative. In either case, the dependent variable (number of cups of coffee consumed) would have been quantitative.

The results of this experiment are presented in Table 3.1, and they show that, on the average, the group with access to cream and sugar drank more cups of coffee ($\overline{X}_B = 4.00$) than the group without access to cream and sugar ($\overline{X}_A = 3.50$), and it is the magnitude of this difference ($d = 0.50$) that we wish to evaluate. This is accomplished in terms of conventional hypothesis testing, which rests on three assumptions: (1) that the population or populations sampled (coffee drinkers in this case) are normally distributed, (2) that the members of each group are obtained through random sampling techniques that insure independence of selection, and (3) that the variances within the groups are equivalent. The statistical test at issue involves the group means, and the *null hypothesis* asserts the

TABLE 3.1

Subjects	*Group A*		*Group B*
	(Cups of coffee consumed)		
1	5		3
2	3		6
3	3		2
4	3		5
Mean	3.50		4.00
S^2	1.00		3.33
S	1.00		1.83
$S_{\bar{X}}$	0.50		0.91
d		0.50	
S_d		1.04	
t		0.48	
df		6	

equivalence of the population means for which they are estimates—or, formally stated,

$$H_0\colon \quad \mu_A - \mu_B = 0$$

where H_0 is the null hypothesis. The alternative hypothesis, H_1, which remains viable in the event H_0 is judged untenable, is

$$H_1\colon \quad \mu_A - \mu_B \neq 0$$

These are two competing versions of reality, and a choice between them is made by determining the probability of H_0 being correct, a determination accomplished via the appropriate statistical test.

In choosing between H_0 and H_1, it is first necessary to evaluate the dispersion of scores within each group in order to give operational substance to the principle that

> Before it is possible to conclude with confidence that two groups are different from one another with respect to some characteristic, any difference *between* them must substantially exceed the differences *within* them with respect to that characteristic.

In the present example, therefore, were there great variability in the number of cups of coffee consumed *within* both groups A and B but very little difference *between* the average number consumed in A compared with B, it would be difficult to sustain a belief that the availability of cream and sugar is functionally important to coffee consumption.

Given that the difference in group means ($d = \overline{X}_A - \overline{X}_B$) defines the magnitude of between-group dissimilarity in performance, it remains to determine the magnitude of within-group dissimilarity in terms of which d is to be evaluated. As noted previously, the standard deviation (S) is a rough indicator of the average extent to which each individual score deviates from the group mean. S therefore applies to raw scores. A comparable expression applicable to the mean is the standard error of the mean:

$$S_{\overline{X}} = S/\sqrt{n} \qquad [3.1]$$

In the cases of groups A and B, therefore,

$$S_{\overline{X}(A)} = 1.00/\sqrt{4} = 0.50$$

$$S_{\overline{X}(B)} = 1.83/\sqrt{4} = 0.91$$

Repeated sampling from the population of coffee drinkers would produce a distribution of means, and $S_{\overline{X}}$ for the group in question is the best estimate, using that group's data, of what the standard deviation of that distribution of means would be—that is, comparable with S in relation to individual scores, $S_{\overline{X}}$ would be a rough indicator of the average amount by which each sample mean would deviate from the population mean (which is unknown).

Because the scores in each group comprise only a sample rather than the entire population, $S_{\overline{X}(A)}$ and $S_{\overline{X}(B)}$ both represent unexplained variability—that is, they are expressions of the extent, on the average, to which a group of persons who have been treated identically have inexplicably failed to behave in the same way. It is therefore permissible to merge these two conceptually equivalent figures into a single measure of collective within-group variability, which is referred to as the standard error of the difference between means:

$$\begin{aligned} S_d &= \sqrt{S^2_{\overline{X}(A)} + S^2_{\overline{X}(B)}} \\ &= \sqrt{0.50^2 + 0.91^2} = 1.04 \end{aligned} \qquad [3.2]$$

The ratio between $d = 0.50$ (between-group difference) and $S_d = 1.04$ ("average" within-group difference) is referred to as a t test,

$$\begin{aligned} t &= d/S_d \\ &= 0.50/1.04 = 0.48 \end{aligned} \qquad [3.3]$$

and it expresses in numerical terms the principle, spelled out above, that prior to declaring two groups to be distinguishable, the explainable performance differential between the differently treated groups (numerator) must exceed the unexplainable differences among persons treated identically (denominator). How many times larger the former must be than the latter in order to be judged statistically significant is a matter of convention, and probability theory is relied upon to assess the probability of obtaining a difference as large as *d* if the null hypothesis is true. The smallest magnitude which a *t* score must reach in order for its associated mean difference to be judged significant is given in *t* tables for df $= n_A + n_B - 2$ and selected alpha levels (see Appendix A), where alpha (α) refers to probability levels considered too low to support the null hypothesis. In this example, df $= 4 + 4 - 2 = 6$; at $\alpha = .05$, therefore, *t* would have to exceed 2.45—that is, the variability between the two groups would have to be almost $2\frac{1}{2}$ times greater than the standard error before the null hypothesis could be rejected and the groups could be declared to have performed in significantly different ways.

4. ANALYSIS OF VARIANCE

The two-group *t* test example of the previous section is reexamined below in terms of analysis of variance (ANOVA), which is the primary statistical method employed in the univariate case, that is, in those cases in which only a single dependent variable, such as the number of cups of coffee consumed, is being appraised. (For a more detailed introduction to ANOVA, see Iversen and Norpoth, 1976; on multivariate ANOVA involving multiple dependent variables, consult Bray and Maxwell, 1986.) From the two-group case, ANOVA procedures can then be extended to greater numbers of groups and to more complex experimental situations.

The statistical decomposition effected by ANOVA is shown in Table 4.1, where the *X* scores in 4.1(a) are the same scores as in Table 3.1, and the scores in 4.1(b) are the raw scores squared. As specified in Chapter 2, the total sum of squared scores is designated TSS, where TSS = 126.00 in this case. In addition to group means—3.50 and 4.00 for groups A and B, respectively—an overall or grand mean is also calculated (GM = 3.75) which is the mean of all eight scores, or the mean of the two group means when $n_A = n_B$.

The scores in 4.1(c) are the original scores with GM subtracted, that is, $X - 3.75$. These are deviation scores and, by convention, are desig-

TABLE 4.1

Subjects	(a) X A	B		(b) X^2 A	B	
1	5	3		25	9	
2	3	6		9	36	
3	3	2		9	4	
4	3	5		9	25	
Sum	14	16	30	52	74	126.00 (TSS)
Mean	3.50	4.00	3.75 (GM)			
	(c) $x = X - \text{GM}$			(d) x^2		
1	1.25	−0.75		1.56	0.56	
2	−0.75	2.25		0.56	5.06	
3	−0.75	−1.75		0.56	3.06	
4	−0.75	1.25		0.56	1.56	
Sum	−1.00	1.00	0.00	3.25	10.25	13.50 (SS_T)
Mean	−0.25	0.25	0.00			
	(e) $e = x - \bar{x}$			(f) e^2		
1	1.50	−1.00		2.25	1.00	
2	−0.50	2.00		0.25	4.00	
3	−0.50	−2.00		0.25	4.00	
4	−0.50	1.00		0.25	1.00	
Sum	0.00	0.00	0.00	3.00	10.00	13.00 (SS_e)
Mean	0.00	0.00	0.00			

nated with the lower case x. The overall sum of Table 4.1(c) is now 0.00, and the group means have now been reduced to −0.25 and 0.25, respectively. Table 4.1(d) contains the squared deviation scores, and SS_T = 13.50 is the corrected total sum of squares, that is, the total sum of squares with the effect of the grand mean taken out. As shown in Chapter 2, SS_T can be calculated directly by subtracting the correction factor (CF) from TSS, where in this instance CF $= (\frac{1}{8})30^2 = 112.50$; hence, SS_T = TSS − CF = 126 − 112.50 = 13.50.

Table 4.1(e) contains the x scores in 4.1(c) with the group means ($\bar{x}$) of these deviation scores subtracted. These scores are designated e (for error) and express what is unique to each subject after removal of the effects of being in the experiment itself (GM) and being in a particular experimental group ($\bar{x}$). The two columns in 4.1(e) now sum to zero, and the means ($\bar{e}$) are, of course, also zero. Table 4.1(f) contains the errors squared, the total being designated SS_e. The e^2s are therefore the same squared within-group deviations that, in Table 3.1, led to the calculation of variance. In fact, the column totals in Table 4.1(f), when divided by df = 3, are the same as the group variances in Table 3.1.

Table 4.1 breaks down the raw scores into their component parts—grand mean (GM), group mean ($\bar{x}$) after the grand mean has been removed, and individual uniqueness or error (e)—and by recombining the components, the original scores can be reconstituted, as shown in Table 4.2: GM is a constant in all scores; $\bar{x}$, the group mean, is a constant within each group, but varies in value between groups (and it is the difference between these group means which the t test evaluates); and e varies randomly both between and within groups. This demonstrates the additivity assumption of ANOVA—namely, that the total deviation of a score from the mean of all scores (GM) can be broken down into two additive components: (1) The deviation of the group mean from GM, and (2) the deviation of the particular score from the mean of its group. It is this additive sum of deviations that, when squared, produces the two component sums of squares, as shown below.

As in the case of the t test, the e values express *unexplained variability* within groups of persons treated identically, whereas the group effects (-0.25 and 0.25, respectively, $d = 0.50$) express *explainable variability* between groups of persons treated differently. In ANOVA, the former is used to evaluate the latter, as in t test expression 3.3. This is accomplished by determining how much of the total sum of squares (SS_T) is attributable to differences between groups (SS_G) as compared with differences within groups (SS_e). The relevant calculations are as follows, based on Table 4.1.

TABLE 4.2

Group A $X = GM + \bar{x}_A + e$	*Group B* $X = GM + \bar{x}_B + e$
3.75 + (−0.25) + (1.50) = 5	3.75 + (0.25) + (−1.00) = 3
3.75 + (−0.25) + (−0.50) = 3	3.75 + (0.25) + (2.00) = 6
3.75 + (−0.25) + (−0.50) = 3	3.75 + (0.25) + (−2.00) = 2
3.75 + (−0.25) + (−0.50) = 3	3.75 + (0.25) + (1.00) = 5
Totals	
15.00 + (−1.00) + (0.00) = 14	15.00 + (1.00) + (0.00) = 16

The total sum of squares (uncorrected) is given in 4.1(b) and is formally calculated according to the expression

$$\begin{aligned} \text{TSS} &= \sum_g \sum_n X^2 \\ &= 5^2 + 3^2 + \cdots + 2^2 + 5^2 = 126.00 \end{aligned} \qquad [4.1]$$

where Σ_n is the sum of scores across all n subjects in a group, and Σ_g is the sum of all the g group sums. However, this figure includes the effect of the overall average (GM). If there are $g = 2$ groups and $n = 4$ persons per group—and given an overall sum of 30—the correction factor for the grand mean is calculated by

$$\text{CF} = \frac{1}{gn}\left(\sum_g \sum_n X\right)^2 = \left(\tfrac{1}{8}\right)30^2 = 112.50 \qquad [4.2]$$

CF is therefore equivalent to gn times the grand mean squared, that is, $\text{CF} = 8(3.75^2) = 112.50$. The corrected total sum of squares is now equal to

$$\begin{aligned} \text{SS}_\text{T} &= \text{TSS} - \text{CF} \\ &= 126.00 - 112.50 = 13.50 \end{aligned} \qquad [4.3]$$

as shown in Table 4.1(d). If there were no groups—that is, if we were merely analyzing eight ungrouped scores—the variance would be $S^2 = \text{SS}_\text{T}/\text{df} = 13.50/(8 - 1) = 1.93$.

The corrected total sum of squares is composed of the sum of squares attributable to differences between groups (SS_G) and the sum of squares attributable to differences arising within groups (SS_e), that is, $\text{SS}_\text{T} = \text{SS}_\text{G} + \text{SS}_e$. That portion of SS_T which is attributable to the differences between the groups arises in terms of the variability of the group means ($\overline{X}$) around the grand mean (GM), that is:

$$\begin{aligned} \text{SS}_\text{G} &= n\left[(\overline{X}_\text{A} - \text{GM})^2 + (\overline{X}_\text{B} - \text{GM})^2\right] \\ &= 4\left[(3.50 - 3.75)^2 + (4.00 - 3.75)^2\right] = 0.50 \end{aligned} \qquad [4.4]$$

In the above calculation, the sum of the squared deviations is multiplied by n because each group mean is based on $n = 4$ observations.

As shown in Chapter 2 (compare expressions 2.3 and 2.4), it is usually more convenient to avoid calculating deviations, and instead to use raw (uncorrected) sums and then to subtract the correction factor. The uncorrected sum of squares for groups (GSS) can be calculated using the column sums in Table 4.1(a):

$$\text{GSS} = \frac{1}{n}\left[\left(\frac{\Sigma X_A}{n}\right)^2 + \left(\frac{\Sigma X_B}{n}\right)^2\right] \qquad [4.5]$$

$$= \tfrac{1}{4}(14^2 + 16^2) = 113$$

The corrected sum of squares for groups is therefore

$$SS_G = \text{GSS} - \text{CF} \qquad [4.6]$$

$$= 113 - 112.50 = 0.50$$

And because $SS_T = SS_G + SS_e$, the latter value can be gotten through subtraction, as a residual term:

$$SS_e = SS_T - SS_G \qquad [4.7]$$

$$= 13.50 - 0.50 = 13.00$$

Alternatively, SS_e can be calculated directly from the uncorrected sums of squares:

$$SS_e = \text{TSS} - \text{GSS} \qquad [4.8]$$

$$= 126.00 - 113.00 = 13.00$$

What has been calculated so far is summarized in Table 4.3. As can be seen, $SS_G + SS_e = 13.50$ (SS_T). The sum of squares associated with the correction factor is 112.50 which, when added to the corrected total, produces TSS = 126.00, the uncorrected sum of squares. The sums of squares in the upper half of Table 4.3 are therefore independent of the mean, and it is only this information which is of experimental interest.

The degrees of freedom for within groups is obtained in the same way as in the case of the *t* test (Table 3.1), that is, there are $n - 1 = 3$ df for

TABLE 4.3

Source of Variance SV	*Degrees of Freedom df*	*Corrected Sums of Squares SS*	*Mean Square MS*	*F Ratio*
Between Groups	$g - 1 = 1$	0.50	0.50	0.23
Within Groups	$g(n - 1) = 6$	13.00	2.17	
Total	$gn - 1 = 7$	13.50	1.93	
Grand Mean	CF = 1	112.50		
Grand Total	$gn = 8$	126.00		

each group, and $g = 2$ groups, hence $g(n - 1) = 2(3) = 6$ df. The between-group df $= g - 1 = 1$ in this case; the total df is therefore $\text{df}_G + \text{df}_e = 7$.

The *mean squares* are the sums of squares divided by their respective degrees of freedom, that is,

$$\text{MS} = \text{SS}/\text{df} \qquad [4.9]$$

hence they are variance estimates. In this case, $\text{MS}_T = \text{SS}_T/\text{df}_T = 13.50/7 = 1.93$, which would be the overall variance of these eight scores if they were ungrouped, and is therefore of virtually no interest.

$\text{MS}_e = \text{SS}_e/\text{df}_e = 13.00/6 = 2.17$, and represents the variance occurring within groups A and B combined. Compare this with the two variances in Table 3.1: As is apparent, the error mean square is merely their average, that is, $\frac{1}{2}(S_A^2 + S_B^2) = \frac{1}{2}(1.00 + 3.33) = 2.17$. MS_e in ANOVA is therefore a straightforward averaging, or pooling, of variability occurring within all groups, and is an expression of what is unexplained in the experiment.

$\text{MS}_G = \text{SS}_G/\text{df}_G = 0.50/1 = 0.50$. This reflects the average amount of variability arising from differences between groups, that is, the variability of the group means around the grand mean; therefore, this also includes the effect of the independent variable, which is explainable in terms of the design of the experiment.

MS_G and MS_e therefore stand in the same relationship as explainable to unexplainable in expression 3.3 of the *t* test, and in ANOVA this is given form in the *F* ratio:

$$\begin{aligned} F_{1,6} &= \text{MS}_G/\text{MS}_e \\ &= 0.50/2.17 = 0.23 \end{aligned} \qquad [4.10]$$

What this explainable/unexplainable ratio represents can be alternatively conceptualized in terms of the ratio between signal and noise. Had the eight subjects in Table 4.1(a) been randomly assigned to the two groups but with no experiment having taken place, this so-called "uniformity trial" would still have produced *X* scores indicating the number of cups of coffee consumed prior to experimental intervention; moreover, there would doubtless have been within-group variability much like that shown in the table, and it is this variability, arising because of individual differences, that constitutes the noise in the experiment. Superimposed on this background noise of uninterpretable, or random, variability in the performance of the subjects is the experimental signal, that is, the additional variability arising because of the effectiveness of the independent variable (in this case, the availability or unavailability of cream and sugar) with respect to the dependent variable (coffee consumption). If an experiment is well conducted and the independent variable truly influences behavior, the signal will be strong enough to be distinguishable from the noise, and it is this relationship that the F ratio incapsulates and appraises. What it seeks to determine, in sum, is whether there is signal variance hidden within the noise of random behavior.

Originally referred to as the variance ratio, the F ratio was given this name by George Snedecor in honor of Sir Ronald A. Fisher, and the subscripts associated with it denote the degrees of freedom for the between-group and within-group sources of variance, respectively—1 and 6 in this case. As in the case of the t test, the significance of the F ratio is determined by consulting an F table (see Appendix B), and in this instance the F table is entered in column 1 ($df_G = 1$) and row 6 ($df_e = 6$), that is, the degrees of freedom indicate where to look in the F table. Had a decision been made previously to accept as statistically significant only those mean differences that produced an F in excess of the $\alpha = .05$ tabular F value, the calculated F would have had to exceed 5.99, which it obviously does not—hence, the means of groups A and B are judged not to be significantly different.

This was the same conclusion reached using the t test, and this is necessarily so because with $g = 2$ groups, $F = t^2$: The ratio in Table 3.1 is $t = 0.48$, and $t^2 = 0.23$, which is the F ratio above. Hence, the square root of the F values in column 1 of the F table will always equal the t values from the t table for the same number of df_e and alpha level.

In the t test, with $\alpha = .05$, if the two group means are judged to be significantly different, the experimentalist theoretically runs a 5% chance of having made an erroneous judgment—that is, of having committed a *Type I error* in which a true H_0 is falsely rejected. Therefore, if the availability of cream and sugar really has no impact on the number of cups of coffee consumed, then 5% of the observed mean differences arising under repeated sampling will appear to be significant when they really are not, their apparent significance being due to the vicissitudes of sampling and other random influences. With four groups, there would be six t tests (1 vs. 2, 1 vs. 3, 1 vs. 4, 2 vs. 3, 2 vs. 4, and 3 vs. 4). In general, therefore, with g groups, there are $c = g(g - 1)/2$ comparisons, and the experimenter runs a 5% risk of making an error with each test, which means that the likelihood of making a mistake in judgment increases so that alpha no longer really describes the level of risk. With $c = 6$ comparisons and

$\alpha = .05$, for example, the level of accumulated risk is

$$\begin{aligned} \text{Risk} &= 1 - (1 - \alpha)^c \\ &= 1 - (1 - .05)^6 = 0.26 \end{aligned} \quad [4.11]$$

Starting with the case of the t test for two groups ($c = 1$ comparison), a 5% risk quickly balloons to 26% when four groups are involved ($c = 6$). The value of ANOVA and the F test—which are equivalent to t in the two-group case—is that they can generalize the logic of the t test to cases in which $g > 2$ without increasing risk. As illustrated in subsequent sections, experiments can be designed in which significant differences among any number of groups can be detected with alpha set at any desired level.

5. COMPLETELY RANDOMIZED DESIGN

Completely randomized are the most elementary of experimental designs, and for purposes of notation will be tentatively designated CR-g (where g equals the number of groups), as suggested by Kirk (1982). (A more descriptive designation will be introduced in Section 8.1.) The design in Chapter 4, for example, was of the type CR-2, and $g = 2$ is of course the lower bound, but in principle g could extend to infinity. As noted previously, the CR design is so called because subjects are assigned randomly to experimental conditions—or, alternatively, experimental treatments are randomly applied to subjects—so that each subject initially has an identical probability of $1/g$ of being exposed to any one of the treatments.

In Table 5.1, to provide a concrete illustration, the $N = 16$ persons who agreed to participate in this experiment were blindly assigned to one of the $g = 4$ groups, those $n = 4$ persons ending up in any group being thrown together by accident. Hence, the only thing that the four subjects in group 1 have in common (at least insofar as is known) is exposure to the same experimental condition, and similarly for those in group 4. If the mean scores for those two groups differ substantially, therefore, the difference in experimental conditions is the only plausible explanation. Political party preference would be an improbable explanation, for example, because Democratic subjects are no more likely than Republican subjects to end up in either group 1 or group 4 under conditions of random assignment. And the same is true of any and all other variables—age, sex, race, personality, etc.—so that all effects except the experimental variable

TABLE 5.1

Subjects	*Group 1* (*3 libs*)	*Group 2* (*2 libs*)	*Group 3* (*1 lib*)	*Group 4* (*0 libs*)	
	(Lib/Con scores, 9 = Lib, 1 = Con)				
1	5	3	6	6	
2	3	6	5	5	
3	3	2	6	6	
4	3	5	5	7	
Sum	14	16	22	24	76 = Total sum
Mean	3.50	4.00	5.50	6.00	4.75 = GM
SS	52	74	122	146	394 = TSS
S^2	1.00	3.33	0.33	0.67	1.33 = Mean S^2

are converted into random error. And because within-group variability is an expression of all uncontrolled influences, it provides a measure of the amount of random error in the experiment, which, as demonstrated previously, can be used to evaluate the magnitude of the experimental effects.

It is to be noted, incidentally, that in this and all subsequent examples, equal *n*s per group are assumed. This is the goal typically sought in experimentation for reasons of computational simplicity and also because of problems that arise in the independent assessment of treatment effects in designs with more than one independent variable.

Substantively, the experimental situation that resulted in Table 5.1 consisted of subjects being instructed to evaluate President Jimmy Carter along a nine-point liberalism/conservatism continuum (1 = conservative). The experiment was conducted in February 1980, prior to the state primaries and Carter's eventual loss to Ronald Reagan. Ideology was widely believed to be a salient consideration in that election, and theoretical interest was in the salience of cognitive anchors (Rotter and Rotter, 1966), that is, in the extent to which Carter's perceived ideological position might be seen to shift under different experimental conditions. The ideological context was controlled by placing Carter's name within each of four different groups of names, as follows:

Group 1 (3 libs): Jerry Brown, Ted Kennedy, George McGovern
Group 2 (2 libs): Ted Kennedy, George McGovern, Ronald Reagan
Group 3 (1 lib): Ted Kennedy, Ronald Reagan, Gerald Ford
Group 4 (0 libs): Ronald Reagan, Gerald Ford, John Connolly

Hence, subjects in group 1 were instructed to evaluate each of four political figures—Carter plus liberals Brown, Kennedy, and McGovern—in terms of their perceived liberalism or conservatism; subjects in group 4 evaluated Carter plus conservative candidates Reagan, Ford, and Connolly. In terms of cognitive anchor theory, it was expected that Carter would be assessed as more conservative in group 1 and progressively more liberal in groups 2 through 4. The actual results are in Table 5.1.

One of the assumptions of ANOVA is that the within-group variances of the four groups are equal, that is, that they represent samples from populations with equal variances. This is the *homogeneity of variance* assumption. Some degree of difference in variance is of course to be expected because of sampling error, but this discrepancy should not be statistically significant. The variances for groups 1 through 4, as shown in Table 5.1, are 1.00, 3.33, 0.33, and 0.67, respectively. Applied to this case, a computationally simple test for homogeneity of variance is:

$$F_{max} = \frac{\text{largest } S^2}{\text{smallest } S^2} = \frac{3.33}{0.33} = 10.00 \qquad [5.1]$$

F_{max} therefore tests the equivalence of the two most discrepant variances, which are judged to be equal so long as the calculated F_{max} does not exceed the tabular F_{max} (see Appendix C). In this instance, $g = 4$ and $n - 1 = 3$ are the degrees of freedom necessary to enter the table, which shows the tabular value to be $F_{max} = 39.2$ ($\alpha = .05$), indicating that the calculated F_{max} above is well within limits. Homogeneity of variance therefore prevails, and consequently we can proceed to the analysis of variance.

The need for homogeneous variances across all groups prior to ANOVA arises from the fact that the within-group mean square, which serves as the summary expression of experimental error and which appears as the denominator of the F ratio, is itself simply the average of the g group variances, given equal group ns. (Note that the average group variance of 1.33 in Table 5.1 is the same as the error mean square in Table 5.2.) This average within-group variance can serve as a common measure of error variance for the experiment as a whole only if what is occurring errorwise in one group is essentially indistinguishable from what is occurring in every other group, so that the averaging of their variances does not, so to speak, involve mixing apples with oranges.

TABLE 5.2

SV	*df*	*SS*	*MS*	*F*
Groups	$g - 1 \quad = 3$	17	5.67	4.25*
Error	$g(n - 1) = 12$	16	1.33	
Total	$gn - 1 \quad = 15$	33		

*$p < .05$

The above warning having been issued, it is nevertheless somewhat rare for variances to be heterogeneous, especially with equal *n*s per group. If F_{max} proves significant, however, it may be necessary, prior to performing the ANOVA, to transform the data in one of the appropriate ways described by Howell (1987: 298–305) or Kirk (1982: 79–84).

The ANOVA of the four-group data in Table 5.1 proceeds in the same manner outlined in the two-group problem of Chapter 4. Three figures are required and are obtained using expressions 4.1, 4.2, and 4.5 from the previous chapter: the uncorrected total sum of squares (TSS), the correction factor (CF), and the uncorrected sum of squares for groups (GSS). With $g = 4$ groups and $n = 4$ subjects per group, the figures are:

$$\text{TSS} = \sum_g \sum_n X^2$$

$$= 5^2 + 3^2 + \cdots + 6^2 + 7^2 = 394$$

$$\text{CF} = \frac{1}{gn}\left(\sum_g \sum_n X\right)^2$$

$$= \tfrac{1}{16}(76^2) = 361$$

$$\text{GSS} = \frac{1}{n}\sum_g\left(\sum_n X\right)^2 = \frac{1}{n}\left[\left(\sum_n X_1\right)^2 + \cdots + \left(\sum_n X_4\right)^2\right]$$

$$= \tfrac{1}{4}(14^2 + 16^2 + 22^2 + 24^2) = 378$$

The corrected sums of squares (i.e., corrected for the mean) are given as follows:

$$SS_G = \text{GSS} - \text{CF} = 378 - 361 = 17$$

$$SS_e = \text{TSS} - \text{GSS} = 394 - 378 = 16$$

$$SS_T = \text{TSS} - \text{CF} = 394 - 361 = 33$$

These same general steps apply to any completely randomized design in which there are equal numbers of subjects per group. The ANOVA summary for this experiment is summarized in Table 5.2. As before, the sums of squares for (between) Groups plus Error (within groups) add up to Total (SS_T), as do the degrees of freedom, and the general formulas for df are also the same for any completely randomized design (i.e., $g - 1$ always designates the between-group df no matter how large g is), and again assuming equal ns per experimental treatment. The mean squares, as before, are calculated by dividing each SS by its respective df. The F ratio is always calculated by MS_G/MS_e—for example, $5.67/1.33 = 4.25$ in this case. The F table (Appendix B) indicates in column 3 ($df_G = 3$) and row 12 ($df_e = 12$) that any calculated F which exceeds $F_{3,12} = 3.49$ is significant beyond the .05 level.

In this instance, a significant F indicates that at least two (and perhaps more) of the four group means are significantly different from one another; it does not tell us which means are different, however. That determination requires more detailed comparisons, such as those found in Chapter 6.

It is frequently of interest in experimental design to determine the importance of a statistical finding. Although it is known in the present case that the Groups factor is significant at a probability level less than .05 (Table 5.2), the importance or practical meaning of this result cannot be judged from the probability statement: we know only that the finding should be considered nonchance (Harcum, 1989).

There are several commonly used measures of the magnitude of a treatment effect. Perhaps the most widely used is omega-squared (ω^2), the general formula for which is

$$\omega^2 = \frac{SS_{effect} - df_{effect} MS_e}{MS_e + SS_T} \qquad [5.2]$$

where SS_{effect} and df_{effect} are associated with the treatment effect being measured. This statistic can vary from 0 to 1 (although negative values can occur when $F < 1$) and is interpreted as the proportion of the total variance in a set of data that can be accounted for or explained by the experimental factor. It should be pointed out that this formula is for the most common design situation, that is, one in which the treatment variable is a "fixed" factor (see Chapter 8 for the distinction between fixed and random effects).

For the findings in Table 5.2, expression 5.2 yields

$$\omega^2 = \frac{SS_G - (g - 1)MS_e}{SS_T + MS_e}$$

$$= \frac{17 - (3)1.33}{33 + 1.33} = 0.38$$

Interpretations of ω^2 usually follow Cohen (1977), who suggests that a large effect has an $\omega^2 \geq 0.15$, a medium effect about 0.06, and a small effect 0.01. The above finding of a significant Groups effect would have to be considered large because 38% of the variance in the data can be accounted for by knowing the ideological context group to which subjects belong.

An excellent discussion of ω^2 can be found in Keppel (1982: 89–96). Howell (1987) gives a thorough account of alternatives, such as eta-squared and the squared intraclass correlation coefficient. O'Grady (1982) offers a well-reasoned critique of the use of measures of strength of an effect in the ANOVA.

6. COMPARISONS AND TRENDS

Performing an ANOVA on the data of a particular design may appear to represent a necessary and sufficient course of action for detecting the effectiveness of experimental manipulations, but this is not the case on either account. In order to understand why, however, it is helpful to think of an experimental design as a construction that can be built of several components; conversely, it can also be conceived as one that can be broken down or decomposed into its constituent parts.

The CR design of the previous chapter, for example, can be thought of as being composed of several alternative *comparisons* between different ideological context groups. An alternative to performing an overall ANOVA involving all the groups in the CR design would therefore be to examine one or more comparisons that involve some subset of the groups. Thus it may really only be of interest to see if there is a significant difference between group 4 (no liberals) and each of the other three groups, and this set of three comparisons could be used instead of the overall ANOVA. On the other hand, there may be only one comparison that is of interest, for example, the average of the means of groups 1, 2, and 3 versus group 4's mean. This is a "complex" comparison whereas the group versus group comparisons are denoted as "simple" or "pairwise" comparisons. The F statistic, in actuality, is a simultaneous test of all possible simple and complex comparisons involving the same groups. If F is significant, then there is some comparison that would also be significant. The problem is to identify it.

So far, reasons have been given for not considering an overall ANOVA as a necessary mode of analysis for any particular design. The reason it is also not likely to be sufficient is that the overall ANOVA generally answers questions that are only preliminary or broadly focused, that is, that lead to more specific inquiries. Consequently, many investigators will perform an overall ANOVA on a CR design, and most other designs as well, but will follow it with a set of comparisons. For instance, it may be theoretically important for a researcher to be able to state that ideological context is a significant influence on voting behavior, but this same researcher may also have a need to know if it is as effective with a weak anchor (as in group 3) as it is with a strong anchor (group 1).

6.1. A Priori Comparisons

When comparisons are established before an experiment is executed, they are termed *a priori* or *planned*, and are usually driven by previous research findings and/or theoretical considerations. Before conducting the experiment on ideological context, for example, interest may have centered on determining whether the extreme cases might at least be significantly different—that is, in learning whether evaluations of Carter's liberalism were altered depending on whether his name appeared with three liberals and no conservatives (group 1) or with three conservatives and no liberals (group 4). This would mean ignoring groups 2 and 3, and this is symbolized in row $C1$ of Table 6.1, which contains the group totals (G) from Table 5.1 plus the lambda (λ) coefficients that are used to define the comparisons. The coefficients for planned comparison $C1$, when multiplied by the group totals, will have the effect of canceling out groups 2 and 3 and determining the magnitude of difference between groups 1

TABLE 6.1

	Groups					
	1	*2*	*3*	*4*		
	Group Totals (G)					
Planned Comparisons	*14*	*16*	*22*	*24*	$\Sigma\lambda$	$\Sigma\lambda^2$
$C1$: 1 vs. 4	1	0	0	−1	0	2
$C2$: 2 vs. 3	0	1	−1	0	0	2
$C3$: 1, 4 vs. 2, 3	$\frac{1}{2}$	$-\frac{1}{2}$	$-\frac{1}{2}$	$\frac{1}{2}$	0	1
$C1 \times C2$	0	0	0	0	0	
$C1 \times C3$	$\frac{1}{2}$	0	0	$-\frac{1}{2}$	0	
$C2 \times C3$	0	$-\frac{1}{2}$	$\frac{1}{2}$	0	0	

and 4, namely:

$$\sum \lambda G = (1)(14) + (0)(16) + (0)(22) + (-1)(24)$$
$$= 14 - 24 = -10$$

The set of lambda coefficients is considered legitimate if $\Sigma\lambda = 0$, which is the case for *C*1. It will be noted that when this is true, there is always a specific difference being examined—namely, that between the group (or groups) whose data are weighted by positive coefficients and those whose data are weighted by negative coefficients. Note also that $\Sigma|\lambda|$, that is, the sum of the absolute values for this set of coefficients, is 2. Whereas this is not a requirement for legitimacy, it is a convenient situation for complex comparisons such as *C*3, as will be seen.

In general the corrected sum of squares attributable to a comparison is given by the expression:

$$SS_C = \frac{(\sum \lambda G)^2}{n \sum \lambda^2} \qquad [6.1]$$

where in this case $\Sigma\lambda G = -10$, as calculated above; $n = 4$ persons per group; and $\Sigma\lambda^2 = 2$ (see Table 6.1). Hence:

$$SS_{C1} = \frac{(-10)^2}{(4)(2)} = 12.5$$

Comparison *C*2 in Table 6.1 pits group 2 against group 3:

$$SS_{C2} = \frac{[(0)(14) + (1)(16) + (-1)(22) + (0)(24)]^2}{(4)(2)}$$
$$= \frac{(-6)^2}{8} = 4.5$$

Comparison *C*3 focuses on combined groups and as such is a complex comparison. Here the average performance of groups 1 and 4 combined is compared with that of groups 2 and 3:

$$SS_{C3} = \frac{[(\frac{1}{2})(14) + (-\frac{1}{2})(16) + (-\frac{1}{2})(22) + (\frac{1}{2})(24)]^2}{(4)(1)}$$
$$= \frac{(19 - 19)^2}{4} = 0$$

The number of planned comparisons to be made and the manner in which the corrected sums of squares associated with them are to be evaluated depends on whether or not these comparisons are *orthogonal.* When comparisons are orthogonal, they are independent, the information used in one comparison being different from that used in another. The number of orthogonal planned comparisons is constrained by the between-groups degrees of freedom. For the experimental design of Table 6.1, $g - 1 = 3$ represents the size of the set of orthogonal comparisons, and $C1$, $C2$, and $C3$ are the three members of this set. In order to establish that a pair of comparisons is orthogonal, it is necessary to cross multiply their lambda coefficients, that is, to multiply the first coefficient of $C1$ by the first coefficient of $C2$, and so forth for the other pairs of coefficients. When the sum of cross products is zero, the comparisons are orthogonal. Thus, $C1$ and $C2$ are orthogonal because $\Sigma(\lambda_{C1}\lambda_{C2}) = (1)(0) + (0)(1) + (0)(-1) + (-1)(0) = 0$.

The value of restricting comparisons to an orthogonal set is in the maintenance of Type I error control. Recall that in performing an ANOVA, the probability of rejecting H_0 when it is in fact true (i.e., a Type I error) is restricted, typically, to $\alpha = .05$. When a set of comparisons is conducted, however, there is the possibility of a Type I error occurring in any one of them. Ordinarily, the concept of a Type I error rate must be considered *familywise*—that is, the probability of at least one Type I error for the set or family of comparisons, a matter to be addressed in greater detail subsequently. For the moment, it is sufficient to acknowledge that orthogonal comparisons escape such concern because they involve independent pieces of information. What are essentially being conducted are separate, stand-alone ANOVAs that do not constitute some higher-order entity or family.

Consider the independent ANOVAs for the set of orthogonal comparisons in Table 6.1. First note that it makes good theoretical sense to compare the most extreme groups 1 and 4 (comparison $C1$), and an investigator might even mount a case for studying any fine difference between middle groups 2 and 3 ($C2$); however, comparing the average of groups 1 and 4 with that of 2 and 3 ($C3$), although making no obvious sense theoretically, is forced on the investigator by virtue of the prior choice of $C1$ and $C2$—that is, with $C1$ and $C2$ specified, $C3$ is the only remaining comparison that will complete an orthogonal set.

The sums of squares for a set of orthogonal comparisons add up to the between-groups sum of squares for that variable, as shown in Table 6.2—that is, SS_G has been decomposed into the three components represented

TABLE 6.2

SV	*df*	*SS*	*MS*	*F*
Groups	3	17.00	5.67	4.25**
(*C*1)	(1)	(12.50)	12.50	9.38***
(*C*2)	(1)	(4.50)	4.50	3.38*
(*C*3)	(1)	(0.00)	0.00	0.00
Error	12	16.00	1.33	
Total	15	33.00		

*$p < .10$, **$p < .05$, ***$p < .01$

by the orthogonal comparisons: $\text{SS}_\text{G} = \text{SS}_{C1} + \text{SS}_{C2} + \text{SS}_{C3} = 12.50 + 4.50 + 0.00 = 17.00$. Likewise, $\text{df}_\text{G} = 3$ has also been decomposed, with 1 df going to each comparison. The *F* ratio for the Groups effect remains the same as reported previously. The *F* ratios for the comparisons ($F = \text{MS}_C/\text{MS}_e$) are compared with $F_{1,12}$ from Appendix B. The large *F* for *C*1 indicates that the difference between the group 1 and 4 means is highly significant ($p < .01$); the *F* for *C*2 is significant at $p < .10$ (an alpha level best used only for exploratory research); *F* for *C*3 is not significant.

It is important to point out that the set of orthogonal comparisons used in Table 6.1 is not the only possible set. For example, consider C', an alternative set of lambda coefficients that are also orthogonal:

$$C1'\!: \quad 1 \quad -1 \quad 0 \quad 0 \qquad \text{SS}_{C1'} = 0.50 \quad (F = .38)$$

$$C2'\!: \quad 0 \quad 0 \quad 1 \quad -1 \qquad \text{SS}_{C2'} = 0.50 \quad (F = .38)$$

$$C3'\!: \quad \tfrac{1}{2} \quad \tfrac{1}{2} \quad -\tfrac{1}{2} \quad -\tfrac{1}{2} \qquad \text{SS}_{C3'} = 16.00 \ (F = 12.03,\, p < .01)$$

Which of several possible sets of orthogonal contrasts is constructed depends on which comparisons are deemed to be of a priori importance by the experimenter, who cannot examine more than one set and still use the procedures introduced above for evaluating the significance of the resulting *F* ratios.

6.2. The Dunn Test

In the event that the a priori or planned comparisons of interest are greater in number than $g - 1$ and/or are not orthogonal to each other, the most common strategy is to use the *Dunn multiple comparison test*, which is based on the *Bonferroni inequality*. The latter expresses the relationship between the alpha level (probability of a Type I error) per comparison (α_{pc}) and the alpha level familywise (α_{fw}), namely: $\alpha_{fw} \leq \Sigma\alpha_{pc}$. The implication of this inequality is that α_{fw} can be divided among the members of the set of comparisons. This new α_{pc} level is then used for testing the significance of each comparison. In this way, α_{fw} can be maintained no matter how many comparisons are involved. Consider the specific example in which there are four comparisons. Here, α_{pc} would be set at .0125 (i.e., $\alpha_{fw}/4$), and, given the Bonferroni inequality, we would be certain that α_{fw} is not greater than .05 (i.e., 4 × .0125) for the set of four comparisons.

An obvious question that arises is, Where are *F* or *t* values to be found for alpha levels such as .0125? Fortunately, the table used with the Dunn test (see Appendix E) incorporates the adjustment of α_{pc} for each particular number of comparisons, and simply requires looking up a critical value for that particular number of comparisons and df_e .

Rather than the *F* of the ANOVA, the Dunn test employs a *t* statistic, a particularly useful version of which is:

$$t = \frac{C_a\overline{X}_a + C_b\overline{X}_b + \cdots + C_p\overline{X}_p}{\left[\text{MS}_e(C_a^2/n_a + \cdots + C_p^2/n_p)\right]^{1/2}} \qquad [6.2]$$

This formula can be used for both simple and complex comparisons, as well as in situations in which the groups do not have equal numbers of subjects. When only pairwise comparisons are to be made and both groups have the same number of subjects, the formula simplifies to:

$$t = \frac{C_a\overline{X}_a + C_b\overline{X}_b}{\sqrt{2\text{MS}_e/n}} \qquad [6.3]$$

In both formulas, each C represents a coefficient for a comparison, each $\overline{X}$ represents a group mean that will be multiplied by that coefficient, *n* is the number of scores in each group, and MS_e is the error mean square taken from the ANOVA analysis.

Assume that the two planned comparisons of greatest interest from the ideological context study are (1) a comparison of groups 1 and 4, and (2) a comparison involving the average of groups 1, 2, and 3 in contrast to the performance of group 4. The coefficients defining the first comparison ($C1$) are 1 0 0 −1, whereas those defining the second ($C2$) are $\frac{1}{3}$ $\frac{1}{3}$ $\frac{1}{3}$ −1. The $C1 \times C2$ sum of cross products is $1\frac{1}{3}$, indicating that these two comparisons are not orthogonal. Table 6.3 contains the means for the

TABLE 6.3

	Group Means				
	1	2	3	4	
	3.5	4.0	5.5	6.0	*Sum*
*C*1	1	0	0	−1	0
*C*2	$\frac{1}{3}$	$\frac{1}{3}$	$\frac{1}{3}$	−1	0
*C*1 × *C*2	$\frac{1}{3}$	0	0	1	$1\frac{1}{3}$

four ideological context groups. The final piece of information required is found in Table 6.2: $MS_e = 1.33$, $df_e = 12$.

From a Dunn's table (Appendix E), it is determined that when the number of comparisons is $c = 2$, $\alpha_{fw} = .05$, and $df_e = 12$, the t_D required for rejecting H_0 is 2.56. (It should be clear from the previous discussion that each comparison is actually being tested with $\alpha = .025$.) Using expression 6.3 and computing t_D for $C(1)$:

$$t_D = \frac{(1)(3.5) + (-1)(6.0)}{\sqrt{(2)(1.33)/4}}$$

$$= -3.06$$

which allows the rejection of H_0. (Because the test is two-tailed, the direction of the difference between groups 1 and 4 is irrelevant.)

For $C(2)$, expression 6.2 is employed:

$$t_D = \frac{(\frac{1}{3})(3.5) + (\frac{1}{3})(4.0) + (\frac{1}{3})(5.5) + (-1)(6.0)}{\left\{1.33\left[(\frac{1}{3})^2/4 + (\frac{1}{3})^2/4 + (\frac{1}{3})^2/4 + (-1)^2/4\right]\right\}^{1/2}}$$

$$= \frac{4.33 - 6.00}{\sqrt{(1.33)(.33)}} = -2.50$$

which is not significant.

It is advisable to restrict usage of Dunn's test to as small a set of planned comparisons as possible, the reason being that α_{pc} is inversely proportional to the number of comparisons made. When the number of comparisons is large and, therefore, an extremely small alpha is used—for example, .005 for 10 comparisons and α_{fw} at .05—the probability of *Type II errors* will be very high; that is, it will be increasingly difficult to reject H_0 when it is false.

Extended discussions of the Dunn test can be found in Marascuilo and Serlin (1988). Keppel (1982) offers a useful modification of the Dunn-Bonferroni strategy for large sets of comparisons.

6.3. Trend Analysis

The raw data in Table 5.1 are *quantitative* in nature, that is, the experimental contrivance involved reducing the number of liberals with whom Jimmy Carter's name appeared; moreover, it also involved a known interval, each group (after group 1) being decreased by one liberal figure. These two features, quantitative data and intervals of known size, permit the analysis of trends.

The trends for which any data set can be tested are a function of the number of degrees of freedom for Groups: In this case, there are $g - 1 = 3$ trends, as shown in Figure 6.1. If the data behave in a linear fashion (L), then estimations of Jimmy Carter's liberalness will show a progressive increase or decrease as the number of conservative names increases. If the data behave quadratically (Q), there will be a drop followed by a subsequent rise, or vice versa; that is, there will be one change of direction in the trend. Cubic data (C) will change directions twice. The actual data configuration in this case also appears in Figure 6.1.

L, Q, and C are orthogonal polynomials which express these trends numerically, and the sums of squares for trends can be calculated using the same expression as 6.1 above, namely

$$SS_{\text{trend}} = \frac{(\sum \lambda G)^2}{n \sum \lambda^2} \qquad [6.4]$$

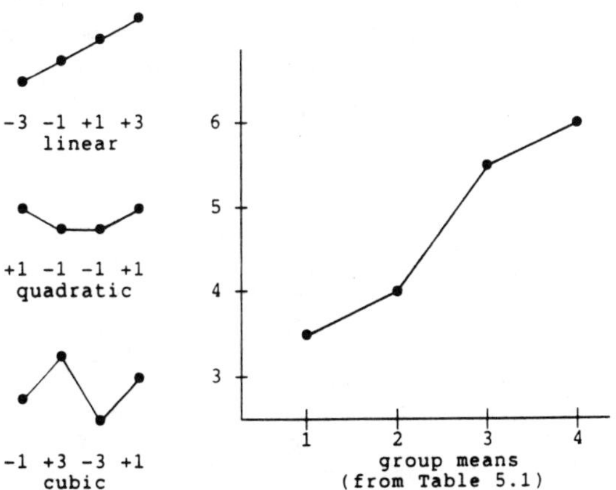

Figure 6.1.

TABLE 6.4

	Groups					
	1	*2*	*3*	*4*		
	Group Totals (G)					
Trends	*14*	*16*	22	24	Σλ	$\Sigma\lambda^2$
L	−3	−1	1	3	0	20
Q	1	−1	−1	1	0	4
C	−1	3	−3	1	0	20

where G is the group total. (The λs in equation 6.4 are different from those in equation 6.1, and can be found in specialized tables for trend analysis located in advanced texts, e.g., Kirk, 1982.) The relevant data are in Table 6.4, and the computations are as follows:

$$SS_L = \frac{[(-3)(14) + \cdot \cdot \cdot + (3)(24)]^2}{(4)(20)} = 16.20$$

$$SS_Q = \frac{[(1)(14) + \cdot \cdot \cdot + (1)(24)]^2}{(4)(4)} = 0.00$$

$$SS_C = \frac{[(-1)(14) + \cdot \cdot \cdot + (1)(24)]^2}{(4)(20)} = 0.80$$

The ANOVA summary in Table 6.5 reveals that only the linear trend is significant ($p < .01$)—that is, as anchor theory would predict, estimations of Jimmy Carter's liberalness varied linearly (and positively) with increases in the number of conservative figures with whom he was com-

TABLE 6.5

SV	*df*	*SS*	*MS*	*F*
Groups	3	17.00	5.67	4.25*
L	(1)	(16.20)	16.20	12.15**
Q	(1)	(0.00)	0.00	0.0C
C	(1)	(0.80)	0.80	0.60
Error	12	16.00	1.33	
Total	15	33.00		

$^*p < .05$, $^{**}p < .01$

pared, although, as will be shown, only the means of the first and fourth groups are actually significantly different. In sum, the trend is marked although the actual group differences are modest.

It is worth noting that of the trend sums of squares in Table 6.5, the linear trend accounts for $16.20/17.00 = 0.95$ (95%) of the Groups sum of squares, the square root of which is a correlation ($r = 0.98$), which expresses the relationship between the linear polynomial (L) and the group totals in Table 6.4.

6.4. A Posteriori Comparisons

It is not always the case that an experimenter knows beforehand what comparisons will be worth evaluating. Many times, comparisons are suggested by the fact that a significant F was obtained and the researcher desires to know more about the source of this result. Perhaps hypotheses about the independent variable came to mind only after conducting the experiment. These *a posteriori* or *unplanned* comparisons can greatly increase the probability of Type I errors (i.e., inflate α_{fw}) because they are often large in number, use nonindependent sources of information, and are based on knowledge already gained via the ANOVA. There are many specific tests for unplanned comparisons, only two of which will be described here: the Tukey HSD (Honestly Significant Difference) test for simple (pairwise) comparisons and the Scheffé test for complex ones.

Tukey HSD Test. The HSD test uses the Studentized range distribution rather than the t or F distribution. Ordinarily a table is created, such as Table 6.6, in which the group means are ranked in order and all differences between these means are calculated. In Table 6.6, it can be seen that the largest difference between means is 2.5, and this difference

TABLE 6.6

	Group Means			
	4	3	2	1
	6.0	5.5	4.0	3.5
4	—	0.5	2.0	2.5*
3		—	1.5	2.0
2			—	0.5
1	$S_{\bar{X}} = 0.58$			—

*$p < .05$

involves a range spanning four ordered means. This information is necessary for performing the HSD test.

The Studentized range distribution appears in Appendix D, and its critical value, labeled q, is obtained by entering the table with α_{fw}, df_e, and r (range), the latter being the number of places, or "steps," between the two most extreme of the ordered means. For Table 6.6, with $r = 4$, $df_e = 12$, and $\alpha_{fw} = .05$, the critical value of q is 4.20.

The statistic q is similar to t and, in fact, differs only by a constant value of $\sqrt{2}$. q_{HSD} can be computed for each of the six differences in Table 6.6 by using the formula:

$$q_{HSD} = \frac{\overline{X}_i - \overline{X}_j}{\sqrt{S_{\overline{X}}}} \qquad [6.5]$$

where $\overline{X}_i$ and $\overline{X}_j$ are any two means and $S_{\overline{X}}$ is the standard error of the mean, which, in turn, is equal to $\sqrt{MS_e/n}$, where MS_e is from the ANOVA (Table 6.2, $MS_e = 1.33$) and n is group size ($n = 4$ in this case).

For the comparison of groups 1 and 4,

$$q_{HSD} = \frac{2.50}{\sqrt{1.33/4}} = 4.33$$

which is significant ($p < .05$), because it exceeds the critical value of 4.20.

The other five comparisons can now be conducted, but it is easier to use a "critical difference" approach for all six comparisons, because with this procedure only one computation is required, that being the minimum difference that must exist between *any* pair of means in order to reject H_0. This critical difference (CD) value, which can be used simultaneously to examine all entries in Table 6.6, is calculated as follows:

$$CD_{HSD} = q_{r,\alpha,df_e}\sqrt{MS_e/n} \qquad [6.6]$$

where q is from the Studentized range for $r = 4$, $\alpha = .05$, and $df_e = 12$, as determined previously, and equals 4.20. Similarly, $\sqrt{MS_e/n} = .58$; therefore, $CD_{HSD} = (4.20)(.58) = 2.44$. In examining Table 6.6, only the difference between groups 1 and 4 is large enough to be significant, that is, only $d = 2.50$ exceeds $CD = 2.44$.

Tukey's HSD test works by maintaining α_{fw} for the entire set of pairwise comparisons. This widely researched test is discussed at length in Kirk (1982). It should be noted that there are alternative versions of this test for designs with unequal group sizes. One peculiarity of the Tukey procedure bears mentioning—namely, that a significant overall F can be obtained when no pairwise comparisons prove significant. One possible reason for this apparent anomaly is that the critical comparisons may be complex rather than the simple ones evaluated by the Tukey test.

Scheffé Test. For complex comparisons, the most widely employed test for unplanned or post hoc comparisons is the Scheffé, which uses the F distribution where the critical difference is obtained employing the following formula:

$$\mathrm{CD_S} = \sqrt{(g - 1)F_{\alpha;\,\mathrm{df}_1,\,\mathrm{df}_2}}\ \sqrt{\mathrm{MS}_e \sum (C^2/n)} \qquad [6.7]$$

In this equation, g refers to the number of groups, $F_{\alpha;\,\mathrm{df}_1,\,\mathrm{df}_2}$ is the critical value from the F table (Appendix B) for that alpha and those numerator and denominator degrees of freedom, MS_e is from the overall ANOVA, C represents a member of the set of coefficients that defines the comparison, and n is group size.

To demonstrate the Scheffé test, a comparison between the average performance of groups 1 and 2 and that of groups 3 and 4 of the ideological context study will be examined. The set of lambda coefficients is $\frac{1}{2}\ \frac{1}{2}\ -\frac{1}{2}\ -\frac{1}{2}$, and the obtained difference, using the means from Table 6.6, is $\frac{1}{2}(4.0 + 3.5) - \frac{1}{2}(6.0 + 5.5) = -2.0$. The critical difference is calculated using expression 6.7 as follows, there $g = 4$, $\mathrm{F}_{.05;\,3,\,12} = 3.49$, $\mathrm{MS}_e = 1.33$, and $n = 4$:

$$\mathrm{CD_S} = \sqrt{(3)(3.49)}\ \sqrt{(1.33)\left\{\left(\tfrac{1}{2}\right)^2/4 + \cdots + \left(-\tfrac{1}{2}\right)^2/4\right\}}$$

$$= (3.24)\ \sqrt{1.33(4)\left(\tfrac{1}{16}\right)} = 1.87$$

The obtained difference of 2.00 (the minus is irrelevant) exceeds the critical value of 1.87, and this difference between groups 1 and 2 versus groups 3 and 4 is therefore significant ($p < .05$).

There are two factors to keep in mind in using the Scheffé test. First, if the overall F is not significant, then no significant comparison can be found, and it would be unprofitable to conduct the Scheffé test under these circumstances. Second, it is plain from the $\mathrm{CD_S}$ formula that this test could also be used for pairwise unplanned comparisons; this would not be wise, however, because Scheffé's is the most conservative of all tests that are available for that purpose, and produces an unacceptably high level of Type II errors.

There is a vast literature on comparison procedures and many specialized texts exist. The discussions by Keppel (1982), Kirk (1982), and

Klockars and Sax (1986) are especially thorough. A valuable advanced treatment of this topic is in Wilcox (1987). Of special importance are procedures to be employed when certain assumptions of the ANOVA are violated, such as the requirement for homogeneous variances.

7. TREATMENTS BY BLOCKS

The randomized block design, or the treatments by blocks design as it is increasingly referred to, is a modification of the completely randomized design that takes into a priori account the possible effect of a *nuisance variable* on the dependent variable. A nuisance variable is one in which there is no experimental interest, but one which, if left unattended, is of sufficient potential danger to the integrity of the experiment that it is considered risky simply to cross one's fingers and hope that its effect will be nullified by the process of random assignment.

In terms of the hypothetical experiment in Table 1.1, as an example: Were there some concern that the most able students might end up in group A and the least able in C—such that subsequent exam performance (dependent variable) might have nothing to do with the relative virtues of the textbooks (independent variable), but with an irrelevant characteristic (i.e., nuisance variable) of the exam takers—then this possibility might be effectively neutralized by randomly assigning the three students with the highest grade averages (block 1) to groups A, B, and C; the three with the next-highest grade averages (block 2) likewise randomly to A, B, and C; etc. In this way, all three groups would in equal measure contain students with the highest and lowest abilities.

The treatments by blocks design is available for situations in which there is a single nuisance variable that is deemed necessary to control on an a priori basis, and for purposes of notation it will tentatively be designated TB-gb, where g stands for the number of treatment groups (as in the CR-g design) and b represents the number of blocks into which the nuisance variable has been divided.

To provide a concrete illustration: In Chapter 5, it was reported that the study of President Carter's perceived liberalism was conducted by gathering 16 persons and assigning them randomly to the four treatment groups; suppose, however, that the data were collected with the assistance of four interviewers, each of whom was instructed to administer the test to four acquaintances. Had this been the case, then the test materials in the possession of each interviewer would have included one administration for each of the $g = 4$ experimental conditions, which would have

TABLE 7.1

Blocks	Group 1 (3 libs)	Group 2 (2 libs)	Group 3 (1 lib)	Group 4 (0 libs)	Sum
Interviewer	(Lib/Con scores, 9 = Lib, 1 = Con)				
1	5	3	6	6	20
2	3	6	5	5	19
3	3	2	6	6	17
4	3	5	5	7	20
Sum	14	16	22	24	76 = Grand sum
Mean	3.50	4.00	5.50	6.00	4.75 = GM

been given to four interviewees on a random basis. For illustrative purposes, the raw scores in Table 7.1 are the same as those in Table 5.1, but the analysis below is somewhat different in order to take into account the above restriction in subject assignment.

In Table 7.1, there is a possibility that something systematic might occur in the rows of the design because of the personal predilections and circumstances of the interviewers. In this connection, the interviewer effect is a nuisance variable of no interest insofar as this particular experiment is concerned, but is a potential source of additional noise which could drown out the signal from the variable of interest (i.e., estimates of Carter's liberalism under the four group conditions) and which will remain disguised as random error if not taken into account. It is the purpose of the TB design to obtain an estimate of the impact of the blocks (interviewers) and to remove it from the error estimate.

The analysis proceeds much as demonstrated in Chapters 4 and 5 for calculating the uncorrected total sum of squares (TSS), the correction factor (CF), and the uncorrected sums of squares for groups (GSS). With $g = 4$ groups and $b = 4$ blocks (the fact that $g = b$ is incidental), and where Σ_g and Σ_b designate summation over groups and blocks, respectively, the calculations are as follows:

$$\text{TSS} = \sum_g \sum_b X^2 = 5^2 + 3^2 + \cdots + 6^2 + 7^2 = 394$$

$$\text{CF} = \frac{1}{gb}\left(\sum_g \sum_b X\right)^2 = \tfrac{1}{16}(76)^2 = 361$$

$$\text{GSS} = \frac{1}{b}(G_1^2 + \cdots + G_4^2) \qquad \text{where } G = \text{group sum } \left(\text{or } \sum_b X\right)$$

$$= \tfrac{1}{4}(14^2 + 16^2 + 22^2 + 24^2) = 378$$

The uncorrected sum of squares for blocks (BSS) is calculated in the same way as GSS, but for the rows; that is, the row totals are squared and then divided by the number of observations ($g = 4$) that entered into the sum:

$$\text{BSS} = \frac{1}{g}(B_1^2 + \cdots + B_4^2) \qquad \text{where } B = \text{block sum } \left(\text{or } \sum_g X\right)$$
$$= \tfrac{1}{4}(20^2 + 19^2 + 17^2 + 20^2) = 362.50$$

The corrected sums of squares for groups, blocks, and total are calculated as follows and are entered in Table 7.2:

$$SS_G = \text{GSS} - \text{CF} = 378 - 361 = 17$$

$$SS_B = \text{BSS} - \text{CF} = 362.5 - 361 = 1.5$$

$$SS_T = \text{TSS} - \text{CF} = 394 - 361 = 33$$

The error sum of squares is simply a residual—that is, the sum of squares that remains after the group and block effects have been accounted for—and so can be calculated by subtraction:

$$SS_e = SS_T - SS_G - SS_B = 33 - 17 - 1.5 = 14.50$$

As in the case of the CR-g design, MS = SS/df, and the F ratio is formed by dividing MS_e into MS_G and MS_B, respectively. It is to be noted that the general formulas for degrees of freedom will be the same for all randomized block designs of this type (i.e., in which there is one observation in each group-block cell), although the size of both g and b will vary from study to study.

Because of blocking and the potentially correlated row errors to which it gives rise, the F for blocks, as calculated above, may not be appropriate; this is of little consequence, however, because there is normally no interest in testing blocks, only the groups—that is, in this case, interviewer differences are a nuisance variable, which it was deemed necessary a priori to control, but not to test as a variable of experimental interest.

TABLE 7.2

SV	*df*		*SS*	*MS*	*F*
Groups	$g - 1$	= 3	17.00	5.67	3.52
Blocks	$b - 1$	= 3	1.50	0.50	0.31
Error	$(g - 1)(b - 1)$	= 9	14.50	1.61	
Total	$gb - 1$	= 15	33.00		

The $F = 3.52$ for groups is significant at only the $\alpha = .10$ level when compared with the tabular F (for $df_G = 3$ and $df_e = 9$), which is below the conventional .05 level; group differences would therefore typically be regarded as not significant, which would preclude the a posteriori testing of group means. On the other hand, if a priori comparisons have been planned, they can be tested using the same procedures described in Chapter 6, but with MS_e and df_e as specified for the TB design. Similarly with respect to trend tests: The linear trend in the CR case in Chapter 6 was significant, and the same trend in the TB case yields significance also ($p < .05$).

The reason for the reduction in significance of the Groups effect in the case of the TB design (compared with the CR design) can be explained in terms of Figure 7.1. In the case of both designs, SS_G is the same; what is different is the magnitude of the error term, which, as the denominator of the F ratio, directly influences whether or not F reaches a significant level. As shown in Figure 7.1, SS_e in the CR design is divided into two parts in the TB design: SS_B and SS_e. But the degrees of freedom are also divided: $df_e = 12$ in the CR design are divided into $df_B = 3$ and $df_e = 9$ in the TB design. Although SS_e is diminished in the TB design, therefore, and although this could reduce MS_e (hence increase the significance of F), the df_e are also diminished to an even greater extent. Consequently, MS_e is actually increased, and the F ratio is thereby reduced.

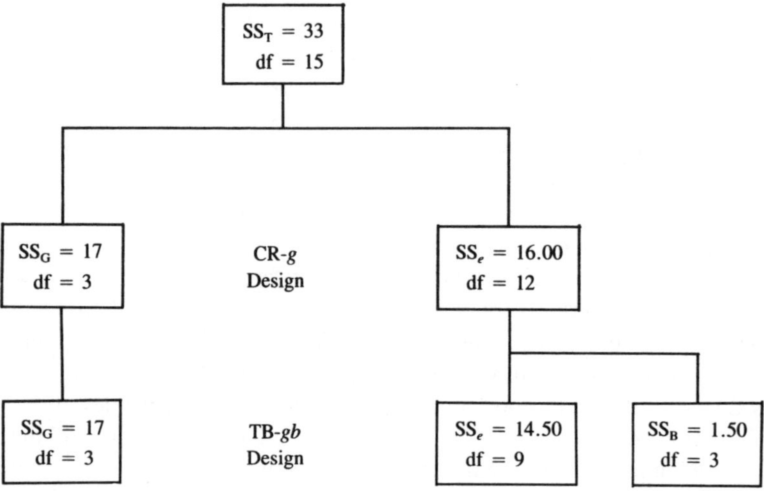

Figure 7.1.

The TB design can therefore be seen to involve a trade-off: Will blocking for the nuisance variable account for a sufficiently large amount of the sum of squares to justify the loss of $b - 1$ degrees of freedom from the error term? As indicated in the row totals of Table 7.1, there turned out to be very little between-row variability, and so in retrospect the blocking was not worth the loss of 3 df from the error term.

Prior to finally accepting the conclusions of the ANOVA in Table 7.2, it is necessary to consider the *additivity assumption* of the TB design—that is, the assumption that each raw score is an additive combination of the overall mean (μ), plus a specific group effect (G), plus a specific block effect (B), plus error (e), or

$$X = \mu + G + B + e$$

In the event of nonadditivity, the variable represented by the blocks (different interviewers in this instance) interacts with the experimental conditions to produce variability over and above the addition of their simple effects. In the nonadditive case,

$$X = \mu + G + B + G \times B + e$$

where $G \times B$ represents the "interaction" of the Groups and Blocks variables. This term signifies that there is a joint effect of these two variables that goes beyond any individual influence.

In this particular experiment, it is possible that the behaviors of subjects within one of the rows are different from those of subjects in the other rows, in which case the overall data configuration represented by the group means would not match the configuration for the deviant row. Were this the case, it would mean that the blocks are interacting with the experimental groups in conflict with the additivity assumption and thereby inflating the error sum of squares, which in turn would increase the size of the denominator of the F ratio and make it more difficult to detect a difference among the various groups.

Tukey's test for additivity is described in reference to Table 7.3. (For further details, consult Kirk, 1982: 250–253.) The unbracketed scores in the interior of the table are the raw scores from Table 7.1; in the side and bottom margins are the row and column means; the overall or grand mean is GM = 4.75; the d scores along the side and bottom are the deviations of the row (d_r) and column (d_c) means around the grand mean; and the numbers in parentheses are the cross-products of the ds in the respective rows and columns. In row 1 and column 3, for example,

$$d_{rc} = d_r \times d_c = d_1 \times d_3 = 0.25 \times 0.75 = 0.19$$

TABLE 7.3

Blocks	*Groups* *1*	*2*	*3*	*4*	*Mean*	d_r
1	5	3	6	6	5.00	0.25
	(−.31)	(−.19)	(.19)	(.31)		
2	3	6	5	5	4.75	0.00
	(.00)	(.00)	(.00)	(.00)		
3	3	2	6	6	4.25	−0.50
	(.63)	(.38)	(−.38)	(−.63)		
4	3	5	5	7	5.00	0.25
	(−.31)	(−.19)	(.19)	(.31)		
Mean	3.50	4.00	5.50	6.00	4.75 = GM	
d_c	−1.25	−0.75	0.75	1.25		

d_r = Row mean − GM
d_c = Column mean − GM

The sums of squares for nonadditivity is given by

$$SS_{\text{nonadd}} = \frac{\left(\sum_{r}\sum_{c} d_{rc}X\right)^2}{\left(\sum d_r^2\right)\left(\sum d_c^2\right)} \qquad [7.1]$$

where the numerator instructs us to multiply the *d*s in parentheses by the raw score in the same cell, to sum this cross-product for the entire matrix, and then to square that sum; and the denominator instructs us to multiply the sum of squared row *d*s by the sum of squared column *d*s:

$$SS_{\text{nonadd}} = \frac{[(-.31)(5) + \cdots + (.31)(7)]^2}{(0.25^2 + \cdots + 0.25^2)(-1.25^2 + \cdots + 1.25^2)}$$

$$= \frac{(-1.25)^2}{(4.25)(0.38)} = 0.98$$

SS_{nonadd} and 1 df are taken from the error term in Table 7.2, leaving a sum of squares for a remainder:

$$SS_{\text{rem}} = SS_e - SS_{\text{nonadd}} = 14.50 - 0.98 = 13.52$$

$$df_{\text{rem}} = df_e - df_{\text{nonadd}} = 9 - 1 = 8$$

The F ratio to determine whether the nonadditivity is significant is obtained by forming the ratio of MS_{nonadd} to MS_{rem}:

$$MS_{nonadd} = SS_{nonadd}/df_{nonadd} = 0.98/1 = 0.98$$

$$MS_{rem} = SS_{rem}/df_{rem} = 13.52/8 = 1.69$$

$$F_{nonadd} = 0.98/1.69 = 0.58$$

The F table is consulted for 1 and 8 df, usually at the $\alpha = .25$ level, which, in this case, is $F_{.25;\,1,8} = 1.54$, indicating no significant group × block interaction, hence the tenability of the additivity assumption. By reducing the alpha level to .25, the experimentalist amplifies sensitivity for the slightest indication of an interaction, at the less serious risk of detecting one where none really exists (Type II error).

If a significant F had been obtained in this example, this would have been an indication that the *sphericity* (or circularity) assumption of randomized block designs had not been met. This assumption concerns a property of the difference scores that can be obtained by subtracting group 2 scores from group 3 scores (for example) for all blocks of subjects. The requirement is that the standard deviations of all possible sets of such difference scores be equivalent (or homogeneous). When this assumption is violated, alternative F tests, adjusted dfs, or data transformations are required. A concise but cogent introduction to this topic is found in Howell (1987).

It is to be noted that the analysis above (see Table 7.1) is based on a situation in which there is only one observation in each group × block cell, and further that the ANOVA situation would have been different if there had been $n > 1$ observations per cell—for example, with respect to Table 7.1, if rows 1 and 2 contained subjects who had been interviewed by interviewer A and rows 3 and 4 by interviewer B. In that case there would have been $n = 2$ observations per group × block cell, which would have given rise to the following sources of variance and degrees of freedom:

Groups	$g - 1$	= 3
Blocks	$b - 1$	= 1
$G \times B$	$(g - 1)(b - 1)$	= 3
Error	$gb(n - 1)$	= 8
Total	$gnb - 1$	= 15

Inasmuch as a design of this kind would be analyzed in precisely the same way (although interpreted somewhat differently) as a completely randomized factorial design with two main effects, the analysis will be postponed to Chapter 9. It should be pointed out, however, that in the TB design when $n > 1$, the interaction between blocks and groups emerges as a separate source of variability, and that there is consequently no need to test for nonadditivity—that is, group × block interaction is a specified part of the design.

It is also to be noted that the structure of the TB-*gb* design, in controlling for a single nuisance variable, can be extended to the control of two (Latin square design) or three (Graeco-Latin square design) nuisance variables. These designs are infrequently used, however, and the interested reader is therefore directed to their treatment in any of the more comprehensive texts noted in the References.

In summary, the purpose of the TB-*gb* design is to control for a potentially contaminating variable or variables (such as interviewer effect in the illustrative case above) which, if left uncontrolled, might inflate the error term and prevent a significant F. Blocking also detracts from the error degrees of freedom, however, and is worthwhile only if the block sum of squares (and/or the interaction sum of squares if $n > 1$) is large enough to offset the loss in error df.

8. ALGORITHMS

To this point, the designs and analyses have been sufficiently straightforward to permit avoidance of complicated subscripts and other notational devices. Similarly, the simplicity of previous designs has rendered the error term (the denominator of the F ratio) fairly obvious: usually it was simply a residual, that is, it was based on the sum of squares remaining after the major effects and their interactions had been accounted for. With the introduction of more complicated designs, however, a more formal notational system becomes advantageous. As will be shown, standardized notation plus a few simple rules will make it possible to employ fairly complicated designs with comparative ease.

8.1. Nesting and Cross-Classifying Subjects

Table 8.1(a) is a completely randomized design and contains the same familiar data as were analyzed in Chapter 5. In this case there is one main

TABLE 8.1

	(B) B1	B2	B3	B4	
	5	3	6	6	
	3	6	5	5	
	3	2	6	6	
	3	5	5	7	
	14	16	22	24	76

(a) Completely randomized: $S(B)$

		(B) B1	B2	B3	B4	
(A)	A1	5	3	6	6	39
		3	6	5	5	
	A2	3	2	6	6	37
		3	5	5	7	
		14	16	22	24	76

(b) Completely randomized factorial: $S(AB)$

		(B) B1		B2		B3		B4	
(A)	A1	5	→	3	→	6	→	6	20
		3	→	6	→	5	→	5	19
	A2	3	→	2	→	6	→	6	17
		3	→	5	→	5	→	7	20
		14		16		22		24	76

(c) Split-plot factorial (mixed): $S(A)B$

effect (B) with four levels ($B1$ through $B4$) and $n = 4$ subjects per group, with the group and grand sums as shown at the bottom of the table. The completely randomized factorial in Table 8.1(b) will be discussed in Chapter 9. It is not really a separate design; rather, as shown here, it is a cross-classification of two completely randomized designs: there are two main effects (variable A with two levels, and B with four levels) with $n = 2$ subjects per cell. The split-plot factorial in Table 8.1(c) will be discussed in greater detail in Chapter 10. It is typically referred to as a mixed design because it is the combination of a completely randomized design (variable A) and a repeated measures design (variable B), the latter design being one in which more than one measure is obtained from each subject. In the present instance, the four scores were obtained from each participant, one for each level of B. Hence, the 16 scores in the completely randomized factorial are produced by 16 separate subjects, whereas the same number of scores in the mixed design are produced by only 4 subjects ($n = 2$ in group $A1$, $n = 2$ in group $A2$), each of whom is measured four separate times (i.e., measured for $B1$, $B2$, $B3$, and $B4$).

Because the subjects in the completely randomized factorial design are *nested*, two by two, in each of the eight $A \times B$ cells, this design will be referred to as $S(AB)$, indicating that subjects are nested within the AB cells. [The CR design in Chapter 5 is therefore of the type $S(A)$.] In the mixed design, subjects are randomly assigned to either group $A1$ or to group $A2$, so the A variable distinguishes *between* subjects, and subjects are therefore nested within the A cells. Subjects are exposed to all four levels of variable B, however, hence B is a *within* subjects variable, and subjects are cross-classified with B rather than nested. A shorthand reference for this design will be $S(A)B$, indicating that subjects are nested within the A groups but cross-classified with B.

This design notation supersedes that used in earlier chapters, and its advantage is that it is less generic and provides a more readily accessible description of how the experiment is designed, that is, how subjects have been assigned to experimental treatments. The advantage of the previous notation is that it specifies the number of groups—for example, CR-4 specifies a completely randomized design with $g = 4$ groups—but this can be overcome under the new notation, if need be, through the use of subscripts: hence $S_{10}(A_2B_4)C_5$ specifies a mixed design with two between-subject variables, A and B, with $a = 2$ and $b = 4$ levels in factorial arrangement; and one within-subjects (repeated measures) variable, C, with $c = 5$ levels; and with $n = 10$ subjects in each of the eight $A \times B$ cells.

8.2. Degrees of Freedom and Sums of Squares

Table 8.2 contains the degrees of freedom for the sources of variance (SV), or variance components, of the $S(AB)$ design in Table 8.1(b). In general, df formulas such as these are obtained by the following heuristic. Let a equal the number of levels of variable A, b equal the number of levels of variable B, etc. Then, for each SV in the ANOVA, let the num-

TABLE 8.2

SV	df Formulas		df		df Formulas Expanded	SS
A	$a - 1$	=	1	=	$a - 1$	SS_A = ASS − CF
B	$b - 1$	=	3	=	$b - 1$	SS_B = BSS − CF
AB	$(a - 1)(b - 1)$	=	3	=	$ab - a - b + 1$	SS_{AB} = ABSS − ASS − BSS + CF
$S(AB)$	$ab(n - 1)$	=	8	=	$abn - ab$	$SS_{S(AB)}$ = TSS − ABSS
Total	$abn - 1$	=	15	=	$abn - 1$	SS_T = TSS − CF

ber of levels minus 1 represent the df (e.g., $b - 1$). When the SV is a compound, such as AB, the df are multiplied—for example, $(a - 1)(b - 1)$. For expressions such as $S(AB)$, in which nesting is indicated, the terms in parentheses do not have 1 subtracted from them; thus $S(AB)$ has df = $ab(n - 1)$, where there are n "levels" of subjects.

Moreover, and of greater importance, the df formulas are analogous to a DNA molecule or a Rosetta Stone which, when decoded, provide instructions concerning how to form the required sum of squares for each of the sources of variance. This is begun by expanding the df as shown in Table 8.2—that is, where necessary, carrying through the multiplication indicated. In the case of the $A \times B$ interaction, for example, df = $(a - 1)(b - 1) = ab - a - b + 1$. A list is then made of all the unique symbols and symbol combinations among the expanded df: In this case there are five—1, a, b, ab, and abn—and each represents a component necessary for calculating the sums of squares, both corrected and uncorrected for the mean.

The symbol 1 in all designs represents the correction factor (CF), which is always calculated by summing all scores, squaring that sum, and dividing by the total N. In the $S(AB)$ design of Table 8.1(b), there are $a = 2$ levels of variable A, $b = 4$ levels of B, and $n = 2$ subjects per cell—hence $N = abn = (2)(4)(2) = 16$. The meaning of the symbol 1 is therefore as follows, using the data in Table 8.1(b):

$$1 = \text{CF} = \frac{\left(\sum_a \sum_b \sum_n X\right)^2}{abn}$$

$$= \frac{1}{abn}\left(\sum_a \sum_b \sum_n X\right)^2 \qquad [8.1]$$

$$= \tfrac{1}{16}(5 + 3 + \cdots + 6 + 7)^2 = 361$$

In this case, the summation signs ($\Sigma_a \Sigma_b \Sigma_n$) indicate that, prior to squaring, the X scores (evaluations of Carter's liberalism) are being summed across all a levels of variable A, all b levels of B, and all n subjects within each cell.

The symbol a represents the uncorrected sum of squares for variable A (ASS), and is decoded as follows:

$$a = \text{ASS} = \sum_a \frac{\left(\sum_b \sum_n X\right)^2}{bn} = \frac{1}{bn} \sum_a \left(\sum_b \sum_n X\right)^2 \qquad [8.2]$$

The rules for decoding a in expression 8.2, and applicable to all other letter symbols, are:

1. For the letter or letters under consideration (a in this case), enter summation signs, hence Σ_a in expression 8.2.
2. For all other letters not included in the symbol under consideration (b and n in this instance), place summation signs within parentheses, add the symbol for the dependent variable (X), and indicate that the sum is to be squared—hence, $(\Sigma_b \Sigma_n X)^2$ in expression 8.2.
3. Divide the squared sum by the number of observations that comprised the sum—that is, divide by the product of the symbols associated with the summation signs within parentheses. In expression 8.2, the summation signs within parentheses are associated with b and n, hence bn is the divisor.

All that then remains is to interpret the computational formula produced by the application of these rules. In expression 8.2, $\Sigma_a(\Sigma_b \Sigma_n X)^2$ instructs us to form a sum of squares around the differences in the levels of the A variable, that is, around the sums of $A1$ and $A2$ in Table 8.1(b). Specifically, it instructs us (1) to begin with level $A1$ and to sum across all $b = 4$ levels of B and all $n = 2$ subjects per cell, and then (2) to move to level $A2$ and do the same. Each of the sums is then squared, the squared sums are then themselves summed, and the total is divided by bn, or, alternatively, multiplied by $1/(bn)$. The operations using the data in Table 8.1(b) and expression 8.2 are as follows:

$$a = \text{ASS} = \tfrac{1}{8}\left[(5 + 3 + \cdots + 6 + 5)^2 + (3 + 3 + \cdots + 6 + 7)^2\right] = \tfrac{1}{8}(39^2 + 37^2) = 361.25$$

By the same token, the symbol *b* designates the uncorrected sum of squares for the *B* variable (BSS)—that is, in terms of the data in Table 8.1(b), the column totals are to be squared and added together, and then divided by $1/(an)$. Applying the decoding rules:

$$
\begin{aligned}
b = \text{BSS} &= \frac{1}{an} \sum_b \left(\sum_a \sum_n X \right)^2 \\
&= \tfrac{1}{4}(14^2 + 16^2 + 22^2 + 24^2) = 378
\end{aligned}
\qquad [8.3]
$$

ab symbolizes the uncorrected sum of squares for the interaction of variables *A* and *B* (indicated by ABSS), and directs comparison of the $ab = 8$ cells in Table 8.1(b):

$$
\begin{aligned}
ab = \text{ABSS} &= \frac{1}{n} \sum_a \sum_b \left(\sum_n X \right)^2 \\
&= \tfrac{1}{2}[(5 + 3)^2 + \cdots + (6 + 7)^2] \\
&= \tfrac{1}{2}(8^2 + 9^2 + \cdots + 11^2 + 13^2) = 381
\end{aligned}
\qquad [8.4]
$$

Finally, *abn* includes all three of the letter symbols in this design, and hence stands for the uncorrected total sum of squares (TSS). Because all letters are included, there are no letters in parentheses and no divisor. The decoding rules applied yield:

$$
\begin{aligned}
abn = \text{TSS} &= \sum_a \sum_b \sum_n X^2 \\
&= 5^2 + 3^2 + \cdots + 6^2 + 7^2 = 394
\end{aligned}
\qquad [8.5]
$$

The degrees of freedom, once decoded, not only give directions about how to calculate the uncorrected sums of squares and the correction factor, but, as shown in Table 8.2, also indicate how to combine these figures to produce the corrected sums of squares. In the case of variable *A*, for example, $\text{df}_A = a - 1$, hence the corrected sum of squares for this variable is given by $\text{SS}_A = \text{ASS} - \text{CF} = 361.25 - 361 = 0.25$. In the case of the *AB* interaction, $\text{df}_{AB} = (a - 1)(b - 1) = ab - a - b + 1$; the corrected sum of squares is therefore $\text{SS}_{AB} = \text{ABSS} - \text{ASS} - \text{BSS} + \text{CF} = 381 - 361.25 - 378 + 361 = 2.75$.

The mean squares are then calculated as in previous sections (i.e., $\text{MS} = \text{SS}/\text{df}$), and the *F* ratio is formed by dividing the MS for each variance component (*A*, *B*, and *AB*) by the error MS. According to the new notation, the error MS for this design is designated $\text{MS}_{S(AB)}$ because $S(AB)$ refers to subjects within a cell, and hence designates the experi-

TABLE 8.3

SV	Degrees of Freedom *Formulas*	*Expanded*	*SS*
Between Subjects	$an - 1$	$= an - 1$	$SS_{BS} = ANSS - CF$
A	$a - 1$	$= a - 1$	$SS_A = ASS - CF$
S(A)	$a(n - 1)$	$= an - a$	$SS_{S(A)} = ANSS - ASS$
Within Subjects	$an(b - 1)$	$= abn - an$	$SS_{WS} = TSS - ANSS$
B	$b - 1$	$= b - 1$	$SS_B = BSS - CF$
AB	$(a - 1)(b - 1)$	$= ab - a - b + 1$	$SS_{AB} = ABSS - ASS - BSS + CF$
S(A)B	$a(b - 1)(n - 1)$	$= abn - ab - an + a$	$SS_{S(A)B} = TSS - ABSS - ANSS + ASS$
Total	$abn - 1$	$= abn - 1$	$SS_T = TSS - CF$

mental space in which subjects are treated identically. Because subjects were assigned to cells on a random basis, their differences in score must therefore be due to random influences.

The same computational logic can be extended to the mixed, or $S(A)B$, design in Table 8.1(c). The expanded degrees of freedom for this design are displayed in Table 8.3. In this case, there are six unique symbols and symbol combinations contained in the expanded df, hence six computations to perform: 1, a, an, b, ab, and abn. The symbol an is the only one not contained in the previous example, and in relation to the figures in Table 8.1(c) produces the following:

$$an = \text{ANSS} = \frac{1}{b}\sum_a\sum_n\left(\sum_b X\right)^2 \qquad [8.6]$$

$$= \tfrac{1}{4}[(5 + 3 + 6 + 6)^2 + \cdots + (3 + 5 + 5 + 7)^2]$$

$$= \tfrac{1}{4}(20^2 + 19^2 + 17^2 + 20^2) = 362.5$$

Hence, ANSS measures the degree of differences among the rows (i.e., overall differences among the subjects) in Table 8.1(c). The corrected sums of squares are obtained by combining the calculations as dictated by the expanded df, as shown in the SS column in Table 8.3.

The decoding rules above can be applied to the completely randomized design and to all designs considered in subsequent chapters, which encompasses a large proportion of the designs in general use in the social and psychological sciences. Given a particular design, therefore, all that is required is to know the general formulas for the degrees of freedom for the variance components. Given the df formulas, it is a simple matter to expand them, to construct the computational formulas to which they lead, and to combine the calculations to provide the corrected sums of squares, which, in turn, lead to the mean squares and F ratios.

8.3. Mean Squares and *F* Ratios

Without going into unnecessary statistical detail, it is important to appreciate that when two or more columns of numbers are separately summed, more than just a group effect is captured. Consider the $S(AB)$ design of Table 8.1(b): When comparing row differences (A), column differences (B), or cell differences (AB), the sums of squares involved necessarily include within-cell variability (error), for which $SS_{S(AB)}$ (in Table 8.2) provides an independent measure. The F ratio for testing variable A is therefore

$$F = \frac{MS_A}{MS_{S(AB)}}$$

$$= \frac{\text{between levels of } A}{\text{error}}$$

$$= \frac{\text{error} + A}{\text{error}} = 1 + \frac{A}{\text{error}}$$

Hence, the F ratio equals 1.00 plus some amount reflecting the extent to which the A effect exceeds within-cell error. If, as under H_0, the levels of A do not differ, then $F = 1.00 + 0.00$. The F ratio will always have an expected value greater than 1.00 when the alternative hypothesis (H_1) is true, and an expected value of approximately 1.00 when H_0 is true.

In general, a *valid F ratio* is one in which the denominator contains all the components that are in the numerator except for the component that is being tested. If the numerator contains error plus A, and if A is the component to be tested, then the denominator must contain error. If the numerator is $A + B + C$ and the effect to be tested is B, then the denominator must be $A + C$. With more complicated designs, simplified rules are needed to designate those F ratios that will provide appropriate tests of the significance of effects of interest.

Focusing on the $S(AB)$ design in Table 8.1(b) and its source of vari-

TABLE 8.4

SV	Mean Square Components: $S(AB)$	AB	B	A	F ratio
1 A	*			*	$\frac{1}{4}$
2 B	*		*		$\frac{2}{4}$
3 AB	*	*			$\frac{3}{4}$
4 $S(AB)$	*				—

(a) $S(AB)$ fixed effects model

SV	$S(A'B')$	$A'B'$	B'	A'	F ratio
1 A'	*	*		*	$\frac{1}{3}$
2 B'	*	*	*		$\frac{2}{3}$
3 $A'B'$	*	*			$\frac{3}{4}$
4 $S(A'B')$	*				—

(b) $S(A'B')$ random effects model

SV	$S(A'B)$	$A'B$	B	A'	F ratio
1 A'	*			*	$\frac{1}{4}$
2 B	*	*	*		$\frac{2}{3}$
3 $A'B$	*	*			$\frac{3}{4}$
4 $S(A'B)$	*				—

(c) $S(A'B)$ mixed effects model

ance table in Table 8.2, the rules for forming the appropriate F ratio can be given with respect to Table 8.4(a) (modified after Schultz, 1955):

1. List all sources of variance below SV (source of variance)—in this case A, B, AB, and $S(AB)$, which are numbered for convenience—and list them again in reverse order across the top of the table.
2. In each row, place an asterisk in the column associated with the variance component under consideration. (Hence, in row 1, which is associated with component A, an asterisk is placed in column A; in row 2, an asterisk is placed in column B; etc.)
3. In each row, also place an asterisk in each column associated with the variance component under consideration if it appears with other components that are not within parentheses and that are random variables.

Rule 3 refers to a distinction to be made below between fixed and random variables. For the moment, suffice it to say for the $S(AB)$ design that variable B is not random: A appears with B in the interaction term, AB, and B is not enclosed within parentheses, so an asterisk would appear in column AB of row 1 if B were random; but B is not random, so that column remains blank. The B column remains blank for row 1 because A does not appear in it. Experimental subjects are always a random effect, hence an asterisk appears in column $S(AB)$ of row 1—that is, A appears in $S(AB)$, S is outside parentheses, and S is a random variable, and this qualifies for an asterisk under rule 3. Rows 2, 3, and 4 are completed in the same fashion.

A valid F ratio, as stated previously, is one in which the denominator contains all the components that are in the numerator except for the component that is being tested. As indicated in the F column of Table 8.4(a), the ratio for testing the A variable is the mean square for component 1 divided by the mean square for component 4:

$$F = \frac{\text{MS}_A}{\text{MS}_{S(AB)}} = \frac{S(AB) + A}{S(AB)}$$

The numerator contains the two components designated by asterisks in row 1, and the denominator contains the one component designated by an asterisk in row 4. The ratio of mean square components therefore satisfies the criterion for a valid F test, and the same procedures are followed to test the significance of B and AB. It should be mentioned that, in the statistical literature, the mean square components in Table 8.4 are typically referred to as *expected mean squares*.

In the $S(A)$ design of Chapter 5, it was assumed that interest focused on the four experimental groups under consideration—that is, group 1 (Carter with three liberals), group 2 (Carter with two liberals and one conservative), and so forth. This is referred to as a *fixed effects model* because interest is in these four groups and no others. However, had the four groups been regarded as simply four representatives drawn at random from a larger population of groups, then the Groups variable would have been a random rather than a fixed variable, hence a *random effects model*. In the latter model, any conclusions reached concerning a statistically significant Groups effect would need to encompass the entire population of treatment conditions from which the four in the experiment were sampled. In a fixed effects model, conclusions would be limited to the actual treatment conditions employed. In the case of the $S(A)$ design, the distinction is of no consequence insofar as the F ratio is concerned because the testing procedure is the same regardless of whether variable A is fixed or random.

In other designs, however, the fixed or random status of variables does influence which mean squares enter into a valid F ratio, and for the sake of clarity a prime sign (′) will henceforth designate variables that are random (with the aforementioned exception of the subjects variable, designated S, which is always random). Variable A is fixed, therefore, whereas A' is random, and AB' specifies an interaction between fixed variable A and random variable B', $S(A'B')$ denotes that subjects are nested in two-variable cells in a design in which both main effects are random variables.

Returning to Table 8.1(b), assume that both main effects are random, that is, that the design is of the type $S(A'B')$. Table 8.4(b) indicates the mean square components and the appropriate F ratios using Schultz's rules above. In this instance, the denominator to test the A' effect would be the $A'B'$ interaction. If A' was random and B fixed, as in Table 8.4(c), the denominator to test A' would be the mean square for within cells, $S(A'B)$. Hence, what qualifies as experimental error and what does not depends on the nature of the design.

To indicate how Schultz's rules operate in the mixed design, assume that the variables in Table 8.1(c) are both fixed, as in Table 8.5(a). In this case, the MS for A is tested against the MS for $S(A)$, whereas the within-subjects components are tested against the MS for $S(A)B$.

With variable B' random, as in Table 8.5(b), the formation of each F ratio is straightforward except in the case of variable A, which requires what is termed a "quasi-F" because of the fact that there is no single mean square with the appropriate characteristics necessary for the denominator. A "pooled" mean square is therefore formed using components 2 plus 4 minus 5:

$$\begin{aligned} MS_{pooled} &= MS_{S(A)} + MS_{AB'} - MS_{S(A)B'} \\ &= [S(A)B' + S(A)] + [S(A)B' + AB'] - S(A)B' \\ &= S(A)B' + AB' + S(A) \end{aligned}$$

The F ratio to test variable A is therefore:

$$\begin{aligned} F &= \frac{MS_A}{MS_{pooled}} \\ &= \frac{S(A)B' + AB' + S(A) + A}{S(A)B' + AB' + S(A)} \end{aligned}$$

TABLE 8.5

	Mean Square Components					
SV	$S(A)B$	AB	B	$S(A)$	A	*F ratio*
Bet. Subjects						—
1 A				*	*	$\frac{1}{2}$
2 $S(A)$				*		—
W/in Subjects						—
3 B	*		*			$\frac{3}{5}$
4 AB	*	*				$\frac{4}{5}$
5 $S(A)B$	*					—
(a) $S(A)B$ fixed effects model						
	$S(A)B'$	AB'	B'	$S(A)$	A	
Bet. Subjects						—
1 A	*	*		*	*	$1/(2 + 4 - 5)$
2 $S(A)$	*			*		$\frac{2}{5}$
W/in Subjects						—
3 B'	*		*			$\frac{3}{5}$
4 AB'	*	*				$\frac{4}{5}$
5 $S(A)B'$	*					—
(b) $S(A)B'$ mixed effects model						

The variance components in the denominator therefore contain all the components that are in the numerator except for that component (variable A in this case) that is being tested, as is required for a valid F. It is to be noted that in order to be exact, this F requires a pooling of degrees of freedom for the denominator, a topic that will be covered in Chapter 10.

The purpose of this notational and algorithmic interlude has been to introduce relatively simple rules that will facilitate the analysis of designs of greater complexity. The design labels, for example, $S(AB)C$, symbolize how the design is structured. The "decoding rules" show how computational formulas for the sums of squares can be constructed, based upon a knowledge of the formulas for degrees of freedom. Once the corrected sums of squares are calculated—and the directions for this are also coded in the degrees of freedom—the mean squares are gotten as usual, MS = SS/df. Schultz's rules then designate which mean squares to combine for valid F ratios. These rules apply retrospectively to the completely randomized design, and to all other designs that will be considered subsequently, and to designs of the fixed, random, or mixed-effects varieties.

9. FACTORIAL DESIGN

The factorial design, as mentioned previously, is not really a separate class of design, but a way of combining two or more designs. As a case in point, consider the completely randomized design discussed in Chapter 5: The investigator, recall, wished to examine the impact of political anchors on assessments of President Carter's liberalism (dependent variable), but suppose that another investigator were interested in examining the impact on the same dependent variable of exposure to a conservative critique of the Carter Administration.

The data in Table 9.1 are for another purpose, to be described momentarily, but the design structure is congruent with the problem just described, where *A*1 through *A*4 would be the same as the anchor variable examined in Chapter 5, and the *B* variable would represent exposure (*B*1) versus no exposure (*B*2) to a conservative critique. There would therefore be $ab = (4)(2) = 8$ cells into which respondents would be assigned. (In this case, there are $n = 5$ subjects per treatment combination.) Although half of the respondents in the *A*1 condition would be exposed to a conservative message and half would not, this would not bias the mean of *A*1 because the respondents in the *A*2, *A*3, and *A*4 conditions would be treated in the same way. The effect of the *B* variable would therefore be balanced across each of the conditions of *A*, and so the 40 responses could be conceived as being devoted solely to a test of the *A* variable; alternatively, the same 40 responses (20 each in *B*1 and *B*2) could be treated as if the *A* variable did not exist. The Table 9.1 design therefore contains two completely randomized designs which have been arranged factorially, and the greater efficiency that this arrangement provides arises from the fact that each respondent serves a double function.

More typically, a single investigator with interest in both variables will enter them into the same experiment in order to estimate their separate plus interactive effects on the dependent variable. In the case of Table 9.1, interest centered on the effect of reading instruction strategy (variable *A*) and gender (*B*) on the percentage increase in reading accuracy (dependent variable based on a word recognition test) of third-grade dyslexic children: *A*1 was a control group (no special instruction), *A*2 received whole word (visual) instruction, *A*3 received phonics instruction, and *A*4 received mulitisensory instruction. Strictly speaking, gender is of course not an experimental variable—rather, it is a subject variable or characteristic—but it will be treated as such for illustrative purposes.

The results of the ANOVA are shown in Table 9.2 (assuming a fixed

TABLE 9.1

	Learning Strategies					
	A1	*A2*	*A3*	*A4*	*Total*	*Mean*
*B*1	44	54	60	86		
Male	33	53	47	89		
	55	55	68	86	1250	62.50
	57	57	72	81		
	51	56	75	71		
	(240)[a]	(275)	(322)	(413)		
*B*2	37	56	54	55		
Female	37	63	37	50		
	30	60	58	44	1017	50.85
	48	61	55	57		
	50	48	61	56		
	(202)	(288)	(265)	(262)		
Total	442	563	587	675	2267	Grand sum
Mean	44.20	56.30	58.70	67.50	56.68	GM
					136,005	TSS

[a]Cell totals are in parentheses.

TABLE 9.2

SV	*df*		*SS*	*MS*	*F*
Strategy (A)	$a - 1$	$= 3$	2770.48	923.49	14.88**
Gender (B)	$b - 1$	$= 1$	1357.23	1357.23	21.87**
$A \times B$	$(a - 1)(b - 1)$	$= 3$	1409.07	469.69	7.57**
$S(AB)$	$ab(n - 1)$	$= 32$	1986.00	62.06	
Total	$abn - 1$	$= 39$	7522.78		

$**p < .01$

effects model) and were obtained by applying the rules discussed in the previous chapter. An expansion of the df, for example, yields five unique symbols and symbol combinations which, when decoded, produce the following computational formulas and uncorrected sums of squares (for $a = 4$ levels of A, $b = 2$ levels of B, and $n = 5$ subjects per cell):

$$1 = \text{CF} = \frac{1}{abn}\left(\sum_a \sum_b \sum_n X\right)^2$$

$$= \tfrac{1}{40}(2267)^2 = 128{,}482.22$$

$$a = \text{ASS} = \frac{1}{bn}\sum_a\left(\sum_b\sum_n X\right)^2$$

$$= \tfrac{1}{10}(442^2 + 563^2 + 587^2 + 675^2) = 131{,}252.70$$

$$b = \text{BSS} = \frac{1}{an}\sum_b\left(\sum_a\sum_n X\right)^2$$

$$= \tfrac{1}{20}(1250^2 + 1017^2) = 129{,}839.45$$

$$ab = \text{ABSS} = \frac{1}{n}\sum_a\sum_b\left(\sum_n X\right)^2$$

$$= \tfrac{1}{5}(240^2 + 202^2 + \cdots + 262^2) = 134{,}019.00$$

$$abn = \text{TSS} = \sum_a\sum_b\sum_n X^2$$

$$= 44^2 + \cdots + 56^2 = 136{,}005.00$$

The expanded df also specify how to combine the uncorrected sums of squares to produce the corrected sums:

$$\text{SS}_A = a - 1 = \text{ASS} - \text{CF} = 131{,}252.70 - 128{,}482.22 = 2770.48$$

$$\text{SS}_B = b - 1 = \text{BSS} - \text{CF} = 129{,}839.45 - 128{,}482.22 = 1357.23$$

$$\text{SS}_{AB} = ab - a - b + 1 = \text{ABSS} - \text{ASS} - \text{BSS} + \text{CF}$$

$$= 134{,}019.00 - 131{,}252.70 - 129{,}839.45 + 128{,}482.22$$

$$= 1409.07$$

$$\text{SS}_{S(AB)} = abn - ab = \text{TSS} - \text{ABSS}$$

$$= 136{,}005.00 - 134{,}019.00 = 1986.00$$

$$\text{SS}_T = abn - 1 = \text{TSS} - \text{CF}$$

$$= 136{,}005.00 - 128{,}482.22 = 7522.78$$

The corrected SS, when divided by their respective df, yield the appropriate mean squares in the MS column of Table 9.2. The next task is to determine which MS to employ in forming valid F tests.

Employing Schultz's algorithm, the components of the four mean squares and the appropriate F ratios are as follows:

1. $\text{MS}_A = S(AB) + A \qquad F = 1/4 = 923.49/62.06 = 14.88$

2. $MS_B = S(AB) + B \qquad F = 2/4 = 1357.22/62.06 = 21.87$

3. $MS_{AB} = S(AB) + AB \qquad F = 3/4 = 469.69/62.06 = 7.57$

4. $MS_{S(AB)} = S(AB)$

In this case—that is, with both A and B fixed, and with subjects nested within AB cells—the mean square for $S(AB)$ is the appropriate divisor for both main effects and their interaction. The df in Table 9.2 then specify which column and row to enter in the F table (Appendix B). For the A effect, the F table is entered for $df_A = 3$ and $df_{S(AB)} = 32$: $F_{.05;3,32} = 2.90$ (approximately), which is exceeded by the above calculated $F = 14.88$, which is therefore significant ($p < .05$). Indeed, all three Fs above are significant beyond the $\alpha = .01$ level.

Before turning to the a posteriori testing of means, consider the modifications in the F test that would have been required had variable A above been random rather than fixed—that is, had the four learning strategies in Table 9.1 been merely four selected at random from a wider collection of possible strategies. In this hypothetical situation, which is somewhat far-fetched conceptually, the mean squares and F ratios would have been as follows:

1. $MS_{A'} = S(A'B) + A'$

   $F = 1/4 = 923.49/62.06 = 14.88$

2. $MS_B = S(A'B) + A'B + B$

   $F = 2/3 = 1357.22/469.69 = 2.89$

3. $MS_{A'B} = S(A'B) + A'B$

   $F = 3/4 = 469.69/62.06 = 7.57$

4. $MS_{S(A'B)} = S(A'B)$

Whereas variable A' and the $A'B$ interaction remain significant ($p < .01$) as before, the B variable is no longer significant because of the fact that a larger number ($MS_{A'B} = 469.69$ rather than $MS_{S(A'B)} = 62.06$) is now required in the denominator for a valid F test. Whether a design is fixed, random, or mixed, therefore, does not influence the sizes of the mean squares, which are calculated in the same way regardless of the type of design; however, design type does influence which MS is chosen for the denominator, and this can influence the size of F and the conclusions drawn.

9.1. A Posteriori Testing

Table 9.2 indicates that both A and B as well as their interaction are significant, which invites the a posteriori testing of means. The significance of the AB interaction implies that the behavior of the A variable was different in $B1$ compared with $B2$—or, in this instance, that the pattern of means (for improvement in reading accuracy) for the various learning strategies was different for male than for female dyslexics. Although A and B were significant, therefore, caution should be taken in rendering general statements about these effects—for example, about the superior effectiveness of a specific learning strategy or of either of the sexes compared with the other—because the performances of either A or B are conditioned by specific levels of the other.

Table 9.3 contains the four teaching strategy means ($A1$ to $A4$) for males ($B1$) and females ($B2$), with significant mean differences shown in the interior of the tables. Tukey's HSD test, defined in expression 6.5, was employed for a posteriori testing and necessitates the calculation of $q_{\text{HSD}} = d/S_{\overline{X}}$, where d stands for any difference under consideration, and the standard error of the mean ($S_{\overline{X}}$) is given by $\sqrt{\text{MS}_e/n}$. In this case, there are $n = 5$ subjects in each of the AB cells to be compared, and the error mean square from Table 9.2 is associated with $S(AB)$, that is, the error estimate placed in the denominator of the F ratio when testing for the significance of the AB interaction. In this instance, therefore, $S_{\overline{X}} = \sqrt{62.06/5} = 3.52$.

Applied to the male subjects' means, the most extreme means yield a difference of $d = 82.60 - 48.00 = 34.60$, and the test value is consequently $q_{\text{HSD}} = 34.60/3.52 = 9.83$, which easily exceeds the critical Studentized range value of 4.80 for a range of $r = 4$ means, $\alpha = .01$, and $\text{df}_e = 32$ from Table 9.2 (see Appendix D). Asterisks in Table 9.3 indicate the other significant differences determined in the same fashion.

The interpretation of the data in Table 9.3 demonstrates the conditional nature of conclusions concerning main effects when their interaction is significant. Whereas the patterns of the means show that the no-treatment control group ($A1$) performed generally less well for both males and females, they also show that the difference for males between control and visual strategy ($A2$) was not significant. Although each of the teaching strategies was better than no treatment for the females, none of the strategies was demonstrably better than any other; for the males, however, the multisensory strategy ($A4$) proved superior to any of the others.

The standard error of the mean above ($S_{\overline{X}} = 3.52$) can also be used to

TABLE 9.3

		Group Means (males)		
	*A*4	*A*3	*A*2	*A*1
	82.60	64.40	55.00	48.00
*A*4 82.60	—	18.20**	27.60**	34.60**
*A*3 64.40		—	9.40	16.40**
*A*2 55.00			—	7.00
*A*1 48.00	$S_{\bar{X}} = 3.52$			—
		Group Means (females)		
	*A*2	*A*3	*A*4	*A*1
	57.60	53.00	52.40	40.40
*A*2 57.60	—	4.60	5.20	17.20**
*A*3 53.00		—	0.60	12.60*
*A*4 52.40			—	12.00*
*A*1 40.40	$S_{\bar{X}} = 3.52$			—

*$p < .05$, **$p < .01$

test the differences between gender means for each of the levels of variable *A*. When this is done, only two emerge as significant—at *A*3 ($p < .05$) and *A*4 ($p < .01$).

The issue of multiple comparisons for interactions is somewhat contentious. It is sometimes suggested that all cells be considered as in an *S*(*A*) design: In the example in Table 9.1, this would lead to the use of Tukey's test with $r = 8$, but this strategy often leads to comparisons that are confounded, for example, *A*1 females versus *A*4 males. Perhaps the most reasonable alternative is that offered by Keppel (1973: 244-246), where α_{fw} is divided over the number of rows or columns to be analyzed. In the example above, there are four columns or two rows to be examined; thus an alpha of .05/2 or .05/4 would be used in each analysis (or .05/6 were the interaction to be examined in terms of rows and also columns). The difficulty of course is that there are no tables for the $q = .05/2 = .025$ level, such as would be necessary for the present analysis of rows. The simplest solution is to adopt a .01 alpha level: This would lead to a loss of power and a consequent increase in Type II errors, but it is recommended given the prevailing view in applied statistics concerning the need to control Type I errors in post hoc analyses. A thorough discussion of simple effects analysis and interaction comparisons is in Keppel (1982: 208–245).

9.2. Hierarchical Designs

Hierarchical designs often bear resemblance to completely randomized factorial designs: they differ inasmuch as they involve multiple nesting, that is, complete cross-classification is lacking. In the factorial design considered previously (see Table 9.1), each level of *B* appears with each level of *A* so that the interaction of the two can be determined; however, the situation in Table 9.4 is different.

In this case, variable *A* represents two different teaching strategies (visual and verbal). The scores are the same as in Table 9.1, but the situation has been restructured to picture an experiment consisting of four teachers of dyslexic students, to each of whom $n = 10$ cases are randomly assigned. (For this design, ignore the gender variable *C*.) Although there are $b = 2$ teachers for each level of *A*, the two assigned to level *A*1 are different from the two under level *A*2; hence, teachers are nested under teaching strategy, that is, $B(A)$, and it is therefore impossible to determine any *AB* interaction.

Similarly, subjects are nested within the *B* variable, that is, $S[B(A)]$; hence it cannot be known whether students nested under teacher *B*1 would have performed in the same way if nested instead under teacher *B*2. The nested effect is random in this instance because it is assumed that the four teachers were randomly chosen from a population of such individuals.

TABLE 9.4

	Teaching Strategy (A)				
	(*A*1) *Visual*		(*A*2) *Verbal*		
	Teachers (B)				
	*B*1	*B*2	*B*3	*B*4	
Male	44	54	60	86	
(*C*1)	33	53	47	89	
	55	55	68	86	
	57	57	72	81	
	51	56	75	71	
Female	37	56	54	55	
(*C*2)	37	63	37	50	
	30	60	58	44	
	48	61	55	57	
	50	48	61	56	
	442	563	587	675	2267

Most often, nested variables are random; consequently, as in the case of the subjects variable S, the prime sign would be redundant and will therefore be omitted in the following analysis.

The ANOVA results are shown in Table 9.5, where $a = 2$ teaching strategies, $b = 2$ teachers nested within each A, and $n = 10$ subjects nested within B. (Note that there are $b = 2$ teachers per level of A although the two in $A1$ are different from those in $A2$.) The four computations for uncorrected sums of squares, based on the symbols in the expanded df, are:

$$1 = \text{CF} = \tfrac{1}{40}(2267)^2 = 128{,}482.22$$

$$a = \text{ASS} = \tfrac{1}{20}\left[(442 + 563)^2 + (587 + 675)^2\right] = 130{,}133.45$$

$$ab = \text{ABSS} = \tfrac{1}{10}(442^2 + \cdots + 675^2) = 131{,}252.70$$

$$abn = \text{TSS} = 44^2 + 33^2 + \cdots + 57^2 + 56^2 = 136{,}005.00$$

The corrected sums of squares, mean squares, and F ratios are displayed in Table 9.5, and the following expected mean square components, based on Schultz's rules, indicate what ratios had to be formed for valid F tests:

1. A $\quad S[B(A)] + B(A) + A \quad F = 1/2$
2. $B(A)$ $\quad S[B(A)] + B(A) \quad F = 2/3$
3. $S[B(A)]$ $\quad S[B(A)]$

According to Schultz's rules, the appropriate ratio for testing variable A is $F = \text{MS}_A/\text{MS}_{B(A)}$, which is not significant. The test for the B variable ($F = \text{MS}_{B(A)}/\text{MS}_{S[B(A)]}$) is significant, however, and would be interpreted as demonstrating that some teachers were more effective than others in producing improvements in reading accuracy, regardless of teaching strategy. Ordinarily, the B variable is not of interest because, as in this

TABLE 9.5

SV	df		SS	MS	F
1 A	$a - 1$	$= 1 = a - 1$	1651.23	1651.23	2.95
2 $B(A)$	$a(b - 1)$	$= 2 = ab - a$	1119.25	559.62	4.24*
3 $S[B(A)]$	$ab(n - 1)$	$= 36 = abn - ab$	4752.30	132.01	
Total	$abn - 1$	$= 39 = abn - 1$	7522.78		

*$p < .05$

instance, the four randomly selected teachers were not intrinsic to the experiment except in the procedural sense of facilitating its execution.

As shown here, variable A is frequently insignificant because the df associated with the denominator of the F test is normally quite small ($\mathrm{df}_{B(A)} = 2$ this example). It is always possible, therefore, that A might prove significant were a more sensitive test available. In the usual case in which $B(A)$ is not significant, this source of variance can be pooled with $S[B(A)]$ for a more powerful error MS. This pooling is inadmissible, however, if there is the slightest chance that $B(A)$ is significant, and so this source of variance is usually tested at a very low level (e.g., $\alpha = .25$). In the above case, as indicated, $B(A)$ is highly significant, and so pooling would be strictly inadmissible. For the sake of illustrating procedure, however, this will be ignored and the pooling will proceed by combining the sums of squares for $B(A)$ and $S[B(A)]$ and dividing by their combined df:

$$\mathrm{MS}_{\mathrm{pooled}} = \frac{\mathrm{SS}_{B(A)} + \mathrm{SS}_{S[B(A)]}}{\mathrm{df}_{B(A)} + \mathrm{df}_{S[B(A)]}}$$

$$= \frac{1119.25 + 4752.30}{2 + 36} = 154.51$$

The revised F ratio, based on the pooling above and the analysis in Table 9.5, is now

$$F = \mathrm{MS}_A / \mathrm{MS}_{\mathrm{pooled}} = 1651.23/154.51 = 10.69 \qquad (p < .01)$$

with 1 and 38 df associated with the numerator and denominator, respectively. Had the pooling been admissible, the result would have indicated a significant difference between teaching strategies $A1$ and $A2$.

Hierarchical designs can also contain variables that are arranged factorially, and this can be demonstrated by returning to Table 9.4 and taking into account the gender variable C. As previously, B is nested within A, but C is cross-classified with both A and B, which gives rise to the sources of variance in Table 9.6.

The calculations leading to the ANOVA in Table 9.6 are left as an exercise. Interpretation of the results would give special emphasis to the significant $B(A)C$ interaction, which indicates that male and female students (variable C) performed differently depending on the teacher to which they were assigned (variable B). It would be the task of a posteriori testing to tease out the salient differences that were contributing to this significant F.

TABLE 9.6

SV	*df*		*SS*	*MS*	*F*
Between					
Levels of *A*					
1 *A*	$a - 1$	= 1	1651.23	1651.23	$\frac{1}{2}$ 2.95
2 *B*(*A*)	$a(b - 1)$	= 2	1119.25	559.63	$\frac{2}{6}$ 9.02**
Within					
Levels of *A*					
3 *C*	$c - 1$	= 1	1357.23	1357.23	$\frac{3}{5}$ 4.75
4 *AC*	$(a - 1)(c - 1)$	= 1	837.23	837.23	$\frac{4}{5}$ 2.93
5 *B*(*A*)*C*	$a(b - 1)(c - 1)$	= 2	571.85	285.93	$\frac{5}{6}$ 4.61*
Subjects					
Within Cells					
6 *S*[*B*(*A*)*C*]	$abc(n - 1)$	= 32	1986.00	62.06	
Total	$abcn - 1$	= 39	7522.78		

*$p < .05$; **$p < .01$

Factorial designs are probably the most widely used in the social sciences because of their simplicity as well as the fact that they permit the simultaneous examination of two or more main effects plus their interactions. A major advantage is their efficiency because each subject is, in effect, used in two or more experiments—that is, each subject's dependent score (e.g., reading improvement) is used as part of the design evaluating variable *A* and again for evaluating *B* (and *C*, *D*, etc.). Hierarchical designs are useful when it is not convenient completely to cross-classify the variables of interest. Nested effects are generally of little interest, but (as in the case of the teachers in Table 9.4) are necessary to expedite the experiment. The impact of their presence in the experiment must therefore be evaluated.

10. SPLIT-PLOT AND REPEATED MEASURES DESIGNS

The split-plot and repeated measures designs differ from others previously covered by virtue of the fact that subjects are measured more than once on the dependent variable—hence the term "repeated measures," a design that has been somewhat controversial (Lovie, 1981). The split-plot terminology derives from agriculture, where plots of ground were divided, each subplot then receiving a different experimental treatment. Within the human sciences, the term *mixed design* has been increasingly adopted to refer to those experiments in which there are both within-subjects (repeated measures) and between-subjects variables. Another way of viewing the designs described in this chapter is to regard them as a subset of the treatments × blocks designs of Chapter 7, with individual subjects being analogous to blocks in the TB design.

Consider Table 10.1 as an example. In this study, subjects were instructed to respond to a set of possible public policies (e.g., reducing taxes, increasing social security benefits), first in terms of the extent to which they saw these policies as benefitting or costing them personally (along a 2 to −2 benefit/cost continuum), and second in terms of the extent to which they thought the current Republican Administration supported or opposed the same policies (assessed along the same 2 to −2 continuum). The policies reflected a range of values, including *wealth* (*W*), for example, protecting banks and businesses from failure; *well-being* (*B*), increasing the availability of low-cost medical treatment; *respect* (*R*), equalizing opportunities for women and minorities; and *rectitude* (*D*), legalizing prayer in the public schools. The resulting difference scores reflected the extent to which subjects judged their value preferences to be in accord with the Republican Administration's policy initiatives—positive scores indicating congruence, negative scores incongruence. Each subject therefore provided four scores, one for each of the four values.

It will be recalled that in the completely randomized design considered in Chapter 5, there were 16 subjects (each of whom was measured only once), with $n = 4$ being nested within each group; this was referred to as an $S(A)$ design, indicating that subjects were nested within each level of

TABLE 10.1

	Values (A)					
Subjects	*W*	*B*	*R*	*D*	*Sum*	
*S*1	1	4	0	−1	4	
*S*2	2	−8	2	1	−3	
*S*3	2	−7	1	2	−2	
*S*4	0	−5	−7	1	−11	
*S*5	−2	−8	0	−4	−14	
Sum	3	−24	−4	−1	−26	Grand sum
Mean	0.60	−4.80	−0.80	−0.20	−1.30	GM
					308	TSS

A. By way of contrast, the repeated measure design in Table 10.1 is of the type *SA*, with subjects being cross-classified with each level of *A*. In the *S*(*A*) design, the error MS contains all uncontrolled sources of variance, including variability arising from individual differences among subjects. One of the advantages of the *SA* design, therefore, is that it provides an assessment of the amount of total sum of squares attributable to differences among subjects, which is then subtracted from the error term, thereby reducing the size of the denominator of the *F* ratio.

The ANOVA of the data in Table 10.1 is summarized in Table 10.2. As illustrated previously, the expanded df can be used to determine the corrected SS, following the decoding rules of Chapter 8. In this case, there are four symbols and symbol combinations:

$$1 = \text{CF} = \frac{1}{an}\left(\sum_a \sum_n X\right)^2$$
$$= \tfrac{1}{20}(-26)^2 = 33.80$$

$$n = \text{SSS} = \frac{1}{a}\sum_n\left(\sum_a X\right)^2$$
$$= \tfrac{1}{4}[(4)^2 + \cdots + (-14)^2] = 86.50$$

$$a = \text{ASS} = \frac{1}{n}\sum_a\left(\sum_n X\right)^2$$
$$= \tfrac{1}{5}[(3)^2 + \cdots + (-1)^2] = 120.40$$

$$an = \text{TSS} = \sum_a \sum_n X^2$$
$$= 1^2 + 2^2 + \cdots + 1^2 + (-4)^2 = 308.00$$

where SSS is the uncorrected sum of squares arising from differences among subjects. The expanded df for the *SA* term is $(a - 1)(n - 1) =$

TABLE 10.2

SV	*df*		*SS*	*MS*	*F*
Among subjects (*S*)	$n - 1$	= 4	52.70	13.18	—
Values (*A*)	$a - 1$	= 3	86.60	28.87	2.57
SA	$(a - 1)(n - 1)$	= 12	134.90	11.24	—
Total	$an - 1$	= 19	274.20		

$an - a - n + 1$. The corrected SS is therefore given by $SS_{SA} = TSS - ASS - SSS + CF = 308.00 - 120.40 - 86.50 + 33.80 = 134.90$.

According to Schultz's rules, the three mean squares contain the following components:

1. $MS_S = S$
2. $MS_A = SA + A$
3. $MS_{SA} = SA$

As presented here, MS_{SA} implies that nonadditivity exists for this design—that is, MS_{SA} represents, in part, an interaction of subjects and treatment. At present, it is sufficient to note that as a result of this nonadditivity, experimental variable A is testable—$F = MS_A/MS_{SA} = 28.87/11.24 = 2.57$ (not significant)—whereas the among subjects variable (S) is not. We are not normally interested in testing S, however, which represents *systematic* differences among subjects. As in the case of the randomized block design (Chapter 7), a value of the SA design is that it permits assessment of a source of variability that can be subtracted from the error term, thereby reducing error and enhancing the likelihood that the F ratio for the experimental variable will prove significant.

The additivity assumption for the SA design states that each dependent score (X, representing the congruence/incongruence of personal values and perceived Republican Administration policy positions) equals the sum of the effects of the main variables, plus the grand mean and error, that is, $X = \mu + S + A + SA$, where SA is assumed to contain residual error only. But because there is only $n = 1$ score per cell in Table 10.1, residual error cannot be measured separately from any interaction that might exist between variables S and A; consequently, the SA term may contain both residual error plus variability arising because of nonadditivity, that is, because of subjects' performances interacting with the A variable.

More specifically, an interaction arises, in part, when one or more subjects' individual performances depart significantly from the mean performances of the group. For example, if, on the average, X scores increase steadily from value W to value B to R and to D, then for additivity to hold, individual subjects would be expected to follow the same course. But it is also possible that some subjects would have high X scores at the outset (condition W), leaving little room for higher scores during subsequent testing. Tukey's test for nonadditivity takes into account both the subject's mean performance over all levels of A and the subject's rate of change relative to the group's rate of change.

Tukey's test for nonadditivity was illustrated previously (Table 7.3 and surrounding text) and, when applied to the data in Table 10.1, shows the additive assumption to be tenable ($F_{\text{nonadd}} = 1.07$, not significant, $\alpha = .25$). Had the results been otherwise, the data might have required transformation or an adjustment in the procedure for determining the critical F ratio in examining the null hypothesis. There are certain benefits accruing from additivity—for example, it permits a test of the Subjects effect in Table 10.2—but its importance should not be overly stressed insofar as most practical situations are concerned. It is normally simpler to assume the worst (i.e., to assume that nonadditivity exists), and this conservative bias is built into the analysis culminating in Table 10.2, as well as in subsequent analyses.

A related problem in designs involving repeated measures, and which has already been discussed for this entire class of designs (i.e., randomized block designs), is the assumption of sphericity, or circularity. A comparatively simple modification of F testing procedures can compensate for the violation of this assumption (modified from Myers, 1979: 173–174). Table 10.3(a) displays the correlations among the $a = 4$ treatments (i.e., the four columns of Table 10.1), whereas Table 10.3(b) contains the variances (in parentheses) and covariances. (The covariance between any two levels of variable A is obtained by multiplying their correlation by the product of their respective standard deviations; therefore, for the values of W and B, for example, $\text{COV} = (0.13)(\sqrt{2.80})(\sqrt{25.70}) = 1.10$.)

TABLE 10.3

	W	*B*	*R*	*D*		
(a) Correlation matrix						
W	1.00	.13	.35	.85		
B	.13	1.00	−.10	−.08		
R	.35	−.10	1.00	−.11		
D	.85	−.08	−.11	1.00		
(b) Variance-covariance matrix						
W	(2.80)	1.10	2.09	3.40		
B	1.10	(25.70)	−1.82	−0.95		
R	2.09	−1.82	(12.70)	−0.94		
D	3.40	−0.95	0.25	(5.70)		
$\bar{X}$	2.35	6.01	3.31	1.80	3.37	GM
$\bar{X}^2$	5.51	36.09	10.92	3.25	55.77	$\Sigma\bar{X}^2$
					906.58	$\Sigma\Sigma X^2$

The column averages are recorded in row $\overline{X}$ of Table 10.3(b), and the square of the column averages in row $\overline{X}^2$; the average of the column averages (grand mean) is therefore GM = 3.37, and the sum of the squared column averages is $\Sigma\overline{X}^2 = 55.77$; the sum of squares of all 16 variances and covariances is $\Sigma\Sigma X^2 = 906.58$. In addition, the average of the four variances is $\overline{S}^2 = \frac{1}{4}(2.80 + 25.70 + 12.70 + 5.70) = 11.73$. The following three calculations are also required:

$$A \quad (\overline{S}^2 - \text{GM})^2 = (11.73 - 3.37)^2 = 69.89$$

$$B \quad 2a\sum\overline{X}^2 = (2)(4)(55.77) = 446.16$$

$$C \quad a^2\text{GM}^2 = (16)(3.37)^2 = 181.71$$

An estimated adjustment factor ($\hat{\epsilon}$), to be employed subsequently, is obtained as follows:

$$\begin{aligned}\hat{\epsilon} &= \frac{a^2 A}{(a-1)\left(\sum X^2 - B + C\right)} \\ &= \frac{(16)(69.89)}{(3)(906.58 - 446.16 + 181.71)} \qquad [10.1] \\ &= 0.58\end{aligned}$$

In the case of nonadditivity, the F test in Table 10.2 would still be an exact test so long as the sphericity requirement is met, in which case the adjustment factor would be $\hat{\epsilon} = 1.00$. To compensate for lack of sphericity, the degrees of freedom are modified as a function of $\hat{\epsilon}$. As shown in Table 10.2, $\text{df}_A = 3$ and $\text{df}_{SA} = 12$ are the numerator and denominator degrees of freedom, respectively, used in entering the F table (Appendix B), which indicates that the calculated F must exceed $F_{3,12} = 3.49$ in order to be significant at the $\alpha = .05$ level. Given that $\hat{\epsilon} = 0.58$, which reflects the magnitude of variance-covariance heterogeneity, the above degrees of freedom are adjusted as follows:

$$\text{df}'_A = \hat{\epsilon}(\text{df}_A) = 0.58(3) = 1.74 \simeq 2$$

$$\text{df}'_{SA} = \hat{\epsilon}(\text{df}_{SA}) = 0.58(12) = 6.97 \simeq 7$$

The adjusted df′ are rounded to the nearest whole number (2 and 7, respectively), and the corrected values now indicate that the calculated F must exceed $F_{2,7} = 4.74$ in order to be significant at the $\alpha = .05$ level.

The Geisser-Greenhouse correction (Keppel, 1982: 470–471) always adopts an adjustment factor of $\hat{\epsilon} = 1/(a-1)$—in this case $1/3 = 0.33$—

TABLE 10.4

	Party (A)								
	Republican				Democratic				
	Values (B)								
Subjects	*W*	*B*	*R*	*D*	*W*	*B*	*R*	*D*	*Sum*
*S*1	1	4	0	−1	−3	2	2	0	5
*S*2	2	−8	2	1	2	6	−2	4	7
*S*3	2	−7	1	2	2	7	−2	0	5
*S*4	0	−5	−7	1	3	7	9	2	10
*S*5	−2	−8	0	−4	1	10	0	4	1
Sum	3	−24	−4	−1	5	32	7	10	28 Sum
									.70 GM
									702 TSS

which is the smallest possible value of $\hat{\epsilon}$ and therefore the most conservative adjustment (albeit the simplest to calculate) that can be made. Given $\hat{\epsilon} = 0.33$, the degrees of freedom of $\text{df}'_A = 1$ and $\text{df}'_{SA} = 4$ would require a calculated F in excess of $F_{1,4} = 7.71$ in order to reach significance at the $\alpha = .05$ level.

The *SAB* variant of the repeated measures design, as shown in Table 10.4, involves the cross-classification of three variables: *A*, *B*, and *S* (subjects). In this case, subjects were asked to assess the extent to which the current Republican Administration favored certain policies (representative of the same four values in Table 10.1), but in addition to assess the extent to which a Democratic Administration would favor the same policies were it in power. As previously, the dependent variable represents the congruence or incongruence of each subject's own assessment of personal cost/benefit and the subject's perception of the parties' policy positions.

Table 10.5 shows the sources of variance associated with the *SAB*-type design, as well as the general df, which will always be the same regardless of the sizes of *a*, *b*, or *n* (assuming equal *n*s per *AB* groups). In this instance, as before, the among-subjects (S) df and the within-subjects (WS) df sum to total df, and the same applies for the sums of squares. There is usually no interest in the overall WS effect, however, because it is broken down into six components—*A*, *B*, and *AB* interaction, plus three error terms (*SA*, *SB*, and *SAB*).

The expanded df reveal eight unique symbols and symbol combinations which, when decoded, produce the following uncorrected SS (based on the data in Table 10.4):

TABLE 10.5

SV	Degrees of Freedom General		Expanded	SS	MS
S	$n - 1$	= (4)	$= n - 1$	(5.40)	1.35
WS	$n(ab - 1)$	= (35)	$= abn - n$	(677.00)	19.34
A	$a - 1$	= 1	$= a - 1$	160.00	160.00
SA	$(a - 1)(n - 1)$	= 4	$= ab - a - n + 1$	105.50	26.38
B	$b - 1$	= 3	$= b - 1$	2.20	0.73
SB	$(b - 1)(n - 1)$	= 12	$= bn - b - n + 1$	43.80	3.65
AB	$(a - 1)(b - 1)$	= 3	$= ab - a - b + 1$	178.20	59.40
SAB	$(a - 1)(b - 1)(n - 1)$	= 12	$= abn - ab - an + a - bn + b + n - 1$	187.30	15.61
Total	$abn - 1$	= (39)	$= abn - 1$	(682.40)	

$$1 = \text{CF} = \tfrac{1}{40}(28)^2 = 19.60$$

$$n = \text{SSS} = \tfrac{1}{8}(5^2 + 7^2 + 5^2 + 10^2 + 1^2) = 25.00$$

$$abn = \text{TSS} = 1^2 + 2^2 + \cdots + 2^2 + 4^2 = 702.00$$

$$a = \text{ASS} = \tfrac{1}{20}[(3 - 24 - 4 - 1)^2 + (5 + 32 + 7 + 10)^2] = 179.60$$

$$an = \text{ANSS} = \tfrac{1}{4}[(1 + 4 + 0 - 1)^2 + \cdots + (1 + 10 + 0 + 4)^2] = 290.50$$

$$b = \text{BSS} = \tfrac{1}{10}[(3 + 5)^2 + \cdots + (\{-1\} + 10)^2] = 21.80$$

$$bn = \text{BNSS} = \tfrac{1}{2}[(1 + \{-3\})^2 + \cdots + (\{-4\} + 4)^2] = 71.00$$

$$ab = \text{ABSS} = \tfrac{1}{5}[(3)^2 + (-24)^2 + \cdots + (10)^2] = 360.00$$

an and *bn* are perhaps the least obvious components. Decoded, the former reads as follows:

$$\begin{aligned} an = \text{ANSS} &= \frac{1}{b}\sum_a\sum_n\left(\sum_b X\right)^2 \\ &= \tfrac{1}{4}[(A_1B_1S_1 + A_1B_2S_1 + A_1B_3S_1 + A_1B_4S_1)^2 \\ &\quad + \cdots + (A_2B_1S_5 + A_2B_2S_5 + A_2B_3S_5 + A_2B_4S_5)^2] \\ &= \tfrac{1}{4}[(1 + 4 + 0 + \{-1\})^2 + \cdots + (1 + 10 + 0 + 4)^2] \\ &= 290.50 \end{aligned}$$

That is, the levels of *B* are summed while the levels of *A* and *S* remain constant. Similarly for *bn*:

$$
\begin{aligned}
bn = \text{BNSS} &= \frac{1}{a}[(A_1B_1S_1 + A_2B_1S_1)^2 + (A_1B_1S_2 + A_2B_1S_2)^2 \\
&\quad + \cdots + (A_1B_4S_5 + A_2B_4S_5)^2] \\
&= \tfrac{1}{2}[(1 + \{-3\})^2 + (2 + 2)^2 + \cdots \\
&\quad + (\{-4\} + 4)^2] \\
&= 71.00
\end{aligned}
$$

By this point it should be clear that calculations of the uncorrected SS merely indicate different ways to cut the cake represented by the matrix of raw scores: The squares of the row totals, when summed, reflect differences among subjects (SSS); columns one through four squared, when compared with columns five through eight squared, reflect differences between the levels of variable *A* (ASS); columns one and five versus two and six versus three and seven, etc. contrast levels of *B* (BSS); and so forth, each SS being divided by the number of scores entering into each sum.

The expanded df in Table 10.5 show how to combine the various uncorrected SS in order to calculate the corrected SS. The mean squares, as usual, are obtained by MS = SS/df. The mean square for within subjects (WS) is of no importance because interest normally focuses on the various components (*A*, *B*, *AB*) into which the WS variability can be divided.

It remains only to form the correct *F* ratios, and this, as shown previously, depends on whether the components represent fixed or random effects. Table 10.6 displays the results of two situations: *SAB*, in which *A* and *B* are both fixed effects (*S* is always a random variable); and *SAB′*, a mixed design in which *A* is fixed (i.e., experimental interest is in the responses to the Republican and Democratic alternatives only) and *B′* is random (i.e., the four values—*W*, *B*, *R*, and *D*—are only randomly selected from a larger universe to which any conclusions will be generalized). As is indicated, the calculations of SS and MS remain the same in both *SAB* and *SAB′*, although the ways in which the mean squares are combined in the *F* ratios differ.

Before proceeding, note that nonadditivity will be assumed in both instances (i.e., that the *SAB* and *SAB′* components represent a confounding of random influences plus the interaction of subjects with *AB* combi-

TABLE 10.6

(a) Fixed effects model (*SAB*)

	SV	*MS*	*Mean Square Components*	*F Ratios*	
1	S	1.35	*S*	—	
	WS	19.34	—	—	
2	*A*	160.00	*SA* + *A*	$\frac{2}{3}$	6.07
3	*SA*	26.38	*SA*	—	—
4	*B*	0.73	*SB* + *B*	$\frac{4}{5}$	0.20
5	*SB*	3.65	*SB*	—	—
6	*AB*	59.40	*SAB* + *AB*	$\frac{6}{7}$	3.81*
7	*SAB*	15.61	*SAB*		
	Total				

(b) Mixed effects model (*SAB*′)

	SV	*MS*	*MS Components*	*F Ratios*	
1	S	1.35	*SB*′ + *S*	$\frac{1}{5}$	0.37
	WS	19.34	—	—	—
2	*A*	160.00	*SAB*′ + *AB*′ + *SA* + *A*	2/(3 + 6 − 7)	2.28
3	*SA*	26.38	*SAB*′ + *SA*	$\frac{3}{7}$	1.69
4	*B*	0.73	*SB*′ + *B*′	$\frac{4}{5}$	0.20
5	*SB*	3.65	*SB*′	—	—
6	*AB*	59.40	*SAB*′ + *AB*′	$\frac{6}{7}$	3.81*
7	*SAB*	15.61	*SAB*′		
	Total				

*$p < .05$

nations), although in practical situations it would be wise to test for nonadditivity because there are certain advantages that accrue if additivity does in fact pertain. With nonadditivity, it may also be necessary to modify *F* testing procedures when the sphericity assumption is violated (see Table 10.3). Were the Geisser-Greenhouse strategy to be employed, therefore, $\hat{\epsilon} = 1/(a - 1)$ or $1/(b - 1)$ would be used as the adjustment factors for the *A* or *B* variables, respectively—and for the *AB* interaction.

The *A* effect for the *SAB*′ design is the most complicated and serves to illustrate the testing principles involved. According to Schultz's rules, MS_A contains within it variance components $SAB' + AB' + SA + A$, that is, the variability associated with the levels of *A* itself, plus variability associated with those other components containing *A* in which all other included factors are random. Because there is no other MS that contains all of the components in MS_A except for A itself, it is necessary to piece together a quasi-F, in this case $\mathrm{MS}_A/(\mathrm{MS}_{SA} + \mathrm{MS}_{AB'} - \mathrm{MS}_{SAB'})$, which produces the following ratio:

$$F_1 = \frac{SAB' + AB' + SA + A}{(SAB' + SA) + (SAB' + AB') - SAB'}$$
$$= \frac{SAB' + AB' + SA + A}{SAB' + AB' + SA}$$

There are sometimes alternative quasi-F ratios that can be constructed, as for example $(\mathrm{MS}_A + \mathrm{MS}_{SAB'})/(\mathrm{MS}_{AB'} + \mathrm{MS}_{SA})$, which produces

$$F_2 = \frac{(SAB' + AB' + SA + A) + SAB'}{(SAB' + AB') + (SAB' + SA)}$$
$$= \frac{SAB' + SAB' + AB' + SA + A}{SAB' + SAB' + AB' + SA}$$

F_1 and F_2 display the necessary property that all the terms in the numerator are contained in the denominator except for the term being tested (in this case A). Numerically, the F ratios are:

$$F_1 = \frac{\mathrm{MS}_A}{\mathrm{MS}_{SA} + \mathrm{MS}_{AB'} - \mathrm{MS}_{SAB'}}$$
$$= \frac{160}{26.38 + 59.40 - 15.61} = 2.28$$

$$F_2 = \frac{\mathrm{MS}_A + \mathrm{MS}_{SAB'}}{\mathrm{MS}_{AB'} + \mathrm{MS}_{SA}}$$
$$= \frac{160 + 15.61}{59.40 + 26.38} = 2.05$$

It is perhaps worth noting that it is possible for the quasi-F to be negative, a computational possibility which is theoretically senseless.

There are $a - 1 = 1$ df associated with the numerator of the quasi-F_1 ratio, but it remains to determine the number of df associated with the denominator. According to Keppel (1982: 330–333), the df for a combination of mean squares (involving $\mathrm{MS}_1, \mathrm{MS}_2, \ldots, \mathrm{MS}_k$) is obtained as follows:

$$\mathrm{df} = \frac{(\mathrm{MS}_1 \pm \cdots \pm \mathrm{MS}_k)^2}{(\mathrm{MS}_1^2/\mathrm{df}_1) + \cdots + (\mathrm{MS}_k^2/\mathrm{df}_k)} \qquad [10.1]$$

In the case of the variance components involved in variable A in Tables 10.5 and 10.6(b), the df for the denominator of the F_1 ratio are calculated as follows:

$$\text{df} = \frac{\text{MS}_{SA} + \text{MS}_{AB'} - \text{MS}_{SAB'}}{(\text{MS}^2_{SA}/\text{df}_{SA}) + (\text{MS}^2_{AB'}/\text{df}_{AB'}) + (\text{MS}^2_{SAB'}/\text{df}_{SAB'})}$$

$$= \frac{26.38 + 59.40 - 15.61}{(26.38^2/4) + (59.40^2/3) + (15.61^2/12)}$$

$$= 3.59 \simeq 4$$

The result is rounded to the nearest whole number. The tabular $F_{.05;\,1,4} =$ 7.71 indicates that the calculated $F = 2.28$ is not significant.

In the case of quasi-F_2 above, df must be calculated for the numerator and denominator because both are composites. These calculations are left as an exercise, which should produce 1.20 and 5.45 for the numerator and denominator df, respectively. Rounded to 1 and 5, the tabular $F_{.05;\,1,5}$ $= 6.61$ indicates that the calculated F still falls short of significance.

In the *SA* and *SAB* designs illustrated above, no distinctions were made between subjects, but in Table 10.7 a distinction is made between subjects assessed as democratic versus undemocratic in attitude. (As was the case with the gender variable in Chapter 9, attitude is a subject trait rather than an experimental variable.) The between-subjects variable is therefore cross-classified factorially with the within-subjects variable, with $n = 2$ subjects (in this instance) being nested within each of the two levels of A, but all subjects being exposed to all four levels of B—hence the designation $S(A)B$. This is referred to generically as a *mixed design*, and it gives rise to two different sources of error variance—between subjects (BS) and within subjects (WS).

TABLE 10.7

Attitude (A)	*Trials (B)* *1*$^+$	*2*^{o}	*3*$^+$	*4*^{o}	*Row Sum*	*Type Sum*
(*A*1)	5	6	6	7	24	41
Democratic	4	4	6	3	17	
(*A*2)	−1	−2	−5	−3	−11	−24
Nondemocratic	−4	0	−4	−5	−13	
Sum	4	8	3	2	17	Sum
					319	TSS

The experiment consisted of presenting subjects with 100 cards, on each of which was a set of pronouns (I, you, he, she, it, we, they), an infinitive (e.g., ''to throw''), and an object (e.g., ''the ball''). Each subject's task was to select a pronoun, match it with the correct form of the verb, and read the sentence aloud—for example, ''He threw the ball.'' During the first 20 readings, a count was made of the number of times the subject used first-person pronouns ''I'' or ''we'' in a sentence (operant level). During the second 20 readings, the subject was given a social reinforcement (e.g., ''good,'' ''uh-huh'') for each first-person pronoun used. The figures in column 1^+ indicate the number of first-person pronouns expressed by each subject over and above his or her operant level. In trials 2° and 4° (20 cards each) no reinforcement was given for selecting first-person pronouns; in trial 3^+, as in 1^+, reinforcement was given. The theory proposed that persons with democratic inclinations are more adaptable to subtle social cues. Under the null hypothesis, therefore, it would be expected that democratic subjects would respond to social reinforcements by expressing larger numbers of reinforced responses (in this case first-person pronouns).

As shown in Table 10.8, the sums of squares for between subjects (SS_{BS}) and within subjects (SS_{WS}) add to the total SS. In turn, SS_{BS} is divided into SS_A and $SS_{S(A)}$, that is, into the sums of squares attributable to differences between the two different attitude types and among subjects nested within levels of A. The SS_{WS} is divided into sums of squares attributable to performance differences among trials, to differences among AB cells (interaction), and to differences arising because of the interaction of subjects with variable B within levels of variable A ($SS_{S(A)B}$).

The formulas required to calculate the sums of squares are straightforward and should by now be obvious; they are therefore left as an exercise.

TABLE 10.8

SV	*df*	*SS*	*MS*	*F*
BS	$an - 1 = 3$	(270.69)		
A (Attitude)	$a - 1 = 1$	264.06	264.06	79.72*
$S(A)$	$a(n - 1) = 2$	6.63	3.31	
WS	$an(b - 1) = 12$	(30.25)		
B (Trials)	$b - 1 = 3$	5.19	1.73	0.81
AB	$(a - 1)(b - 1) = 3$	12.19	4.06	1.89
$S(A)B$	$a(b - 1)(n - 1) = 6$	12.88	2.15	
Total	$abn - 1 = 15$	(300.94)		

*$p < .05$

Similarly, the application of Schultz's rules for determining valid F ratios should also be routine: The ratios shown in Table 10.8 assume a fixed effects model, but the proper ratios would be somewhat different were either A or B a random variable.

The A effect is significant, and inspection of the data in Table 10.7 indicates that the subjects assessed as democratic responded to social reinforcements by emitting larger numbers of reinforced responses, whereas the nondemocratic responded with fewer. Because there are only $a = 2$ levels of A, both a priori and a posteriori testing as well as trend testing are superfluous. With $a > 2$, however, such testing would be in order and the standard error for the a posteriori testing of means, using Tukey's HSD test (see expression 6.5), would be

$$S_{\overline{X}_A} = \sqrt{\mathrm{MS}_{S(A)}/bn}$$

which in the above example would be

$$S_{\overline{X}_A} = \sqrt{3.31/8} = 0.64$$

By the same token, a test of a significant Trials effect (variable B) would involve the error term associated with within-subjects differences:

$$S_{\overline{X}_B} = \sqrt{\mathrm{MS}_{S(A)B}/an} = \sqrt{2.15/4} = 0.73$$

Similarly, in the use of Scheffé's or of a priori testing, care must be taken to utilize that error term associated with the effect being tested.

Testing is more complicated in the case of a significant interaction. The AB interaction in Table 10.8 is not significant; if it were, however, it would indicate differences in the levels of one variable at various levels of the other—for example, that the pattern of scores at $B1$, $B2$, $B3$, and $B4$ were different at $A1$ than at $A2$. In terms of Table 10.7, this would require testing the differences among the B means at $A1$ and again at $A2$, or testing the differences between $A1$ and $A2$ at the four levels of B. (To guard against Type I errors, only one of these sets of analyses would be undertaken.) Because A is a between-subjects variable and B a within-subjects variable, the testing of levels of A at each level of B involves both between- and within-subjects error, hence it is necessary to calculate a composite mean square ($\mathrm{MS}_{\mathrm{comp}}$) based on the figures in Table 10.8:

$$\mathrm{MS}_{\mathrm{comp}} = \frac{\mathrm{SS}_{S(A)} + \mathrm{SS}_{S(A)B}}{\mathrm{df}_{S(A)} + \mathrm{df}_{S(A)B}} \qquad [10.2]$$

$$= \frac{6.63 + 12.88}{2 + 6} = 2.44$$

The standard error for testing mean differences using Tukey's HSD test is

$$S_{\bar{X}_{AB}} = \sqrt{\mathrm{MS}_{\mathrm{comp}}/n}$$
$$= \sqrt{2.44/2} = 1.10$$

The degrees of freedom would also have to be pooled, as follows:

$$\mathrm{df}_{\mathrm{pooled}} = \frac{(\mathrm{SS}_{S(A)} + \mathrm{SS}_{S(A)B})^2}{(\mathrm{SS}_{S(A)})^2/\mathrm{df}_{S(A)} + (\mathrm{SS}_{S(A)B})^2/\mathrm{df}_{S(A)B}}$$
$$= \frac{(6.63 + 12.88)^2}{(6.63)^2/2 + (12.88)^2/6} \qquad [10.3]$$
$$= 7.67$$

The pooled df are rounded to the nearest whole number (df = 8 in this case), and the testing then proceeds as outlined in section 6.4.

If the levels of *B* had been examined at A_1 and again at A_2, then $\mathrm{MS}_{S(A)B}$ would have been sufficient as an error term. The difference here, although perhaps not obvious from the computational formulas, is that the *B* comparisons (at the various levels of *A*) employ only sums of squares that are derived from within-subjects sources of variance, whereas the *A* comparisons (at the various levels of *B*) employ both between- and within-subjects sources. The general principles behind the derivations of these procedures for analyzing interactions in mixed designs are presented in detail in Howell (1987) and Kirk (1982).

The repeated measures and mixed designs, as was the case with the factorial design, are capable of being extended ad infinitum with additional between-subjects and within-subjects variables, although larger designs require considerably greater numbers of subjects and produce higher-order interactions which, if significant, are usually difficult to interpret. This type of design is especially useful when relatively small numbers of subjects are available, when it is desirable to examine the behavior of individuals under a variety of treatments and treatment combinations, and in those cases in which duration plays an important role. Examples of the latter include the many learning experiments in which subjects' abilities to master various tasks are repeatedly examined across several trials.

APPENDIX A
Percentage Points of *t* Distribution (2-Tailed)

	alpha			alpha	
df	.05	.01	df	.05	.01
1	12.71	63.66	22	2.08	2.82
2	4.31	9.93	24	2.07	2.80
3	3.19	5.85	26	2.06	2.78
4	2.78	4.61	28	2.05	2.77
5	2.58	4.04	30	2.05	2.75
6	2.45	3.71	40	2.03	2.71
7	2.37	3.45	50	2.01	2.68
8	2.31	3.36	60	2.00	2.66
9	2.27	3.25	80	1.99	2.64
10	2.23	3.17	100	1.99	2.63
11	2.21	3.11	200	1.98	2.61
12	2.18	3.06	400	1.97	2.59
13	2.16	3.02	∞	1.96	2.58
14	2.15	2.98			
15	2.14	2.95			
16	2.12	2.93			
17	2.11	2.90			
18	2.11	2.88			
19	2.10	2.87			
20	2.09	2.85			

NOTE: Table values calculated by the authors.

APPENDIX B
Upper Percentage Points of *F* Distribution

df denom-inator	df numerator 1	2	3	4	5	6	7	8	9	10
	alpha = .05									
1	161.4	199.5	215.8	224.8	230.0	233.8	236.5	238.6	240.1	242.1
2	18.51	19.00	19.16	19.25	19.30	19.33	19.35	19.37	19.38	19.40
3	10.13	9.55	9.28	9.12	9.01	8.94	8.89	8.85	8.81	8.79
4	7.71	6.94	6.59	6.39	6.26	6.16	6.09	6.04	6.00	5.96
5	6.61	5.79	5.41	5.19	5.05	4.95	4.88	4.82	4.77	4.74
6	5.99	5.14	4.76	4.53	4.39	4.28	4.21	4.15	4.10	4.06
7	5.59	4.74	4.35	4.12	3.97	3.87	3.79	3.73	3.68	3.64
8	5.32	4.46	4.07	3.84	3.69	3.58	3.50	3.44	3.39	3.35
9	5.12	4.26	3.86	3.63	3.48	3.37	3.29	3.23	3.18	3.14
10	4.96	4.10	3.71	3.48	3.33	3.22	3.14	3.07	3.02	2.98
11	4.84	3.98	3.59	3.36	3.20	3.09	3.01	2.95	2.90	2.85
12	4.75	3.89	3.49	3.26	3.11	3.00	2.91	2.85	2.80	2.75
13	4.67	3.81	3.41	3.18	3.03	2.92	2.83	2.77	2.71	2.67
14	4.60	3.74	3.34	3.11	2.96	2.85	2.76	2.70	2.65	2.60
15	4.54	3.68	3.29	3.06	2.90	2.79	2.71	2.64	2.59	2.54
16	4.49	3.63	3.24	3.01	2.85	2.74	2.66	2.59	2.54	2.49
17	4.45	3.59	3.20	2.96	2.81	2.70	2.61	2.55	2.49	2.45
18	4.41	3.55	3.16	2.93	2.77	2.66	2.58	2.51	2.46	2.41
19	4.38	3.52	3.13	2.90	2.74	2.63	2.54	2.48	2.42	2.38
20	4.35	3.49	3.10	2.87	2.71	2.60	2.51	2.45	2.39	2.35
22	4.30	3.44	3.05	2.82	2.66	2.55	2.46	2.40	2.34	2.30
24	4.26	3.40	3.01	2.78	2.62	2.51	2.42	2.36	2.30	2.25
26	4.23	3.37	2.98	2.74	2.59	2.47	2.39	2.32	2.27	2.22
28	4.20	3.34	2.95	2.71	2.56	2.45	2.36	2.29	2.24	2.19
30	4.17	3.32	2.92	2.69	2.53	2.42	2.33	2.27	2.21	2.16
40	4.08	3.23	2.84	2.61	2.45	2.34	2.25	2.18	2.12	2.08
60	4.00	3.15	2.76	2.53	2.37	2.25	2.17	2.10	2.04	1.99
120	3.92	3.07	2.68	2.45	2.29	2.18	2.09	2.02	1.96	1.91
500	3.86	3.01	2.62	2.39	2.23	2.12	2.03	1.96	1.90	1.85
1000	3.85	3.01	2.61	2.38	2.22	2.11	2.02	1.95	1.89	1.84

alpha = .01

df denom-inator	1	2	3	4	5	6	7	8	9	10
1	4048	4993	5377	5577	5668	5924	5992	6096	6132	6168
2	98.50	99.01	99.15	99.23	99.30	99.33	99.35	99.39	99.40	99.43
3	34.12	30.82	29.46	28.71	28.24	27.91	27.67	27.49	27.34	27.23
4	21.20	18.00	16.69	15.98	15.52	15.21	14.98	14.80	14.66	14.55
5	16.26	13.27	12.06	11.39	10.97	10.67	10.46	10.29	10.16	10.05
6	13.75	10.92	9.78	9.15	8.75	8.47	8.26	8.10	7.98	7.87
7	12.25	9.55	8.45	7.85	7.46	7.19	6.99	6.84	6.72	6.62
8	11.26	8.65	7.59	7.01	6.63	6.37	6.18	6.03	5.91	5.81
9	10.56	8.02	6.99	6.42	6.06	5.80	5.61	5.47	5.35	5.26
10	10.04	7.56	6.55	5.99	5.64	5.39	5.20	5.06	4.94	4.85
11	9.65	7.21	6.22	5.67	5.32	5.07	4.89	4.74	4.63	4.54
12	9.33	6.93	5.95	5.41	5.06	4.82	4.64	4.50	4.39	4.30
13	9.07	6.70	5.74	5.21	4.86	4.62	4.44	4.30	4.19	4.10
14	8.86	6.51	5.56	5.04	4.69	4.46	4.28	4.14	4.03	3.94
15	8.68	6.36	5.42	4.89	4.56	4.32	4.14	4.00	3.89	3.80
16	8.53	6.23	5.29	4.77	4.44	4.20	4.03	3.89	3.78	3.69
17	8.40	6.11	5.18	4.67	4.34	4.10	3.93	3.79	3.68	3.59
18	8.29	6.01	5.09	4.58	4.25	4.01	3.84	3.71	3.60	3.51
19	8.18	5.93	5.01	4.50	4.17	3.94	3.77	3.63	3.52	3.43
20	8.10	5.85	4.94	4.43	4.10	3.87	3.70	3.56	3.46	3.37
22	7.95	5.72	4.82	4.31	3.99	3.76	3.59	3.45	3.35	3.26
24	7.82	5.61	4.72	4.22	3.90	3.67	3.50	3.36	3.26	3.17
26	7.72	5.53	4.64	4.14	3.82	3.59	3.42	3.29	3.18	3.09
28	7.64	5.45	4.57	4.07	3.75	3.53	3.36	3.23	3.12	3.03
30	7.56	5.39	4.51	4.02	3.70	3.47	3.30	3.17	3.07	2.98
40	7.31	5.18	4.31	3.83	3.51	3.29	3.12	2.99	2.89	2.80
60	7.08	4.98	4.13	3.65	3.34	3.12	2.95	2.82	2.72	2.63
120	6.85	4.79	3.95	3.48	3.17	2.96	2.79	2.66	2.56	2.47
500	6.69	4.65	3.82	3.36	3.05	2.84	2.68	2.55	2.44	2.36
1000	6.67	4.63	3.80	3.34	3.04	2.82	2.66	2.53	2.43	2.34

SOURCE: Adapted from Howell (1987: Appendix F, pp. 577–579)

APPENDIX C
Upper Percentage Points of the F_{max} Statistic

alpha = .05

df= n−1	df=g 2	3	4	5	6	7	8	9	10
2	39.0	87.5	142	202	266	333	403	475	550
3	15.4	27.8	39.2	50.7	62.0	72.9	83.5	93.9	104
4	9.60	15.5	20.6	25.2	29.5	33.6	37.5	41.1	44.6
5	7.15	10.8	13.7	16.3	18.7	20.8	22.9	24.7	26.5
6	5.82	8.38	10.4	12.1	13.7	15.0	16.3	17.5	18.6
7	4.99	6.94	8.44	9.70	10.8	11.8	12.7	13.5	14.3
8	4.43	6.00	7.18	8.12	9.03	9.78	10.5	11.1	11.7
9	4.03	5.34	6.31	7.11	7.80	8.41	8.95	9.45	9.91
10	3.72	4.85	5.67	6.34	6.92	7.42	7.87	8.28	8.66
12	3.28	4.16	4.79	5.30	5.72	6.09	6.42	6.72	7.00
15	2.86	3.54	4.01	4.37	4.68	4.95	5.19	5.40	5.59
20	2.46	2.95	3.29	3.54	3.76	3.94	4.10	4.24	4.37
30	2.07	2.40	2.61	2.78	2.91	3.02	3.12	3.21	3.29
60	1.67	1.85	1.96	2.04	2.11	2.17	2.22	2.26	2.30
∞	1.00	1.00	1.00	1.00	1.00	1.00	1.00	1.00	1.00

SOURCE: *Biometrika Tables for Statisticians* (3rd ed., Vol. 1, Table 31) edited by E. S. Pearson and H. O. Hartley, 1966, New York: Cambridge University Press. Reproduced by the kind permission of the trustees of *Biometrika*.

APPENDIX D
Studentized Range (Tukey's HSD Test)

alpha = .05

df error	range (r) 2	3	4	5	6	7	8	9	10
1	18.0	27.0	32.8	37.1	40.4	43.1	45.4	47.4	49.1
2	6.09	8.3	9.8	10.9	11.7	12.4	13.0	13.5	14.0
3	4.50	5.91	6.82	7.50	8.04	8.48	8.85	9.18	9.46
4	3.93	5.04	5.76	6.29	6.71	7.05	7.35	7.60	7.83
5	3.64	4.60	5.22	5.67	6.03	6.33	6.58	6.80	6.99
6	3.46	4.34	4.90	5.31	5.63	5.89	6.12	6.32	6.49
7	3.34	4.16	4.68	5.06	5.36	5.61	5.82	6.00	6.16
8	3.26	4.04	4.53	4.89	5.17	5.40	5.60	5.77	5.92
9	3.20	3.95	4.42	4.76	5.02	5.24	5.43	5.60	5.74
10	3.15	3.88	4.33	4.65	4.91	5.12	5.30	5.46	5.60
11	3.11	3.82	4.26	4.57	4.82	5.03	5.20	5.35	5.49
12	3.08	3.77	4.20	4.51	4.75	4.95	5.12	5.27	5.40
13	3.06	3.73	4.15	4.45	4.69	4.88	5.05	5.19	5.32
14	3.03	3.70	4.11	4.41	4.64	4.83	4.99	5.13	5.25
15	3.01	3.67	4.08	4.37	4.60	4.78	4.94	5.08	5.20
16	3.00	3.65	4.05	4.33	4.56	4.74	4.90	5.03	5.15
17	2.98	3.63	4.02	4.30	4.52	4.71	4.86	4.99	5.11
18	2.97	3.61	4.00	4.28	4.49	4.67	4.82	4.96	5.07
19	2.96	3.59	3.98	4.25	4.47	4.65	4.79	4.92	5.04
20	2.95	3.58	3.96	4.23	4.45	4.62	4.77	4.90	5.01
24	2.92	3.53	3.90	4.17	4.37	4.54	4.68	4.81	4.92
30	2.89	3.49	3.84	4.10	4.30	4.46	4.60	4.72	4.83
40	2.86	3.44	3.79	4.04	4.23	4.39	4.52	4.63	4.74
60	2.83	3.40	3.74	3.98	4.16	4.31	4.44	4.55	4.65
120	2.80	3.36	3.69	3.92	4.10	4.24	4.36	4.48	4.56
∞	2.77	3.31	3.63	3.86	4.03	4.17	4.29	4.39	4.47

alpha = .01

df error	2	3	4	5	6	7	8	9	10
1	90.0	135	164	186	202	216	227	237	246
2	14.0	19.0	22.3	24.7	26.6	28.2	29.5	30.7	31.7
3	8.26	10.6	12.2	13.3	14.2	15.0	15.6	16.2	16.7
4	6.51	8.12	9.17	9.96	10.6	11.1	11.5	11.9	12.3
5	5.70	6.97	7.80	8.42	8.91	9.32	9.67	9.97	10.24
6	5.24	6.33	7.03	7.56	7.97	8.32	8.61	8.87	9.10
7	4.95	5.92	6.54	7.01	7.37	7.68	7.94	8.17	8.37
8	4.74	5.63	6.20	6.63	6.96	7.24	7.47	7.68	7.87
9	4.60	5.43	5.96	6.35	6.66	6.91	7.13	7.32	7.49
10	4.48	5.27	5.77	6.14	6.43	6.67	6.87	7.05	7.21
11	4.39	5.14	5.62	5.97	6.25	6.48	6.67	6.84	6.99
12	4.32	5.04	5.50	5.84	6.10	6.32	6.51	6.67	6.81
13	4.26	4.96	5.40	5.73	5.98	6.19	6.37	6.53	6.67
14	4.21	4.89	5.32	5.63	5.88	6.08	6.26	6.41	6.54
15	4.17	4.83	5.25	5.56	5.80	5.99	6.16	6.31	6.44
16	4.13	4.78	5.19	5.49	5.72	5.92	6.08	6.22	6.35
17	4.10	4.74	5.14	5.43	5.66	5.85	6.01	6.15	6.27
18	4.07	4.70	5.09	5.38	5.60	5.79	5.94	6.08	6.20
19	4.05	4.67	5.05	5.33	5.55	5.73	5.89	6.02	6.14
20	4.02	4.64	5.02	5.29	5.51	5.69	5.84	5.97	6.09
24	3.96	4.54	4.91	5.17	5.37	5.54	5.69	5.81	5.92
30	3.89	4.45	4.80	5.05	5.24	5.40	5.54	5.65	5.76
40	3.82	4.37	4.70	4.93	5.11	5.27	5.39	5.50	5.60
60	3.76	4.28	4.60	4.82	4.99	5.13	5.25	5.36	5.45
120	3.70	4.20	4.50	4.71	4.87	5.01	5.12	5.21	5.30
∞	3.64	4.12	4.40	4.60	4.76	4.88	4.99	5.08	5.16

SOURCE: *Biometrika Tables for Statisticians* (3rd ed., Vol. 1, Table 29) edited by E. S. Pearson and H. O. Hartley, 1966, New York: Cambridge University Press. Reproduced by the kind permission of the trustees of *Biometrika*.

APPENDIX E
t_D Distribution (Dunn's Test)

alpha = .05

df error	No. of comparisons 2	3	4	5	6	7	8	9	10
5	3.16	3.53	3.81	4.03	4.22	4.38	4.53	4.66	4.77
6	2.97	3.29	3.52	3.71	3.86	4.00	4.12	4.22	4.32
7	2.84	3.13	3.34	3.50	3.64	3.75	3.86	3.95	4.03
8	2.75	3.02	3.21	3.36	3.48	3.58	3.68	3.76	3.83
9	2.69	2.93	3.11	3.25	3.36	3.46	3.55	3.62	3.69
10	2.63	2.87	3.04	3.17	3.28	3.37	3.45	3.52	3.58
11	2.59	2.82	2.98	3.11	3.21	3.29	3.37	3.44	3.50
12	2.56	2.78	2.93	3.05	3.15	3.24	3.31	3.37	3.43
13	2.53	2.75	2.90	3.01	3.11	3.19	3.26	3.32	3.37
14	2.51	2.72	2.86	2.98	3.07	3.15	3.21	3.27	3.33
15	2.49	2.69	2.84	2.95	3.04	3.11	3.18	3.23	3.29
16	2.47	2.67	2.81	2.92	3.01	3.08	3.15	3.20	3.25
17	2.46	2.65	2.79	2.90	2.98	3.06	3.12	3.17	3.22
18	2.45	2.64	2.77	2.88	2.96	3.03	3.09	3.15	3.20
19	2.43	2.63	2.76	2.86	2.94	3.01	3.07	3.13	3.17
20	2.42	2.61	2.74	2.85	2.93	3.00	3.06	3.11	3.15
21	2.41	2.60	2.73	2.83	2.91	2.98	3.04	3.09	3.14
22	2.41	2.59	2.72	2.82	2.90	2.97	3.02	3.07	3.12
23	2.40	2.58	2.71	2.81	2.89	2.95	3.01	3.06	3.10
24	2.39	2.57	2.70	2.80	2.88	2.94	3.00	3.05	3.09
25	2.38	2.57	2.69	2.79	2.86	2.93	2.99	3.03	3.08
30	2.36	2.54	2.66	2.75	2.82	2.89	2.94	2.99	3.03
40	2.33	2.50	2.62	2.70	2.78	2.84	2.89	2.93	2.97
50	2.31	2.48	2.59	2.68	2.75	2.81	2.85	2.90	2.94
75	2.29	2.45	2.56	2.64	2.71	2.77	2.81	2.86	2.89
100	2.28	2.43	2.54	2.63	2.69	2.75	2.79	2.83	2.87
∞	2.24	2.39	2.50	2.58	2.64	2.69	2.73	2.77	2.81

alpha = .01

df error	2	3	4	5	6	7	8	9	10
5	4.77	5.25	5.60	5.89	6.14	6.35	6.54	6.71	6.87
6	4.32	4.70	4.98	5.21	5.40	5.56	5.71	5.84	5.96
7	4.03	4.36	4.59	4.79	4.94	5.08	5.20	5.31	5.41
8	3.83	4.12	4.33	4.50	4.64	4.76	4.86	4.96	5.04
9	3.69	3.95	4.15	4.30	4.42	4.53	4.62	4.71	4.78
10	3.58	3.83	4.00	4.14	4.26	4.36	4.44	4.52	4.59
11	3.50	3.73	3.89	4.02	4.13	4.22	4.30	4.37	4.44
12	3.43	3.65	3.81	3.93	4.03	4.12	4.19	4.26	4.32
13	3.37	3.58	3.73	3.85	3.95	4.03	4.10	4.16	4.22
14	3.33	3.53	3.67	3.79	3.88	3.96	4.03	4.09	4.14
15	3.29	3.48	3.62	3.73	3.82	3.90	3.96	4.02	4.07
16	3.25	3.44	3.58	3.69	3.77	3.85	3.91	3.96	4.01
17	3.22	3.41	3.54	3.65	3.73	3.80	3.86	3.92	3.97
18	3.20	3.38	3.51	3.61	3.69	3.76	3.82	3.87	3.92
19	3.17	3.35	3.48	3.58	3.66	3.73	3.79	3.84	3.88
20	3.15	3.33	3.46	3.55	3.63	3.70	3.75	3.80	3.85
21	3.14	3.31	3.43	3.53	3.60	3.67	3.73	3.78	3.82
22	3.12	3.29	3.41	3.50	3.58	3.64	3.70	3.75	3.79
23	3.10	3.27	3.39	3.48	3.56	3.62	3.68	3.72	3.77
24	3.09	3.26	3.38	3.47	3.54	3.60	3.66	3.70	3.75
25	3.08	3.24	3.36	3.45	3.52	3.58	3.64	3.68	3.73
30	3.03	3.19	3.30	3.39	3.45	3.51	3.56	3.61	3.65
40	2.97	3.12	3.23	3.31	3.37	3.43	3.47	3.51	3.55
50	2.94	3.08	3.18	3.26	3.32	3.38	3.42	3.46	3.50
75	2.89	3.03	3.13	3.20	3.26	3.31	3.35	3.39	3.43
100	2.87	3.01	3.10	3.17	3.23	3.28	3.32	3.36	3.39
∞	2.81	2.94	3.02	3.09	3.14	3.19	3.23	3.26	3.29

SOURCE: Adapted from Howell (1987: Appendix t′, pp. 590–593)

REFERENCES

BLACK, V. (1955) "Laboratory versus field research in psychology and the social sciences." British Journal for the Philosophy of Science 5: 319–330.

BOX, J. F. (1978) R. A. Fisher: The Life of a Scientist. New York: John Wiley.

BRAY, J. H. and MAXWELL, S. E. (1986) Multivariate Analysis of Variance (Quantitative Applications in the Social Sciences, Vol. 54). Beverly Hills, CA: Sage.

COCHRAN, W. G. and COX, G. M. (1957) Experimental Designs (2nd ed.). New York: John Wiley.

COHEN, J. (1977) Statistical Power Analysis for the Behavioral Sciences (rev. ed.). New York: Academic Press.

DECONCHY, J-P. (1981) "Laboratory experimentation and social field experimentation: An ambiguous distinction." European Journal of Social Psychology 11: 323–347.

FISHER, R. A. (1960) The Design of Experiments (7th ed.). New York: Hafner. (Originally published 1935).

HARCUM, E. R. (1989) "The highly inappropriate calibrations of statistical significance." American Psychologist 44: 964.

HOWELL, D. C. (1987) Statistical Methods for Psychology (2nd ed.). Boston: PWS-Kent.

IVERSEN, G. R. and NORPOTH, H. (1976) Analysis of Variance (Quantitative Applications in the Social Sciences, Vol. 1). Beverly Hills, CA: Sage.

KEPPEL. G. (1973) Design and Analysis: A Researcher's Handbook (1st ed.). Englewood Cliffs, NJ: Prentice-Hall.

KEPPEL. G. (1982) Design and Analysis: A Researcher's Handbook (2nd ed.). Englewood Cliffs, NJ: Prentice-Hall.

KIRK, R. E. (1982) Experimental Design: Procedures for the Behavioral Sciences (2nd ed.). Belmont, CA: Brooks/Cole.

KLOCKARS, A. J. and SAX, G. (1986) Multiple Comparisons (Quantitative Applications in the Social Sciences, Vol. 61). Beverly Hills, CA: Sage.

LOVIE, A. D. (1981) "On the early history of ANOVA in the analysis of repeated measure designs in psychology." British Journal of Mathematical and Statistical Psychology 34: 1–15.

MARASCUILO, L. A. and SERLIN, R. C. (1988) Statistical Methods for the Social and Behavioral Sciences. New York: W. H. Freeman.

MARTIN, M. W. and SELL, J. (1979) "The role of the experiment in the social sciences." Sociological Quarterly 20: 581–590.

MYERS, J. L. (1979) Fundamentals of Experimental Design (3rd ed.). Boston: Allyn & Bacon.

O'GRADY, K. E. (1982) "Measures of explained variation: Cautions and limitations." Psychological Bulletin 92: 766–777.

ROTTER, G. S. and ROTTER, N. G. (1966) "The influence of anchors in the choice of political candidates." Journal of Social Psychology 70: 275–280.

SCHULTZ, E. F., Jr. (1955) "Rules of thumb for determining expectations of mean squares in analysis of variance." Biometrics 11: 123–135.

SELVIN, H. C. (1957) ''A critique of tests of significance in survey research.'' American Sociological Review 22: 519–527.

SPECTOR, P. E. (1981) Research Designs (Quantitative Applications in the Social Sciences, Vol. 23). Beverly Hills, CA: Sage.

WEIR, B. T. (1985) ''The American tradition of the experimental treatment of elections: A review essay.'' Electoral Studies 4(2): 125–133.

WILCOX, R. (1987) New Statistical Procedures for the Social Sciences: Modern Solutions to Basic Problems. Hillsdale, NJ: Lawrence Erlbaum.

Additional References

COHEN, J. (1992). "A power primer." Psychological Bulletin, 112, 155-159.

HOCHBERG, Y. (1988). "A sharper procedure for multiple tests of significance." Biometrika, 75, 800-802.

PART III

ANALYSIS OF VARIANCE

GUDMUND R. IVERSEN

HELMUT NORPOTH

1. INTRODUCTION

How does the public arrive at perceptions of economic well-being? This question has given rise to much speculation, discussion, and some research. One reasonable source of such perceptions is the mass media, particularly when it comes to assessments of the overall state of the economy, because this is something we as individuals do not experience directly. The question we want to study here is whether the mass media raise the public's concern with the economy by their coverage of economic news (see, e.g., Iyengar and Kinder, 1987).

In order to look for answers to this question, we design an experiment with two groups of people. Each group watches a television newscast spliced together from actual stories previously shown on the evening news. One group, known as the experimental group, watches a story on the state of the economy as part of the newscast. The other group watches the same newscast, except that the economic story has been deleted. This group is known as the control group. After watching their respective newscasts, the subjects are asked to fill out a questionnaire where they are asked, among other things, about the importance they

AUTHORS' NOTE: *We are grateful to Lawrence S. Mayer, Eric M. Uslaner, and an anonymous reader of a draft of the first edition and to an anonymous reader of a draft of the second edition for their comments.*

6

attach to "the state of the economy." Importance is measured on a ten-point rating scale.

People were randomly assigned to one of the groups. This is done in order to eliminate effects of other possible variables. For example, if all the young people were assigned to the experimental group and all the old to the control group, we would not know whether differences between the groups were due to age or to the difference in the newscasts they saw on television.

After the data have been collected, we have one set of values on the importance-variable for the experimental group and another set for the control group. An example of such data is shown in Table 1 in the next chapter. If the type of newscast does have an effect, the observed values should be different in the two groups; and we want to study differences between the two groups of data. One way to compare the two groups is to compare the two mean importance-values using a t-test for the difference between two means. Another way to look at the same data is to say that we have a treatment variable with two values: treatment and control. This variable is a categorical (nominal) variable. The other variable is the importance variable, and we take it to be a metric (interval) variable. The example can then be viewed as a study of the effect of a categorical variable on a metric variable. What we need is a way of statistically analyzing a relationship between variables of this kind, and analysis of variance is such a statistical method.

"Analysis of variance" is in some ways a misleading name for a collection of statistical methods and models that deal with differences in the means of a variable across groups of observations. While "analysis of means" may be a better name, the methods all employ ratios of variances in order to establish whether the means differ, and the name analysis of variance is here to stay. The name is often abbreviated to ANOVA, which a student of ours for a long time thought was the name of an Italian statistician.

The various statistical methods that fall under this name are related to other statistical methods. For example, when we study the difference between the means for only two groups of observations, as in the example above, we can find whether there is a significant difference between the means from the t-value for a difference-of-means test. This test is usually not thought of as being an analysis of variance, but we show in the next chapter that it is nothing but a special case of one of the simplest analysis of variance procedures. We show that the square of the t-value is a ratio of two variances, and this ratio gives another way of telling whether there is a statistically significant difference between the two groups.

Analysis of variance methods are also related to the set of statistical methods known as regression analysis. This point is pursued further in Chapter 5; here we note only that analysis of variance is usually the appropriate method when the groups of observations are created by a categorical independent variable. In our example the independent variable is type of newscast, and the variable has two categories (with or without economic news), resulting in two groups of observations of the dependent variable. Our task consists of determining whether the groups differ in their mean level of the dependent variable—here, importance rating. The dependent variable in an analysis of variance is almost always a metric (interval) variable.

But we can have groups formed by metric variables just as well as categorical variables. In that case analysis of variance is usually not the appropriate method for the analysis. Take education as an example of such a metric variable. When measured as number of years completed in school, all members of one group have a score of 6, all members of the next group have a score of 7, etc. With education as the independent variable, regression analysis is the appropriate way of studying whether the importance-variable or some other metric dependent variable, differs across the various education groups. Thus regression is used for the study of the effect of a metric variable on another metric variable, while analysis of variance is used for the study of the effect of a categorical variable on a metric variable. But it should be noted that the differences between analysis of variance and regression are smaller than may seem to be the case, and they can both be seen as special cases of what is known as the general linear model.

Part of the reason why regression and analysis of variance are seen as two separate sets of methods is historical. Different sciences have tended to use different types of statistical methods, and analysis of variance methods originated mostly in agriculture and the work done by the late Sir Ronald A. Fisher in the period between the two world wars. For many years he was a statistician at an agricultural experimental station in England, and a typical question he would be called upon to investigate might be whether different types of fertilizers gave different yields. Type of fertilizer is the categorical, independent variable, and yield is the metric dependent variable. By using each fertilizer on several different plots of land and measuring the yields at the end of the growing season, he would have the basis for concluding whether the fertilizers differ in their effectiveness.

Two different types of data can be analyzed using analysis of variance. The first type is experimental data, and both the television and the agricultural examples above are of this type. They have in common that the elements (people, plots of land, etc.) are randomly assigned to one of the treatments, and then the effect of the treatment is measured. The other type is observational data. In a survey we may ask people for their religious affiliation as well as their income in order to study whether income is affected by religious affiliation. This fits the pattern for analysis of variance with a categorical variable (religion) affecting a metric variable (income). All the computations are the same for the two types of data, but the difference is that with observational data, it is much harder to establish a causal effect. This is because people are not randomly assigned to different religious categories and their incomes observed later. Thus, even if we find income differences, we do not know whether they are caused by people's religion or whether they are caused by some other variable(s) that are related to religious affiliation. In experimental studies with random assignments to treatments, the effects of other variables tend to cancel each other out. Randomization was one of Fisher's major contributions to what is known as experimental design. For a further discussion of observational versus experimental research see Cochran (1965, 1983).

The formal theory of analysis of variance requires the observations to satisfy certain assumptions. There is the usual assumption that the observations have been collected independently of each other. Beyond that there are assumptions about certain quantities being additive and following the normal distribution. It is possible to use the data themselves to check on some of these assumptions, and we spell out the necessary assumptions for each method we discuss. The theory itself is heavily mathematical. We feel, rather reluctantly, that to fully understand a particular method it is necessary to understand the underlying mathematics. But it is also possible to get a very good working understanding of many of the methods without an extensive mathematical background. We present the arguments here with a minimum of mathematics, and instead we rely on intuitive and graphic arguments.

The computations needed for an analysis of variance are mostly done on computers, and we do not give computing formulas for hand calculators. If a data set is small enough that a computer is not needed, it is possible to do the computations directly from the formulas we present. But the required setup for a computer analysis is not always simple to perform, and the meaning of some of the quantities on the output are not always entirely obvious. We make an occasional reference to the SPSS-X software.

The remaining chapters take up some of the simpler analysis of variance models. We progress from one to two independent (explanatory) variables, and the resulting models are known as one-way and two-way analyses of variance, respectively. From there it is possible to go on to more than two explanatory variables. We also have to distinguish between the cases when we have observations on the dependent variable for all categories of the explanatory variable(s) and when we only have data on a subset of the categories. In the first case we have what is called a fixed model, and in the second case we have a random model. The chapters are arranged in the following way:

Ch. 2: One explanatory variable, all categories,

Ch. 3: Two explanatory variables, all categories,

Ch. 4: One explanatory variable, sample of categories,
Two explanatory variables, sample of categories,

Ch. 5: Other models.

Further readings: After this elementary introduction to analysis of variance, it is possible to read further in standard statistical textbooks for the social sciences or other fields. For more extensive treatments on an intermediate level there are books by authors like Cochran and Cox (1957), Hays (1981), Petersen (1986), and Snedecor and Cochran (1967). The classic book on the advanced level is by Scheffé (1959).

2. ONE-WAY ANALYSIS OF VARIANCE, ALL CATEGORIES

Two groups

A t-test for the difference between two means. The fundamental ideas of analysis of variance can be understood better if we first consider in some detail the case in which the explanatory variable has only two categories. In this case the data consist of two groups of observations on the dependent variable, one group for each category of the explanatory variable. For example, we may want to study whether there is a difference in incomes between males and females, or whether there is a difference between Democrats and Republicans on some issues, and so on.

In our example on the economy we have a set of values on the rating of the importance of the economy for the control group and another set of values for the experimental group. There are five values in each of the groups, and we want to investigate whether the two groups differ on the dependent variable importance rating, denoted Y in the formulas. Specifically, we want to find out whether the mean value of the importance rating differs in the two groups. We could conclude that the groups differ if the number of observations differ, or if the standard deviations of Y differ, or if they differ in some other respect; but in analysis of variance we are concerned with whether the means differ.

One simple way to tell whether the two means differ is to compute the means and compare the two numbers. Most likely the two numbers are not the same, and that answers our question right there for the data in the sample. But, what we are more often concerned with is whether the means are different in the two populations of all possible data and not just in the observed sample. Thus we want to determine whether the observed difference between the two sample means is just due to random variations from one sample to the next, or whether the data come from populations where the means are truly different. This is another way of saying that we want to find out whether the difference between the sample means is statistically significant. Finally, even if we conclude that the population means are different, we also need to decide whether they are different enough to be of substantive importance.

These considerations are illustrated by the three different graphs in Figure 1. Graph A shows two numerically different means $\bar{y}_1$ and $\bar{y}_2$. From looking at the two means alone we cannot tell whether they are significantly different or not. In graphs B and C the difference between the two means is the same as in graph A, but graphs B and C also show the values of the five observations in each group. In graph B we see that within each of the two groups the observations are widely scattered around their respective means. Because there seems to be so much randomness in each group of data, we are inclined to say that in this case the difference between the two means is not very convincing.

In graph C the picture is different. Even though the means are the same as in graphs A and B, within each group the observations are now highly clustered. Because the observations are so clustered around the their respective means, the two groups of data seem really separated, and we conclude for graph C that the means are truly different. In this case there is a statistically significant difference between the two means.

The problem for us now becomes how to decide when means are different enough, relative to the spread of the observations in each group, to conclude that there is a statistically significant difference between the means. Analysis of variance helps us answer this question.

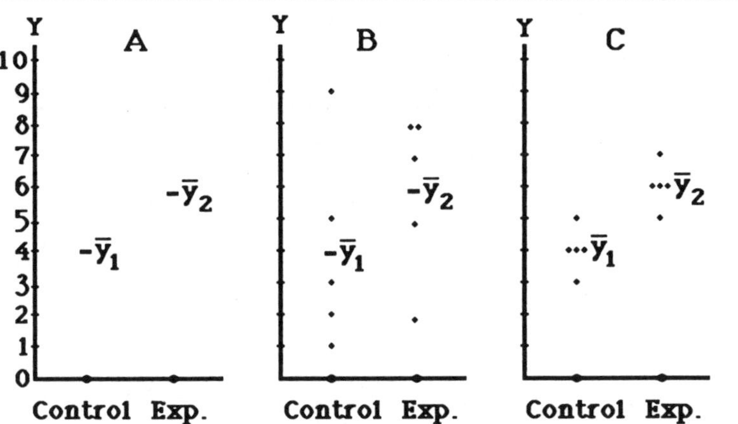

A: Two different group means.

B: Same means with observations spread far apart. Difference between means not statistically significant.

C: Same means with observations close together. Difference between means statistically significant.

Figure 1: Group Means $\bar{y}_1$ and $\bar{y}_2$ with Data

What we have to do is find a way of measuring numerically how different the means are and how much the observations are spread out around their respective means. With those two measures on hand we are then able to tell whether the means differ significantly or not. Before using analysis of variance, however, the data in graph B are analyzed in a more familiar way. Table 1 shows the data in case C and the symbols we use for the observed values of the dependent variable Y.

As already noted in Chapter 1, the t-test for the difference between two means is a special case of analysis of variance, and this t-test can be used here to investigate the difference between the two means. Denote the unknown mean of the control population as μ_1 and the unknown mean for the treatment population as μ_2. The statistical null hypothesis states that these two means are equal. The decision whether or not to reject the hypothesis is based on how likely it is that the two known sample means differ by as much as they do or more, if it really is true that

TABLE 1
Rating Scores of the Importance of the Economy, by Type of Newscast, Hypothetical Data Case C

	Type of Newscast	
	Control Group	Experimental Group
	5	7
	4	5
	4	6
	4	6
	3	6
Mean	4.0	6.0
In symbols:	Control Group	Experimental Group
	y_{11}	y_{21}
	y_{12}	y_{22}
	y_{13}	y_{23}
	y_{14}	y_{24}
	y_{15}	y_{25}
Mean	$\bar{y}_1$	$\bar{y}_2$

the population means are equal. The test statistic for this hypothesis is a t-score where the numerator is

$$(\bar{y}_1 - \bar{y}_2) - (\mu_1 - \mu_2) = (\bar{y}_1 - \bar{y}_2) - 0 = 4 - 6 = -2$$

for both cases B and C. Here $\bar{y}_1$ is the sample mean for the control group and $\bar{y}_2$ is the sample mean for the experimental group. The denominator of the test statistic is slightly more complicated. First we compute the sample variance of Y in each of the two groups, which for the first group yields:

$$\begin{aligned} s_1^2 &= \Sigma(y_{1j} - \bar{y}_1)^2/(n_1 - 1) \\ &= \{(9-4)^2 + (5-4)^2 + (3-4)^2 + (2-4)^2 + (1-4)^2\}/(5-1) \\ &= 40/4 = 10.00 \end{aligned}$$

Similarly, for the observations in the second group we get

$$s_2^2 = \Sigma(y_{2j} - \bar{y}_2)^2/(n_2 - 1) = 26/4 = 6.50$$

The denominator we seek for the t-statistic can now be found from these two variances. Because the numerator is the difference between two means, the denominator becomes the square root of the sum of the variances of the two means, that is,

$$s = \sqrt{s_1^2/n_1 + s_2^2/n_2} = \sqrt{10.00/5 + 6.50/5} = 1.82$$

The resulting ratio gives $t = -2.00/1.82 = -1.10$ with $n_1 + n_2 - 2 = 8$ degrees of freedom. The possible statistical significance of a t-value can be established from a table of the t-distribution, and this value of t is not significant.

Degrees of freedom. With five observations in each group and ten altogether, the t-value of –1.10 has eight degrees of freedom. Here is the first place where we meet the concept of degrees of freedom. This is a quantity that has confused many people. Part of the reason for this confusion is that the formal definition is heavily mathematical. Another reason is that there exists several equivalent definitions, and it is not obvious how they relate to each other.

Degrees of freedom appear any time we compute a sum of squares. One way to define the concept is to say that the degrees of freedom for a particular sum of squares is equal to the smallest number of term in the sum we need to know in order to find the remaining terms and thereby compute the sum. One would think that we need to know all the terms in order to compute a sum. But there are often restrictions imposed on the terms, and these restrictions make it possible to find some of the terms from knowing the others.

For example, the variance s_1^2 computed above is found from the sum of five squared terms. But the terms are all deviations from the mean of the original scores, and it is therefore a restriction on these terms that they add to zero. If we were told that the first four terms were 5, 1, –1, and –2, we would immediately know that the fifth term has to equal –3 since this is the only number that will make the sum of all five terms equal to zero. By squaring each of these five terms and adding the five squares we get a sum of squares equal to 40.00. Because we initially needed to know four of the five terms in order to find the sum of squares equal to 40.00, we say that this sum has four degrees of freedom. Since the sum is the numerator in the expression for the variance in the first group, we also say that the resulting variance has four degrees of freedom. When we add the two variances to get the denominator for the t-value, we also add the corresponding degrees of freedom. Here each variance is based on four degrees of freedom, and there are therefore a total of eight degrees of freedom for the t-value.

In general, with n_1 observations in one group and n_2 in another, there are n_1-1 degrees of freedom for the variance in the first group and n_2-1 degrees of freedom for the variance in the second group. When we combine the two variances to get the denominator for the t-value, we add the degrees of freedom and get a total of n_1+n_2-2 degrees of freedom for the t-value.

We have to realize, however, that when there is a certain number of terms in a sum of squares, the degrees of freedom for this sum could have as many degrees of freedom as there are terms in the sum or as few as one degree of freedom, depending on the nature of the terms in the sum. The actual determination of the correct number of degrees of freedom for a sum of squares can be difficult. The determination is sometimes simplified, however, by the fact that when two sums of squares are added, the degrees of freedom for the two sums are also added. This fact is used several times in this presentation of analysis of variance.

Equal variances. There is a requirement for this t-test that the variances in the two groups do not differ too much. In other words, s_1^2 should be approximately equal to s_2^2. As an example of what is meant by "approximately equal," we note that with five observations in each group, we can tolerate having one variance as much as six times larger than the other and still call the variances approximately equal. With more observations in the two groups, the variances have to be more equal. For example, if there are 100 observations in each of the two groups, one sample variance cannot be more than one-third larger than the other. The equality of two variances is tested by computing the ratio of the two variances, and this ratio follows the F-distribution.

The formal assumption does not state that the two sample variances are equal, but that the variances are equal in the populations from which the two sets of observations came. If the assumption of equal population variances is true, then we should use all the data to estimate this common variance. This is a better use of the data than we made above, where we used part of the data to find the estimates s_1^2 and another part of the data to find the other estimates s_2^2.

One way to find a single, common estimate of the variance is to compute the mean of the two existing estimates; that is,

$$s^2 = (1/2)s_1^2 + (1/2)s_2^2$$

A difficulty with this way of combining the two estimates is that when the two groups do not have the same number of observations, the variance from the group with the larger number of observations is a better quantity, in some sense, and should therefore contribute more to the overall s^2 than the variance from the smaller group. The formula above does not allow for this, however, because it uses ½ as weights for both variances. It is better to use weights that involve the number of observations in each group, and the overall variance is usually found from the expression

$$s^2 = \frac{n_1 - 1}{n_1 + n_2 - 2} s_1^2 + \frac{n_2 - 1}{n_1 + n_2 - 2} s_2^2$$

$$= (4/8)10.00 + (4/8)6.50 = 8.25 \qquad s = 2.87$$

When the number of observations in the two groups is equal, this formula reduces to the first formula with ½ as weights. When the groups have different numbers of observations, the second formula gives more weight to the variance based on the larger number of observations.

Using the common s^2 the denominator for the t-statistic for the difference between two means becomes

$$\sqrt{s^2/n_1 + s^2/n_2} = s\sqrt{1/n_1 + 1/n_2}$$

The t-value itself is found as

$$t = \frac{\bar{y}_1 - \bar{y}_2}{s\sqrt{1/n_1 + 1/n_2}} = \frac{4 - 6}{2.87\sqrt{1/5 + 1/5}} = -1.10 \qquad 8 \text{ df}$$

which, in this particular case with the same number of observations in the two groups, is the same t-value as presented earlier. Instead of first finding the average variance s^2, the following equivalent formula works equally well,

$$t = \frac{\bar{y}_1 - \bar{y}_2}{\sqrt{s_1^2/n_2 + s_2^2/n_1}}$$

In this denominator the variance from the first group is divided by the number of observations in the second group, and vice versa.

Analysis of variance for two groups. The statistical analysis outlined above is the simplest example of an analysis of variance, even though it is usually not thought of a such. But the formula for t can be changed to become an F-ratio as used in analysis of variance. Below we show how this change is done in order to show the connection between the t-test for the equality of two means and analysis of variance.

First it can be noted that except for not being able to tell whether the sign of t is positive or negative, no other information is lost by squaring the t-value. Let us first work with the case where the two groups have the same number of observations on the dependent variable Y, that is, $n_1 = n_2 = n$. Then,

$$t^2 = \frac{(\bar{y}_1 - \bar{y}_2)^2}{s^2(1/n_1 + 1/n_2)} = \frac{n(\bar{y}_1 - \bar{y}_2)^2}{2s^2} = \frac{5(4-6)^2}{2(8.25)} = 1.21$$

tells us just as much as t itself, except whether the difference between the two means is positive or negative. But if the null hypothesis is a two-sided hypothesis, the sign does not matter anyway, since the alternative hypothesis only states that the two population means are different.

It is possible to rewrite the numerator for t^2. It can be shown that the difference between the two means can be written as the sum of two differences where each of the new differences is a difference between a group mean and the overall mean $\bar{y}$. Thus

$$\begin{aligned} &(4-6)^2 \\ &= (\bar{y}_1 - \bar{y}_2)^2 = 2(\bar{y}_1 - \bar{y})^2 + 2(\bar{y}_2 - \bar{y})^2 \\ &\qquad\qquad\qquad = 2(4-5)^2 + 2(6-5)^2 \end{aligned}$$

Then we can rewrite the expression for t^2 the following way,

$$t^2 = \frac{n(\bar{y}_1 - \bar{y})^2 + n(\bar{y}_2 - \bar{y})^2}{s^2} = \frac{5(4-5)^2 + 5(6-5)^2}{8.25}$$

$$= 1.21$$

In the terminology of analysis of variance this quantity is called F with 1 and $2n - 2$ (=8) degrees of freedom. The numerator measures how much the group means differ from the overall mean. The denominator, which is the common variance in each of the groups, measures how much the observations are spread out around the group means. The same formula also applies when the number of observations in the two groups are not equal. When there are n_1 observations in the first group and n_2 in the second group, we get

$$F = \frac{n_1(\bar{y}_1 - \bar{y})^2 + n_2(\bar{y}_2 - \bar{y})^2}{s^2} \qquad 1 \text{ and } n_1 + n_2 - 2 \text{ degrees of freedom}$$

Now it is possible to return to graphs B and C in Figure 1 and see what we achieved. The numerator for the F-ratio will be the same for the two cases since the two group means $\bar{y}_1$ and $\bar{y}_2$ deviate from the overall mean $\bar{y}$ by the same magnitudes. But the denominator s^2 will differ; it will be large for case B and small for case C. In case B the observations are quite far from the mean in each of the two groups, and the variance s^2 (=8.25) will therefore be large. This again means that the F-value (=1.21) will be small.

In case C the situation is different. The observations are quite clustered around their group means, and the variance s^2 (=0.50) is therefore small. The value of F (=20.00) is large. The conclusion is that a large value of F tells us we have a significant difference between the two group means. From the t-table we recall that a value larger than 2 or smaller than –2 is usually significant. This means that with 2 groups, an F-value larger than 4 is similarly significant, since F is the square of t. In this example with 2 groups and 10 observations, we find from tables of the F-distribution that we need an F-value larger than 5.32 in order to call the observed difference $\bar{y}_1 - \bar{y}_2$ significant with a 5% significance level. With more than two groups and with many observations, F-values can be significant when they are as small as 2 or 3.

The value of F is approximately equal to 1.00 where there is no difference between the population means and the difference between the sample means is due only to random fluctuations. The reason for that is as follows. When we have a sample of n observations of a random variable with variance s^2, we can find the variance of the sample mean (s^2) from the equation

$$s_{\bar{y}}^2 = s^2/n$$

Using the data from case B, we have $s^2 = 8.25$ and $n = 5$, which gives

$$s_{\bar{y}}^2 = 8.25/5 = 1.65$$

The interpretation of this variance is that if we had a large number of samples of 5 observations from the same population and computed the mean from each sample, then the variance of these sample means would be approximately equal to 1.65.

We are not in the situation here of having many samples, but we do have two samples and thereby two means $\bar{y}_1$ and $\bar{y}_2$, and we can find the variance of these two means using the ordinary formula for a variance. Thus another estimate of the variance of the means becomes

$$s_{\bar{y}}^2 = \{(\bar{y}_1 - \bar{y})^2 + (\bar{y}_2 - \bar{y})^2\}/(2-1)$$
$$= \{(4-5)^2 + (6-5)^2\}/1 = 2.00$$

If the differences in the sample means are due only to random fluctuations, then these two estimates 1.65 and 2.00 should be about equal. One way to find out how equal they are is to take their ratio, which should be about equal to 1.00. Here

$$F = 2.00/1.65 = 1.21$$

which is the same F-value we had above for these data. Since the ratio is so close to 1.00, we conclude that the difference between the two means is only due to random fluctuations, and the population means are not different.

In case C the situation is different. There the F-ratio equals 20.00, and about the only reason it is that large is that the difference between the two means is due to something more than random fluctuations. Thus there is every reason to believe that the two groups of observations are two samples that do not come from populations with equal means.

The computations necessary for an analysis of variance as it has been performed above are usually summarized in a table like Table 2, which shows the data from case B. The numbers on the first line of the table refer to the group means. The difference between the group means is measured by the sum of squares.

$$n_1(\bar{y}_1 - \bar{y})^2 + n_2(\bar{y}_2 - \bar{y})^2 = 5(4-5)^2 + 5(6-5)^2 = 10.00$$

This sum is sometimes called the between group sum of squares or simply the group sum of squares.

This sum is found from the two terms $\bar{y}_1 - \bar{y}$ and $\bar{y}_2 - \bar{y}$; and if we are told the value of one of these terms, then we automatically know the value of the other term. Another way of saying the same thing is that the between-group sum of squares is based on one degree of freedom when we have two groups. By dividing a sum of squares by its degrees of freedom, we get what is called the corresponding mean square. Here the between-group mean square becomes 10.00/1 = 10.00.

The next entry in Table 2 is the F-ratio, measuring whether or not there is a systematic difference between the group means. The last entry on the first line gives the probability of observing an F-value as large as the one we got or larger, under the assumption that the population means are equal. If the population means are equal, we know that F is approximately equal to 1.00. If the population means are equal, the probability is 0.30 that F is larger than or equal to the observed value 1.21. This probability is quite large, and there is therefore nothing unusual about an F-value of this magnitude. But when the probability is less than 0.05, or 0.01, or whatever significance level we choose, we conclude that the assumption of equal population means must be wrong. In that case the difference between the sample means is significant, and the population means are therefore different. But a small probability only helps us establish that the population means are different; it says nothing about whether the difference is large or small. Usually, only large differences are of any substantive interest.

The numbers on the second line in Table 2 refer to the variation in the observations within the two groups, leading to the common estimate s^2 of the variance within the groups. We have seen above that the numerator for s^2 measures how much the observations differ from their group means. When we add up the deviations of the observations from their respective means, we get the sum of squares

$$\begin{aligned}
&(y_{11}-\bar{y}_1)^2+(y_{12}-\bar{y}_1)^2+\ldots+(y_{15}-\bar{y}_1)^2\\
&+(y_{21}-\bar{y}_2)^2+(y_{22}-\bar{y}_2)^2+\ldots+(y_{25}-\bar{y}_2)^2\\
&=(9-4)^2+(5-4)^2+(3-4)^2+(2-4)^2+(1-4)^2\\
&+(8-6)^2+(8-6)^2+(7-6)^2+(5-6)^2+(2-6)^2=66.00
\end{aligned}$$

Since the sum of squared deviations in each group is based on n–1 = 4 degrees of freedom and there are two groups, this sum of squares has 8 degrees of freedom. The common variance of the dependent variable Y in each of the two groups is obtained by dividing the within-group sum of squares by its degrees of freedom, thereby giving us the within-group

TABLE 2
Analysis of Variance Table for the Data in Case B

Source	*Sum of Squares*	*Degrees of Freedom*	*Mean Square*	*F-ratio*	*Significance*
Between	10.00	1	10.00	1.21	0.30
Within groups	66.00	8	8.25		
Total	76.00	9			

mean square of 66.00/8 = 8.25. Finally, the F-value is obtained by dividing the two mean squares.

The last line in the table, marked total, is obtained by adding the sums of squares and degrees of freedom. These numbers do not have much use in the analysis, even though it is sometimes easier to find the within-group sum of squares as the difference between the total sum of squares and the between-group sum of squares rather than directly, as we did above. The total sum of squares is obtained by subtracting the overall mean from each of the observations, squaring all these differences and adding them. The overall mean in the example is 5, and the total variation of the observations around this mean becomes

$$(y_{11} - \bar{y})^2 + (y_{12} - \bar{y})^2 + \ldots + (y_{15} - \bar{y})^2$$
$$+ (y_{21} - \bar{y})^2 + (y_{22} - \bar{y})^2 + \ldots + (y_{25} - \bar{y})^2$$
$$= (9 - 5)^2 + (5 - 5)^2 + (3 - 5)^2 + (2 - 5)^2 + (1 - 5)^2$$
$$+ (8 - 5)^2 + (8 - 5)^2 + (7 - 5)^2 + (5 - 5)^2 + (2 - 5)^2 = 76.00$$

With 10 observations this sum has 9 degrees of freedom.

Statistical theory. There is a formal mathematical theory that underlies the analysis we have done above; and while we do not present the full theory here, it is important to realize some aspects of that theory. Part of the theory is presented here, and another part is presented at the end of this chapter.

The analysis is founded on the assumption that we can decompose each observed value of the dependent variable into three additive terms; that is, we have to be able to write each observation as a sum of three terms. The decomposition can be written

observation = overall mean
+ deviation of group mean from overall mean
+ deviation of observation from group mean

The overall mean is a constant, common to all the observations. The deviation of a group mean from the overall mean is taken to represent the effect on each observation of belonging to that particular group. In our example, the effect of belonging to the first group is $\bar{y}_1 - \bar{y} = 4 - 5 = -1$, and the effect of belonging to the second group is measured as $\bar{y}_2 - \bar{y} = 6 - 5 = 1$. Thus part of the reason the observed values are what they are is that for each person in the first group a one has been subtracted from the overall mean, and for each person in the second group a one has been added to the overall mean. The –1 is the effect of being in the control group, and the +1 is the effect of being in the experimental group.

Finally, the difference between an observation and the mean for the group is taken to represent the effect of all other variables. These terms are also called the residuals. For the data in case C the residuals are

$$-1, 0, 0, 0, 1 \qquad \text{and} \qquad -1, 0, 0, 0, 1$$

Since each set of residuals is deviations from group means, it is not surprising that they add up to zero in each group. The sum of the squared residuals equals 4.00, and this is the sum we also have called the within sum of squares.

For the 10 observations in case C we get the following decompositions:

$3 = 5 - 1 - 1$	and	$5 = 5 + 1 - 1$
$4 = 5 - 1 + 0$		$6 = 5 + 1 + 0$
$4 = 5 - 1 + 0$		$6 = 5 + 1 + 0$
$4 = 5 - 1 + 0$		$6 = 5 + 1 + 0$
$5 = 5 - 1 + 1$		$7 = 5 + 1 + 1$

The general expression becomes

$$y_{ij} = \bar{y} + (\bar{y}_i - \bar{y}) + (\bar{y}_{ij} - \bar{y}_i)$$

where i equals 1 or 2 and refers to the two groups, while j equals 1, 2, 3, 4, or 5 and refers to the observations within each group.

Use of the F-test requires the residuals to have a normal distribution. The histogram of the 10 residuals for the data in case C is shown in Figure 2. While we do not have a normal distribution in that figure, we do have a unimodal, bell-shaped histogram, satisfactorily indicating that we may well have an underlying normal distribution of the residuals for the entire population.

The residuals will not always display a distribution that follows a normal distribution as closely as the distribution shown in Figure 2. With only moderate departures from normality, experience has shown that the statistical tests discussed here are not affected. Another way of saying the same thing is to say that t-tests and F-tests are robust tests. When the departure from normality is more severe, it may be possible to change the original observations of the dependent variable and thereby make the distribution of the residuals more like a normal distribution.

Such transformations of the observations can be used to make heavily skewed distributions more symmetric. For example, a skewed distribution with many small and few large observations will become more symmetric if we use the square root of each observation in the analysis rather than the original values. Other types of distributions may be more problematic. A u-shaped distribution, for example, cannot be changed into a bell-shaped distribution by any meaningful transformation. In such cases it is still possible to make the computations of all the sums of squares and mean squares, but one must be much more careful in one's interpretation of the significance level used in the test. The distribution of the residuals is discussed further in Chapter 3 in the section on the residual variable.

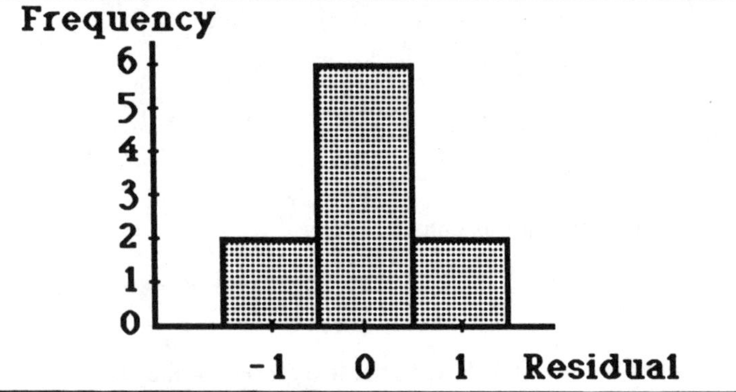

Figure 2: Histogram of Residuals for Data in Case C

There is a major complication with what we have done so far. The differences $\bar{y}_1 - \bar{y}$ and $\bar{y}_2 - \bar{y}$ are only estimates of the true effects on the dependent variable of belonging to the control and experimental groups. Similarly, the residuals are only estimates of the effects of all other variables. Finally, $\bar{y}$ is only an estimate of the overall level of the dependent variable.

The formal model, which specifies an additive model involving the true effects, can be written

$$y_{ij} = \mu + \alpha_i + \epsilon_{ij}$$

As before, i refers to the group, and j refers to the observation within the group. In this model μ is a constant and refers to the overall level of the dependent variable; α_1 and α_2 represent the effect on an observation of being in groups 1 and 2, respectively. The ϵ_{ij} is the effect on the j-th observation in the i-th group of all other variables, and in our example we have 10 such terms: $\epsilon_{11}, \epsilon_{12}, \epsilon_{13}, \epsilon_{14}, \epsilon_{15}, \epsilon_{21}, \epsilon_{22}, \epsilon_{23}, \epsilon_{24}$ and ϵ_{25}. These 10 residual terms are assumed to come from a normal distribution with mean zero and variance σ^2.

Instead of knowing μ, the 2 α's, and the 10 ϵ's, we have 10 observations (the y's) located in two groups. The observations are used to find estimates of the true, unknown effects designated by Greek letters. We can never verify whether the true effects are additive and whether the true residuals have a normal distribution. But we can look at the distribution of the estimated residuals and hope that if this distribution looks fairly normal, then the distribution of the true residuals is not too far from normal. Thus one should always find the estimated residuals and examine their distribution for normality.

More Than Two Groups

Analysis of variance. We can now turn to the case in which the independent variable has more than two categories. If the independent variable is political affiliation, we may have Democrat, Republican, independent, other parties, and apolitical as the categories. With religious affiliation we may have Catholic, Jew, Protestant, other, and none. Each category determines a group of observations of the dependent variable, and in the general case we have k groups rather than two.

The economy, of course, is a book with many chapters, and economic issues come in many versions. Most analyses of economic voting zero in on such indicators as unemployment, inflation, the federal deficit, and foreign trade. Do the mass media affect the salience of each of those four economic issues equally? To answer this question we expand the experimental condition to include four treatments. The control group again will be shown an economy-less newscast, treatment group A will be shown the same newscast plus a story on unemployment; group B one on inflation instead; group C one on the deficit; and group D one on foreign trade. Five subjects will be randomly assigned to each of the five conditions and afterwards asked to fill out a questionnaire in which they are querried, among other things, about the importance of the state of the economy.

The dependent variable is the same as earlier, an evaluation of the importance of the economy on a ten-point scale. Our concern is with whether the five groups differ on this variable, where the groups are thought to be different if their means are different. If the five sample means are not all equal, then we have a relationship between type of newscast and people's view of the economy in the sample. Often, we are more interested in whether the means are equal or not in the corresponding five populations than whether simply the sample means differ.

As before, we have to investigate whether the differences in the sample means are random variations that occurred just by chance or whether there are systematic differences between the means. We have to go through the same type of reasoning we did with two groups and compare the variation in the means with how much the observations vary within each of the groups. The five group means are shown in Table 3, and the observations themselves are shown as points in the scatterplot in Figure 3.

TABLE 3

Evaluation of Economy: Observations and Means by Groups

Group	*Observations*	*Mean*
A Unemployment story	6 6 6 8 9	7.0
B Inflation story	7 8 8 8 9	8.0
C Deficit story	4 4 5 6 6	5.0
D Foreign trade story	5 5 6 6 8	6.0
E No economic story	3 4 4 4 5	4.0
	Overall mean	6.0

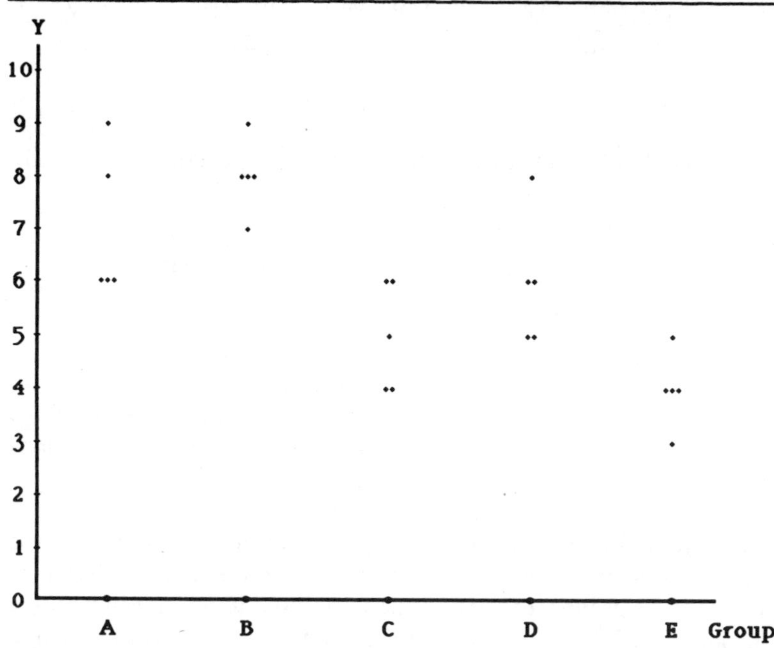

Figure 3: Scatterplot of Data in Table 3

For the sake of simplicity and without any loss of generality, we restrict ourselves in this example to a small number of cases in each group. The numerical values are hypothetical and constructed to be easy to work with. In this example all groups have the same number of observations; but for an analysis of variance as it is done here, it makes little or no difference whether the numbers of observations are the same or not.

The analysis proceeds as follows. The 25 observations have different values, and one way to measure how different they are is to subtract the overall mean $\bar{y} = 6.0$ from each observation, square all the differences, and add the squares. This gives the total sum of squares, TSS, where

$$
\begin{aligned}
\text{TSS} &= \Sigma(y_{ij} - \bar{y})^2 \\
&= (6-6.0)^2 + (6-6.0)^2 + (6-6.0)^2 + (8-6.0)^2 + (9-6.0)^2 \\
&\quad + (7-6.0)^2 + (7-6.0)^2 + (7-6.0)^2 + (8-6.0)^2 + (9-6.0)^2 \\
&\quad + (4-6.0)^2 + (4-6.0)^2 + (5-6.0)^2 + (6-6.0)^2 + (6-6.0)^2
\end{aligned}
$$

$$+ (5 - 6.0)^2 + (5 - 6.0)^2 + (6 - 6.0)^2 + (6 - 6.0)^2 + (8 - 6.0)^2$$
$$+ (3 - 6.0)^2 + (4 - 6.0)^2 + (4 - 6.0)^2 + (4 - 6.0)^2 + (5 - 6.0)^2$$
$$= 72.0$$

There is a simpler and more accurate way to compute this sum, namely

$$\text{TSS} = \Sigma y_{ij}^2 - (\Sigma y_{ij})^2/n$$
$$= (6^2 + 6^2 + \ldots + 5^2) - (6 + 6 + \ldots + 5)^2/25$$
$$= 972 - 150^2/25 = 72.0$$

With this formula it is not necessary to subtract the mean from every term before squaring. Instead, the formula requires the sum of the squared observations minus the squared sum of the observations themselves divided by the total number of observations.

There is another way to think about this total sum of squares. A particular observed value of the economic importance variable has the value it does for two reasons. One reason is that the value is affected by which of the groups the person belongs to, that is, which newscast the person viewed. The other reason is that the person's value is affected by a whole set of other variables, for example, age, education, occupation, etc. The net effect of all these variables is what we call the residual variable. Thus a particular observation is determined by the group and the residual variable. Suppose, for a moment, that neither one of these two had any effect. Then every person would have the same, identical value of the economic importance variable. There would be nothing affecting this variable; and no matter how different people are on other variables, they would have the same value on the economic importance variable.

The best estimate of this common value would be the overall mean 6.0. The degree to which each of the observed values is different from 6.0 then becomes a measure of the combined effect of the group variable and the residual variable. One way to measure how large this effect is to find how different each observation is from 6.0. Next, by squaring each difference and adding the squares, we get a measurement of how large the combined effect is of the group variable and the residual variable. Thus, in this example the combined effect of the type of newscast and the residual variable equals 72.0. An obvious next step is to try to break this combined effect into separate effects for the type of newscast and the residual variable, and that is done below.

The degrees of freedom for this total sum of squares becomes 24. In the general case the degrees of freedom for the total sum of squares equal the total number of observations minus one. There are 25 terms in the total sum of squares here, and having 24 degrees of freedom means we need to know only 24 of the values in order to find all 25. If we know that the first 24 values are

$$0.0\ 0.0\ 0.0\ 2.0\ 3.0\ \ldots\ -2.0\ -2.0$$

then we know from these values that the twenty-fifth value has to equal −1.0. This is because the sum of all 25 values equals zero, and the sum of the first 24 equals 1.0. Thus the last value has to equal −1.0. The reason why the numbers add to zero is that they are deviations from their overall mean.

Because the last value was "hidden" in the previous 24, that value does not contain any new information beyond what we already knew from the first 24 values. Therefore, even though the total sum of squares TSS is computed from a sum of 25 squared numbers, the total information in these numbers is contained in the first 24, and we express this by saying that TSS has 24 degrees of freedom.

The extent to which the means in the groups are different is measured by the between-group sum of squares, BSS. This sum is found by taking the difference between each group mean $\bar{y}_i$ and the overall mean $\bar{y}$, squaring each difference, multiplying the square by the number of observations in the group n_i, and adding these products. This is the same computation we made with two groups. Here we get

$$\begin{aligned} \text{BSS} &= \Sigma n_i(\bar{y}_i - \bar{y})^2 \\ &= 5(7.0-6.0)^2 + 5(8.0-6.0)^2 + 5(5.0-6.0)^2 \\ &+ 5(6.0-6.0)^2 + 5(4.0-6.0)^2 \\ &= 50.0 \end{aligned}$$

This sum has 4 degrees of freedom. There are 5 terms in the sum, but we can find the fifth difference if we know the first 4. In the general case the number of degrees of freedom for the between group sum of squares equals one less than the number of groups.

The between group sum of squares, or simply the group sum of squares, measures how large the effect is of the group variable. In this example 50.0 measures the effect of the different newscasts on the evaluation-of-the-economy variable. Suppose for a moment that type of newscast had no effect. Then the mean of the dependent variable would be the same in all the groups, and they would all equal the overall mean 6.0. But these means are not equal, since type of newscast does have an effect on these individuals. One way to measure that effect for each person is to find the difference between the mean of the group the person belongs to and the overall mean. For exmple, the effect of being in the control groups becomes $\overline{y}_5 - \overline{y} = 4.0 - 6.0 = -2.0$ for each person in that group, and similarly for the people in the other groups. The overall magnitude of these effects can be found by squaring this difference for each person and adding up the squares. Since each person in the fifth group has the effect $(-2.0)^2$, we can multiply this square by five rather than adding it up five times. Doing this for all 25 observation gives a combined effect of 50.0 for the type of newscast.

In addition to being in different groups, the observations are different because people are affected by the residual variable in different ways. Now we need to measure the effect of the residual variable. So far, we have found that the combined effect of type of newscast and the residual variable equals 72.0. Also, the effect of type of newscast alone equals 50.0. This leads us to assigning the difference between the two sums of squares, 72.0 – 50.0 = 22.0, as the effect of the residual variable. Since there are 24 degrees of freedom for the total sum of squares and 4 degrees of freedom for the sum of squares for type of newscast, 20 degrees of freedom are for the residual sum of squares.

There is another way of thinking about the effect of the residual variable. Suppose the residual variable had no effect. Then all the observations in the control group would be the same, since the only effect on those people is that they are in the control group. Similarly for the other groups, within each group the observed values of the dependent variable would be the same. The best estimate of the common value in each group would be the observed mean in that group. In the control group all the observations would be 4.0, in group A they would be 7.0, and so on. But these are not the values we observed, because the residual variable does have an effect. The difference between an observed value and the group mean therefore has to be the effect of the residual variable for that person. For each person we can find the effect of the residual variable; and if we square these effects and add the squares, we find the overall effect of the residual variable.

All 25 residuals are shown in Table 4. The table also shows the sum of squared residuals in each group and the overall residual sum of squares, which is equal to 22.0. This is the same sum we found above as the

TABLE 4
Residuals Arranged by Group, Their Sum of Squares and Degrees of Freedom

Group	*Residuals*					*Sum of Squares*	*Degrees of Freedom*
A	−1.0	−1.0	−1.0	1.0	2.0	8.0	4
B	−1.0	0.0	0.0	0.0	1.0	2.0	4
C	−1.0	−1.0	0.0	1.0	1.0	4.0	4
D	−1.0	−1.0	0.0	0.0	2.0	6.0	4
E	−1.0	0.0	0.0	0.0	1.0	2.0	4
				Residual sum of squares		22.0	20

difference between the total sum of squares and the sum of squares for the type of newscast.

As for degrees of freedom, the residuals add to zero in each group. Thus, if there are n_i observations in the i-th group, the sum of squared residuals in that group have $n_i - 1$ degrees of freedom. In our case, with 5 observations in each group, there are 4 degrees of freedom in each group. Added across all the group, we get 20 degrees of freedom for the residual sum of squares. In the general case the degrees of freedom for the residual sum of squares equal the total number of observations minus the number of groups.

The sums of squares and degrees of freedom we have found are displayed in an analysis of variance table in Table 5. Also, in that table the group and residual sums of squares are divided by their degrees of freedom to get the corresponding mean squares. The group mean square equals 12.5, and the residual mean square equals 1.1. The residual mean square is another name for the estimate of the common variance of the residuals. Since the variance equals 1.1, the standard deviation of the residuals equals the square root, or 1.05. One way to interpret this standard deviation is to say that the average deviation of the observations from their group means, that is, the average residual, equals 1.05. Looking at the magnitudes of the 25 residuals in Table 4, that seems like a reasonable average.

As before, we are usually not as interested in whether the observed sample group means are different as we are in the question of whether the means in the populations from which the samples came are different. The null hypothesis states that the population means are equal, and the hypothesis is tested by the F-ratio. The F is found as the ratio of the

TABLE 5
Analysis of Variance Table for the Data in Figure 3

Source	*Sum of Squares*	*Degrees of Freedom*	*Mean Square*	*F-ratio*	*Significance*
Groups	50.0	4	12.5	11.36	0.00006
Residual	22.0	20	1.1		
Total	72.0	24			
$E^2 = 0.65$					

group mean square to the residual mean square, and in the example F = 12.5/1.1 = 11.36. Again, a value around 1.00 tells us that the differences in the group means is only a random variation from sample to sample. When the F-ratio is a good deal larger than 1.00, we can conclude that the variation in the group means is more than what could have been expected by chance alone, and the population means are therefore different.

From a table of the F distribution we find that with 4 and 20 degrees of freedom, we need a value of F larger than 2.87 in order to reject the null hypothesis with a 5% significance level. With a smaller, 1% significance level, F has to be larger than 4.43. Since our observed value of F is larger than either of these cutoffs, the null hypothesis of equal population means is rejected. Indeed it is possible to find that if the population means are really equal, the probability of observing F equal to or larger than our value 11.36 is only 0.00006. Since this probability is so small, we have strong evidence for the notion that the population means are different.

This immediately raises the next question: How different are the population means? To get some idea of the magnitudes of the differences, we take the sample means as estimates of the corresponding population means. That way, the differences between the sample means become estimates of the differences between the population means. One way to study these differences in more detail is to put confidence intervals around the sample means and examine the evidence in these intervals. Such multiple comparisons of the sample means are commonly discussed in more extensive presentations of analysis of variance.

The residuals should be examined for any unusual patterns like single extreme values and the extent to which they follow a normal distribution. A histogram of the 25 residuals is drawn in Figure 4, and it shows a variable with a mean of zero and a unimodal distribution. In this case

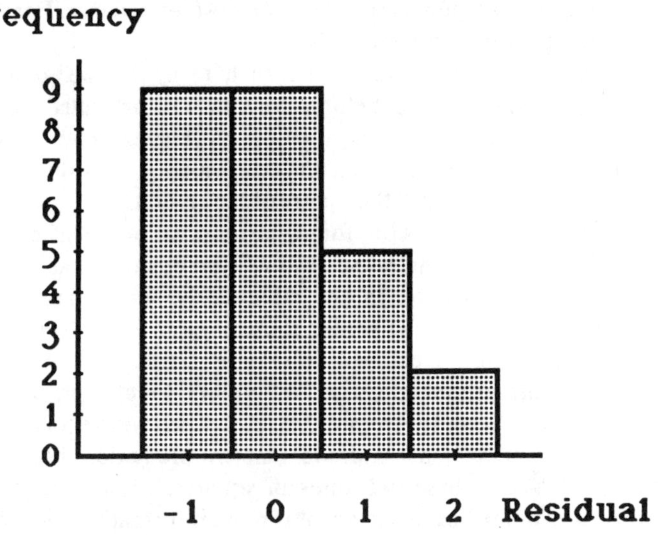

Figure 4: Histogram of Residuals in Table 4

the distribution is somewhat skewed. The distribution of the residuals is discussed further in Chapter 3 in the section on the residual variable.

The correlation ratio. The effect of the newscast variable on the economic variable can be measured in two different ways. The effect of a particular type of newscast on the economic variable can be measured as the difference between the mean for that newscast and the overall mean. The overall effect of all the newscasts, moreover, can be measured by the group (between) sum of squares. But we do not have yet any measure of the relationship between the explanatory and the dependent variable that resembles a correlation coefficient, giving the strength of the relationship between the two variables.

One way to get such a measure is as follows. If we had all the values of Y and were asked to estimate the value for a particular individual, one possible estimate would be the overall mean $\overline{y}$. This is a value located in the middle of the observations; and in the absence of any information about the individual, it seems reasonable to choose such a central value as our estimate. If the true value equals y_{ij}, then the error we make in the estimation becomes the difference $y_{ij} - \overline{y}$. Suppose the "penalty" we have to suffer for this error is the square of the error, that is $(y_{ij} - \overline{y})^2$. If we did this for all the respondents and used the mean as an estimate each time, then the total "penalty" would be the sum of all the squared errors, $\Sigma(y_{ij}$

$-\ y)^2$. This is the total sum of squares in analysis of variance. For the data in our example this number equals 72.0.

Next, change the guessing game in such a way that we are now told what group an observation belongs to. Our best predicted value of Y would then be the mean in that group, $\overline{y}_{i\cdot}$. The error we now make becomes the difference between the true value y_{ij} and this predicted value. The "penalty" is still the square of the error, that is, $(y_{ij} - \overline{y}_i)^2$. The overall "penalty" for doing this for all the observations then becomes the sum of these squares. This is the residual sum of squares as we know it from analysis of variance. In our example the sum equals 22.0, as a measure of how well we can predict the economic scores from knowing which of the groups the people belong to.

Knowing the group improves our ability to predict. There is a reduction in the "penalty" from 72.0 to 22.0 when we are told about the group membership. The improvement in prediction becomes the difference between these two sums of squares, or 50.0. In itself this number does not tell us much, and it is more informative if we compute the relative improvement,

$$E^2 = (72.0 - 22.0)/72.0 = (TSS - RSS)/TSS$$
$$= 0.69$$

Thus there is a 69% improvement in our ability to predict the values of the dependent variable when we know what group an observation belongs to. This quantity is called the correlation ratio and is sometimes denoted as eta squared. It is the ratio of the between group sum of squares to the total sum of squares. It tells us how much of the variation in the dependent variable is explained by the explanatory variable, in the sense of how much our prediction is improved by knowing the group when the "penalty" is measured by the square of the prediction error.

The same quantity is also computed in regression analysis and is there denoted R^2, where R is the multiple correlation coefficient.

Formal model. It is now possible to return in somewhat greater detail to the formal model for what is called a fixed effect one-way analysis of variance. The model specifies that an observed value of the dependent variable Y can be written as a sum of three components. That is, we believe that the substantive process that generated the observed data can be expressed in the equation

Observation

= constant

+ effect of being in a particular group
(effect of the independent variable X)

+ residual

This is a model of the real world, and it can be translated into mathematical symbols. For the j-th observation in the i-th group, we can write the model in the equation

$$y_{ij} = \mu + \alpha_i + \epsilon_{ij}$$

where μ is the constant, α_i is the effect of being in group i, and ϵ_{ij} is the effect of the residual variable, which is the net effect of all other variables, including measurement errors.

As usual with a statistical model of this kind, we want to find estimates of the parameters and thereby investigate the effect of the explanatory variable on the dependent variable, and we want to see how well the data fit the model.

First, we have to realize that the equation above is a very compact way of expressing this model. There is an equation like this for every observation, and in our example we have the following 25 equations:

$$\begin{array}{llllll}
y_{11} = \mu & + \alpha_1 & & & & + \epsilon_{11} \\
\ \ . \quad . \quad . & & & & \text{(group 1)} & \ \ . \\
\ \ . \quad . \quad . & & & & & \ \ . \\
y_{15} = \mu & + \alpha_1 & & & & + \epsilon_{15} \\
y_{21} = \mu & & + \alpha_2 & & & + \epsilon_{21} \\
\ \ . \quad . \quad . & & & & \text{(group 2)} & \ \ . \\
\ \ . \quad . \quad . & & & & & \ \ . \\
y_{25} = \mu & & + \alpha_2 & & & + \epsilon_{25} \\
y_{31} = \mu & & & + \alpha_3 & & + \epsilon_{31} \\
\ \ . \quad . \quad . & & & & \text{(group 3)} & \ \ . \\
\ \ . \quad . \quad . & & & & & \ \ . \\
y_{35} = \mu & & & + \alpha_3 & & + \epsilon_{35} \\
y_{41} = \mu & & & & + \alpha_4 & + \epsilon_{41} \\
\ \ . \quad . \quad . & & & & \text{(group 4)} & \ \ . \\
\ \ . \quad . \quad . & & & & & \ \ .
\end{array}$$

$$
\begin{array}{llll}
y_{45} = \mu & + \alpha_4 & + \epsilon_{45} & \\
y_{51} = \mu & & + \alpha_5 & + \epsilon_{51} \\
\cdot \quad \cdot \quad \cdot & & \text{(group 5)} & \cdot \\
\cdot \quad \cdot \quad \cdot & & & \cdot \\
y_{55} = \mu & & + \alpha_5 & + \epsilon_{55} \\
25 \text{ df} = 1 \text{ df} & + 4 \text{ df} & & + 20 \text{ df}
\end{array}
$$

There are 25 terms on the left side of these equations, and they have a total of 25 degrees of freedom since there are no restrictions on these numbers. On the right side there is one μ, which then has one degree of freedom. There are five α's; but their sum equals zero, and they therefore have four degrees of freedom. There are 25 ϵ's; but since on the average their mean is zero in every group, they have only 20 degrees of freedom. The μ and the α's are the parameters of the model, and the ϵ's measure how well the model fits. Figure 5 gives a graphic representation of the model showing how the observed value of Y is decomposed into the three parts.

The first task is to find numerical estimates of the parameters in the model. We have 25 equations in the example above, and only the Y values are known. But the equations cannot be solved directly for the unknowns. Instead, we use the method of least squares to find estimated numerical values for the unknown. This method uses as estimates the values of the parameters that make the sum of the squared residuals

$$\Sigma \epsilon_{ij}^2 = \Sigma (y_{ij} - \mu - \alpha_i)^2$$

as small as possible. The estimates are denoted by Greek letters with a "^" above. The smallest sum of squares is obtained when

$$
\begin{array}{ll}
\hat{\mu} = \bar{y} & \text{overall mean} \\
\hat{\alpha}_i = \bar{y}_i - \bar{y} & \text{deviation of group mean from overall mean}
\end{array}
$$

For our example we get the estimates

$$
\begin{array}{ll}
\hat{\mu} = \bar{y} = 6.0 & \hat{\alpha}_1 = \bar{y}_1 - \bar{y} = 7.0 - 6.0 = 1.0 \\
& \hat{\alpha}_2 = \bar{y}_2 - \bar{y} = 8.0 - 6.0 = 2.0 \\
& \hat{\alpha}_3 = \bar{y}_3 - \bar{y} = 5.0 - 6.0 = -1.0 \\
& \hat{\alpha}_4 = \bar{y}_4 - \bar{y} = 6.0 - 6.0 = 0.0 \\
& \hat{\alpha}_5 = \bar{y}_5 - \bar{y} = 4.0 - 6.0 = -2.0
\end{array}
$$

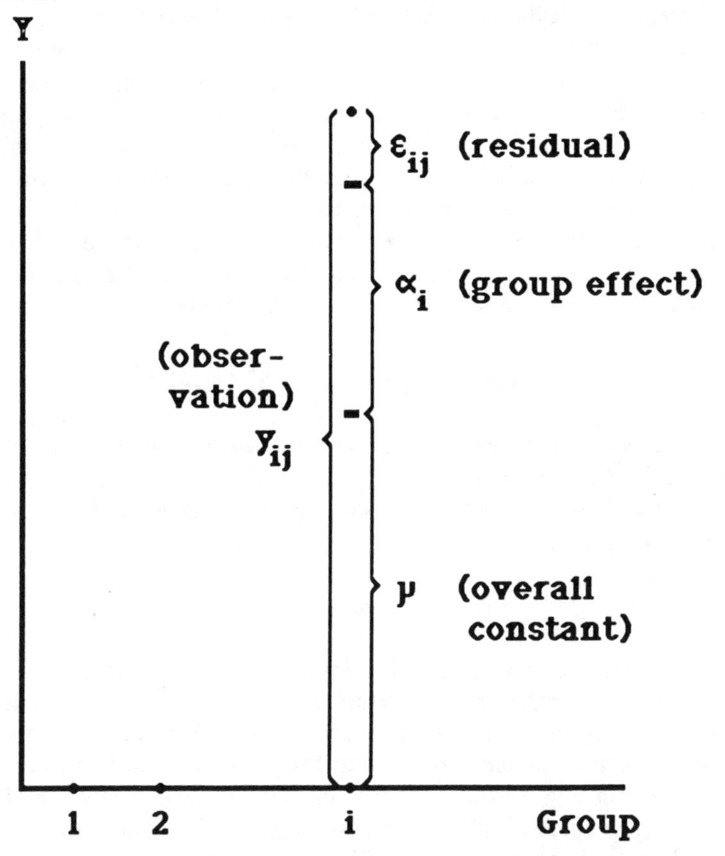

Figure 5: Decomposition of j-th Observation i-th Group into Three Components

With these estimated parameters the estimated residuals are found from the expression

$$\hat{e}_{ij} = y_{ij} - \bar{y}_i$$

The estimated residuals are listed above in Table 4. The sum of the squared residuals equals 22.0, and there is no way we can find other estimates of the parameters that will produce a smaller sum of squared residuals.

The statistical null hypothesis that the population group means are equal is equivalent to the statement that the α's are equal to zero, since they measure the differences between the groups. This hypothesis can be tested using the F-ratio, when the residuals have a normal distribution.

Let us look more closely at why the F-ratio can be used to test this null hypothesis. F is a fraction in which the numerator is the group (between) mean square, and the denominator is the residual (within) mean square. It is possible to show that the denominator is an estimate of the variance of the residuals, σ^2. In the more technical analysis of variance literature this is often expressed by saying that the expected value of the residual mean square equals σ^2. The numerator is more complicated, but it can be shown that it is an estimate of the quantity

$$\sigma^2 + (n_1\alpha_1^2 + n_2\alpha_2^2 + n_3\alpha_3^2 + n_4\alpha_4^2 + n_5\alpha_5^2)/4$$

This expression is known as the expected between group mean square. By dividing the expression for the numerator by the expression for the denominator of F, we get the ratio of the two expected mean squares. This ratio becomes

$$1.00 + (5\alpha_1^2 + 5\alpha_2^2 + 5\alpha_3^2 + 5\alpha_4^2 + 5\alpha_5^2)/4\sigma^2$$

Now there are two possibilities. Either the null hypothesis is true, which means that the α's are all equal to zero, or the null hypothesis is false and the α's are not all equal to zero. If the null hypothesis is true, then the expression above is equal to 1.00. On the other hand, if it is false, then the expression is larger than 1.00. Our observed value of F equals 9.19, which is either a bad estimate of 1.00 or an estimate of something larger than 1.00. Since F is as large as it is, we prefer to think that it is an estimate of something larger than 1.00, which is only possible if at least some of the alphas are different from zero. Thus we conclude that the null hypothesis is false.

Even when the null hypothesis is true, we do not get F-values that are exactly equal to 1.00. Our observed mean squares are only estimates, and they vary from sample to sample. This raises the question of what the cutoff values are for F such that the null hypothesis is not rejected for smaller observed values of F and rejected for values larger than the cutoff. The answers are found in the F-table, which provide us with the proper cutoff values.

Because any F is characterized by a pair of degrees of freedom, the number of groups minus one and the number of observations minus the number of groups, the F-tables are not as detailed as other tables. There is usually a separate table giving F-values for a 5% significance and another table for a 1% significance. The meaning of an entry in, say, the 5% table is that the probability equals only 0.05 of observing an F that large or larger under the condition that the null hypothesis is really true. Thus, when a null hypothesis is actually true, we only get an observed value of F larger than the value in the table 5% of the time across repeated samples. When a null hypothesis is actually false, we get large F-values much more often. Thus, when we observe a large value of F, we conclude that the null hypothesis must be false, even though it is also possible we might have gotten one of those unusual samples with a large F from populations where the group means are equal.

Computing and numerical results. Unless we have a small number of observations and few groups, the computations necessary for a one-way analysis of variance are better done on a computer. All standard statistical program packages have a program for such an analysis. The user only has to specify a few commands on how the data are organized in terms of the independent and the dependent variable and which output is wanted. One commonly used program package in the social sciences is SPSS-X, and it contains two relevant programs called ONEWAY and ANOVA. Analysis of variance programs are also found in the MINITAB package, which is particularly easy to use, and other possible packages are SAS, BMDP, and OSIRIS. Most statistical packages for microcomputers also have facilities for analysis of variance. This software is often much easier to use, even though the programs usually do not include as many options.

3. TWO-WAY ANALYSIS OF VARIANCE, ALL CATEGORIES

Unrelated Explanatory Variables

Introducing one more variable. The economy, like other things, may affect people differently depending on whether the news is good or bad. It has been argued that voters take prosperity for granted and feel no need to reward the incumbent government for what they consider the normal state of the economy. On the other hand, recessions or spurts of inflation lead to "throw the rascals out" reactions, with a negative electoral response being the result (Bloom and Price, 1975; Kernell, 1977; Lanoue, 1986). The assumption is that people only pay attention to the economy as an issue when things go bad. This question can be studied using an experiment with two explanatory variables, also known as factors.

TABLE 6
Allocations of Groups to Factors

Valence of Coverage	Economic Issue Covered in Newscast	
	Unemployment	Inflation
Positive	Group H	Group I
Negative	Group J	Group K

The first variable is the same as the one we used in Chapter 2: economic issues in the newscast. Let us focus on the two economic issues that have most preoccupied the public as well as governments in recent years: unemployment and inflation. Thus, in one type of newscast there is a story on unemployment and in the other type there is a story on inflation. The second, new variable refers to whether the economic news is good or bad: the valence of the coverage, in other words. This variable also has two categories; in one type of newscast the news is positive and in the other the news is negative.

These two variables together define four different experimental conditions, as shown in Table 6. Each condition is used for a separate sample of respondents. All four groups of respondents are shown essentially the same newscast, except for the following modifications. The newscast shown to group H includes a story with good news on unemployment, and the newscast for group I contains a story with good news on inflation. Similarly, the newscast for group J contains a story with bad news about unemployment, and group K gets a story with bad news about inflation. This covers all possible combinations of the two factors, and this plan is an example of what is known as a factorial design.

A total of 12 subjects are randomly allocated to the various experimental conditions in such a way that the same number of subjects sees a particular newscast. That way 3 subjects see each type of newscast. It is an important part of the design of this experiment that the number of subjects is the same for various conditions. We return to this issue below in the section on relationship between explanatory variables.

After watching their respective newscasts, the subjects are asked about the importance of the economy as an issue, using the same ten-point scale as before. The observed values of this dependent variable are shown in Table 7, together with the means in each of the cells in the

TABLE 7
Rating Scores and Means of the Importance of the Economy, by Issue and Valence

Valence of Coverage	Economic Issue Covered in Newscast: Unemployment		Inflation		Mean
Positive	1 2 3	(2.0)	5 6 7	(6.0)	4.0
Negative	7 8 9	(8.0)	7 7 10	(8.0)	8.0
Mean	5.0		7.0		6.0

table and the means for the rows and columns. By reading across the rows of this table, we can sense the differences in the rating of the economy between positive and negative stories. Similarly, focusing on the columns, we get an impression of the differences between unemployment and inflation stories.

There are obvious differences between the means in the rows as well as in the columns. But without further computations, based on an underlying model, we cannot tell whether the differences are due to random variations or whether ratings of the economy are actually affected by the two explanatory variables. In order to develop the necessary formulas for a two-way analysis of variance, we need symbols for the observations and the various means. The symbols are shown in Table 8. Three subscripts are needed to show where an observation is located. The first subscript (i) refers to the row number, the second subscript (j) refers to the column number, and the third (k) counts the observations within a given cell. Since all the observations in the first row have 1 as the first subscript, the mean for those observations also has 1 as the first subscript; and similarly for the second row and the two columns.

Types of effects. Disregarding the columns in Table 7 for a moment, we find that the 6 subjects who saw the positive stories have a mean of 4.0, and those who saw the negative stories have a mean of 8.0. Since these means are different, the valence variable has an effect. A one-way analysis of variance can be used to see if this effect is statistically significant. The valence sum of squares becomes 48.0, and the residual sum of squares becomes 36.0. This results in a significant F of 13.33 on 1 and 10 degrees of freedom, and we conclude valence has an effect.

Similarly, disregarding the rows in Table 7, we see from the columns that the 6 subjects who saw the employment stories have a mean of 5.0,

TABLE 8
Rating Scores and Means of the Importance of the Economy, by Issue and Valence, in Symbols

Valence of Coverage	Economic Issue Covered in Newscast: Unemployment	Inflation	Mean
Postive	y_{111} y_{112} y_{113} ($\bar{y}_{11}$)	y_{121} y_{122} y_{123} ($\bar{y}_{12}$)	$\bar{y}_{1.}$
Negative	y_{211} y_{212} y_{213} ($\bar{y}_{21}$)	y_{221} y_{222} y_{223} ($\bar{y}_{22}$)	$\bar{y}_{2.}$
Mean	$\bar{y}_{.1}$	$\bar{y}_{.2}$	$\bar{y}$

and the 6 subjects who saw the inflation stories have a mean of 7.0. Since the means are different, the issue variable may have a statistically significant effect. We can do a one-way analysis of variance to see if this effect is statistically significant. This analysis results in an issue sum of squares of 12.0 and a residual sum of squares of 72.0. These sum of squares give a nonsignificant F of 1.67 on 1 and 10 degrees of freedom, and we conclude the issue does not have an effect.

In addition to these two effects there is a possible third effect on the dependent variable called the interaction effect. It may be that issue and valence act together in such a way as to produce an effect over and beyond the separate effect of each of the two variables. Such an effect is present in the data in Table 7, and we see this effect in the four cell means.

For those who saw the positive stories, the difference in the means for the inflation story and the unemployment story is 6.0 – 2.0 = 4.0. One way to look at this difference is to say that it measures the effect of issue. But if we look at the same difference for those who saw the negative stories, we find a difference of 8.0 – 8.0 = 0.0. Thus the effect of the issue variable is 4.0 for the positive stories and 0.0 for the negative stories. The effect of the same variable is different for the two categories of the other variable. There is no unique effect of the issue variable, and the only reason the means are what they are must be that there is something else going on as well with these variables.

Similarly, if we look at the table the other way, we find that for the unemployment stories, the difference between the means for the negative and the positive stories is 8.0 – 2.0 = 6.0, while the difference for the inflation stories is 8.0 – 6.0 = 2.0. Thus there is not the same effect in the two columns. This tells us that the four cell means cannot be fully explained by the effects of the issue plus valence. We continue the discussion of the interaction effect below.

Combined effect of both variables. The question now is whether we can do better than the two separate one-way analyses studying the effects of valence and issue. The answer is that we should not analyze the effects of the variables separately but together. This is achieved in a two-way analysis of variance.

The manipulations of a two-way analysis of variance can be broken into several stages. As a first step we can measure the total combined effect of the two explanatory variables. This is done by stringing out the data according to a combined variable, in our case a combined valence-issue variable, and measuring the effect of this combined variable using the methods from one-way analysis of variance. For our example the combined variable leads to four groups of observations, and the data and the results are shown in Table 9.

The analysis of variance table shows that the sum of squares for valence and issue together equals 72, and the residual sum of squares equals 12. Dividing the sums of squares by their degrees of freedom gives the two means squares, and their ratio gives F = 16.00 on 3 and 8 degrees of freedom. This value of F is significant at the 0.009 level; that is, the probability of getting an F-value this large or larger when the two variables have no effect equals as little as 0.009. One noticeable feature of this analysis is that the residual sum of square equals only 12.0, which is much smaller than the residual sums of squares we obtained for the two separate analyses.

In the general case with two explanatory variables A and B, where A has r categories and B has c categories, the number of categories for the combined A and B variable equals rc. Let n_{ij} denote the number of observations in the cell defined by the i-th category of A and the j-th category of B. The sum of squares for the combined A and B variable is then found according to the expression

$$\text{SS A and B} = \Sigma n_{ij}(\bar{y}_{ij} - \bar{y})^2$$

where the summation is across all cells. The total sum of squares is found, as before, by subtracting the overall mean from each observation, squaring these differences, and adding them all. Finally, the residual sum of squares is found as the difference between the total sum of squares and the sum of squares due to the combined A and B variable.

TABLE 9
Rating of Economy for Issue and Valence Analyzed as a One-Way Analysis of Variance

	Unemployment Positive	Inflation Positive	Unemployment Negative	Inflation Negative
	1	5	7	7
	2	6	8	7
	3	7	9	10
Mean	2	6	8	8
			Overall mean $\bar{y} = 6$	

Source	*Sum of Squares*	*Degrees of Freedom*	*Mean Square*	*F-ratio*	*Significance*
Between groups	72	3	24.00	16.00	0.001
Within groups	12	8	1.50		
Total	84	11			

Three separate effects. The next step consists of decomposing the sum of squares for the combined variable into separate parts. One of these is the effect of the valence variable, and another is the effect of the issue variable.

To find the effect of the valence variable, we disregard the columns in Table 7 and do a one-way analysis of the rows. The two row means equal 4.0 and 8.0, and there are 6 observations in each row. With that, the sum of squares for the valence variable becomes

$$6(4.0 - 6.0)^2 + 6(8.0 - 6.0)^2 = 48.00$$

on 1 degree of freedom. This is the same sum of squares reported for the first separate analysis.

Similarly, to find the effect of the issue variable we disregard the rows in Table 7 and do a one-way analysis of variance for the columns. There are 6 observations in each column, and the two column means are 5.0 and 7.0. The overall mean equals 6.0. Thus the sum of squares for the issue variable becomes

$$6(5.0 - 6.0)^2 + 6(7.0 - 6.0)^2 = 12.00$$

on 1 degree of freedom. This is the same sum of squares as we found from the second separate analysis above.

The combined variable has a sum of squares equal to 72.00 on 3 degrees of freedom. Subtracting from that sum the separate sums of square for valence and issue leaves an amount equal to:

$$72.00 - 12.00 - 48.00 = 12.00$$

on 3 – 1 – 1 = 1 degree of freedom. This is a sum of squares which measures the effect of valence and issue over and beyond their two separate effects, and this is known as the interaction effect. Valence and issue act together to produce an effect on people's view of the economy over and beyond their separate effects.

In the general case with r rows and c columns in the data table, the sum of squares for the combined A and B variable can also be decomposed into three components. The sum of squares for the A variable is found from the expression

$$SSA = \Sigma n_{i\cdot}(\overline{y}_{i\cdot} - \overline{y})^2 \qquad r - 1 \text{ df}$$

where the summation is across all r categories of the A variable. Similarly, the sum of squares for the B variable is found from the expression

$$SSB = \Sigma n_{\cdot j}(\overline{y}_{\cdot j} - \overline{y})^2 \qquad c - 1 \text{ df}$$

where the summation is across all c categories of the B variable. The sum of squares for the AB interaction variable can be found by subtracting the sums of squares for A and B from the sum of squares for the combined A and B variable. That is,

$$\text{SSInteraction} = \text{SS A and B} - SSA - SSB$$

on (rc – 1) – (r – 1) – (c – 1) = (4 – 1) (c – 1) degrees of freedom. In our example r = c = 2, and the degrees of freedom for the sum of squares for the interaction equals 1.

Relationship between the explanatory variables. In order to examine the effects of the two categorical, explanatory variables on the metric, dependent variable, we need to turn to another aspect of two-way analysis of variance. This has to do with the relationship between the two explanatory variables themselves, here the relationship between economic issue (unemployment vs. inflation) and valence of coverage

TABLE 10
Contingency Table with Frequencies for Type and Valence

Valence of Coverage	Economic Issue Covered in Newscast		
	Unemployment	Inflation	Total
Positive	3	3	6
Negative	3	3	6
Total	6	6	12

(positive vs. negative). Since these are two categorical variables, their relationship can be examined by considering the contingency table formed by counting the number of observations in each cell of the table. This contingency table is seen in Table 10.

Since the four frequencies are all equal, the chi-square value for Table 10 equals zero, as does any of the correlation coefficients we might use to measure the strength of a relationship between two categorical variables. Thus, for the data in Table 10 there is no relationship between the two variables valence and issue. It should be emphasized that this value of chi-square has nothing to do with the possible effects of the two explanatory variables on the dependent variable. The chi-square analysis is concerned only with the possible relationship between the explanatory variables themselves.

The reason the two explanatory variables are unrelated here is that there is the same number of observations in each of the four cells in the data table. It can also be shown that when the cell frequencies are identical, the interaction variable is unrelated to the two explanatory variables. It is possible to have unequal cell frequencies and still have the two explanatory variables unrelated to each other, but in that case there is a relationship between the interaction variable and each of the explanatory variables.

Equality of cell frequencies is of great importance. When the two explanatory variables and the interaction variable are all unrelated, as they are in this example, it is possible to assess the unique effect of each of the three on the dependent variable in terms of their sums of squares. With unequal frequencies it is not possible to untangle the effects and get three unique sums of squares.

The same problem of unique effects also occurs in multiple regression analysis, where it is labeled the problem of collinearity. That name is not commonly used in connection with analysis of variance. Instead, there is usually a separate presentation of the analysis for the case of equal and unequal cell frequencies.

The problem of collinearity in analysis of variance is one reason why these methods have been little used in nonexperimental studies. In an experiment it is possible to assign equal number of subjects to the various categories of the explanatory variables. With observational data there is not the same freedom. Before collecting the data in a survey, for example, there is no way of knowing what the cell frequencies will be in a table, and most often they are not equal.

Analysis of variance table. The results of a two-way analysis of variance are commonly displayed in an analysis of variance table, and the results from our example is shown in Table 11. The table lists the sums of squares, degrees of freedom, mean squares, and F-ratios. As before, the means squares are found by dividing the sums of squares by their corresponding degrees of freedom. The F-ratios are obtained by dividing the first three means squares by the residual mean square. The table also includes E^2 for the different variables measuring the strengths of their relationship with the dependent variable, and those numbers are found by dividing each sum of squares by the total sum of squares.

The table shows that all three variables, valence, issue and interaction, have a significant effect on people's view of the economy. The highest significance is reached for the valence variable, and this variable also has the strongest relationship with the dependent variable.

The advantage of a two-way analysis of variance versus separate one-way analyses for the two explanatory variables is that with a two-way analysis, the effects of the two variables are pulled out of the residual variable at the same time. If, for example, we had used these data for a one-way analysis studying the effect of the issue variable, the issue sum of squares would have stayed the same at 12, with 1 degree of freedom. Also, the total sum of squares would have stayed the same at 84, with 11 degrees of freedom. But that leaves us with a residual sum of squares of $84 - 12 = 72$, on $11 - 1 = 10$ degrees of freedom. That way the residual means square becomes $72/10 = 7.20$, and the F-ratio for the issue variable becomes $12/7.20 = 1.67$ on 1 and 10 degrees of freedom. With our two-way analysis Table 11 shows an F for this variable of 8.00 on 1 and 8 degrees of freedom, and this F is considerably more significant.

TABLE 11
Analysis of Variance Table for the Data in Table 7

Source	*Sum of Squares*	*Degrees of Freedom*	*Mean Square*	*F-ratio*	*Significance*
Valence	48	1	48.0	32.00	0.0005
Issue	12	1	12.0	8.00	0.02
Interaction	12	1	12.0	8.00	0.02
Residual	12	8	1.5		
Total	84	11			

Valence $E^2 = 48/84 = 0.57$.
Issue $E^2 = 12/84 = 0.14$.
Interaction $E^2 = 12/84 = 0.14$.
Residual $E^2 = 12/84 = 0.14$.

Both the residual sum of squares and the residual degrees of freedom are smaller in a two-way than a one-way analysis of variance. The residual mean square is the ratio of the sum of squares and the degrees of freedom, and the smaller the mean square is, the larger is the resulting F-ratio. A smaller residual sum of squares in the two-way analysis leads to a smaller mean square; but at the same time, a smaller number of degrees of freedom leads to a larger mean square. From this discussion it is not entirely clear if there are any benefits doing a two-way analysis instead of a one-way analysis. However, if the second variable has any kind of effect on the dependent variable, the resulting reduction in the residual sum of squares more than offsets the reduction in its degrees of freedom, and the two-way analysis results in a smaller mean square and a larger F than the one-way analysis.

Effects of being in a particular row, column, and cell. The overall effects of the variables are shown in the sums of squares in Table 11. The valence variable is the most important, with a contribution of 48 to the total sum of squares. But this and the other sums of squares are overall measures, and they do not explain why it is that a particular observation has the value that it does. In addition to the sums of squares, we want to measure the effects of the variables on each of the observations.

The first observed value in the upper left cell of Table 7 equals 1. That observation equals 1 because that person has been affected by four effects:

(1) the story was on unemployment,
(2) the story was positive,

(3) the story was a positive unemployment story,

(4) the residual variable, that is, the net effect of all other variables.

Each of the twelve people were affected by the four variables in a similar way, and we see the presence of the effects in that the observations differ from each other. If the variables did not have any effects, the observations would all be equal.

We postulate that for a particular observation the four effects are additive, meaning that we can get any of the twelve observations in Table 7 by adding four effects, depending on which categories an observation belongs to. In order to better understand these variables, we would like to measure their effects for each of the categories. One way to get at the effects is to decompose the observed values, one step at a time, the way it is done below.

The first step consists of subtracting the overall mean $\overline{y}$ (= 6) from each observation. That centers the data, and it becomes a little easier to find the various effects. The resulting scores are shown in Table 12. The four types of effects are still just as present, since we only subtracted a constant in order to make the overall mean equal to zero.

Let us consider the effect of the valence variable, which defines the rows in the data table. The mean of the first row equals –2.0, and we interpret that to say that a value of 2.0 has been subtracted from the score of each person who saw a positive story. Thus the effect of seeing a positive story equals –2.0. Similarly, the mean of the second row equals 2.0, and we say that the effect of seeing a negative story equals 2.0.

In symbols, let $\hat{\alpha}_1$ denote the estimated effect of being in the first row of the table (positive story) and $\hat{\alpha}_2$ the effect of being in the second row (negative story). We find these effects from the expressions

$$\hat{\alpha}_1 = \overline{y}_{1\cdot} - \overline{y} = 4 - 6 = -2$$

$$\hat{\alpha}_2 = \overline{y}_{2\cdot} - \overline{y} = 8 - 6 = 2$$

where $\overline{y}_{1.}$ and $\overline{y}_{2.}$ are the original means of rows 1 and 2. In the general case the effect of the i-th category of the row variable is found as the difference between the row mean $\overline{y}_{i.}$ and the overall mean y. Because the effects are measured this way, the effects are restricted in such a way that when each effect is multiplied by the number of observations in the same row, then the sum of these products equals zero.

Now that the effects of positive and negative stories have been identified, we can subtract these effects and see what, if anything, remains to be explained. By subtracting –2 from all the observations in

TABLE 12
Rating Scores and Means of the Importance of the Economy by Issue and Valence after Subtracting Overall Mean

Valence of Coverage	Economic Issue Covered in Newscast: Unemployment				Inflation				Mean
Positive	−5	−4	−3	(−4.0)	−1	0	1	(0.0)	−2.0
Negative	1	2	3	(2.0)	1	1	4	(2.0)	2.0
Mean		−1.0				1.0			0.0

the first row and 2 from all the observations in the second row of Table 12, we get the data in Table 13.

The two row means are now the same and equal to zero because the row effects have been subtracted from the data. But the four cell means are still different, as are the column means. Since the column mean for unemployment equals −1, the effect of seeing a story on unemployment has the effect of subtracting 1. Similarly, the effect of seeing a story on inflation has the effect of adding 1. Thus the effects of being in columns 1 and 2 can be measured by the column mean minus the overall mean, in this case

$$\hat{\beta}_1 = \overline{y}_{\cdot 1} - \overline{y} = 5 - 6 = -1$$
$$\hat{\beta}_2 = \overline{y}_{\cdot 2} - \overline{y} = 7 - 6 = 1$$

In the general case the effect of the j-th category of the column variable is found as the difference between the column mean $\overline{y}_{\cdot j}$ and the overall mean $\overline{y}$. The restriction on these effects is such that when each effect is multiplied by the number of observations in the same column, then the sum of these products equals zero.

Next we subtract the effect of the unemployment story from all the observations in the first column in Table 13 and the effect of the inflation story from all the observations in the second column. This takes out the column effects and leaves us with the data in Table 14.

Now we have subtracted from each observation the effect of being in a particular row and the effect of a particular column. In Table 14 the row means and the column means are all zero, and this verifies that there are no row or column effects in the data any longer. A two-way analysis of variance on the data in Table 14 would give row and column sums of

TABLE 13

Rating Scores and Means of the Importance of the Economy by Issue and Valence after Subtracting Overall Mean and Row Effects

Valence of Coverage	Economic Issue Covered in Newscast: Unemployment				Inflation				Mean
Positive	−3	−2	−1	(−2.0)	1	2	3	(2.0)	0.0
Negative	−1	0	1	(0.0)	−1	−1	2	(0.0)	0.0
Mean		−1.0				1.0			0.0

TABLE 14

Rating Scores and Means of the Importance of the Economy by Issue and Valence after Subtracting Overall Mean, Row Effects, and Column Effects

Valence of Coverage	Economic Issue Covered in Newscast: Unemployment				Inflation				Mean
Positive	−2	−1	0	(−1.0)	0	1	2	(1.0)	0.0
Negative	0	1	2	(1.0)	−2	−2	1	(−1.0)	0.0
Mean		0.0				0.0			0.0

squares equal to zero, indicating no effects. But the interaction and residual effects are still present, and a two-way analysis of variance of the data in Table 14 gives the same interaction and residual sums of squares as we have in the original analysis in Table 11.

The four cell means give us clues to the magnitudes of the effects of the interaction variable. The mean score for those who saw a positive story on unemployment is still equal to −1, even after we have subtracted the effect of the story being about unemployment as well as the effect of the story being positive. If those were the only two variables that had any effect, we would expect the mean in each cell to equal zero after the two effects have been taken out. But the mean in the first cell is still equal to −1, and it must be the interaction variable that brought the mean from 0 to −1. Thus the effect of the interaction variable for a positive unemployment story equals −1. Similarly, the effect of the interaction variable for positive inflation stories equals 1, for negative unemployment stories it also equals 1, and for negative inflation stories it equals -1.

The interaction effects can also be expressed in formulas. To find the effects we subtracted the overall mean $\overline{y}$ as an estimate of the overall constant μ, the row effect $\hat{\alpha}_i$, and the column effect $\hat{\beta}_j$. In symbols, the interaction effects $\hat{\gamma}_{ij}$ can be found from the equations

Positive unemployment:
$$\begin{aligned}\hat{\gamma}_{11} &= 2 - 6 - (-2) - (-1)\\ &= \overline{y}_{11} - \hat{\mu} - \hat{\alpha}_1 - \hat{\beta}_1\\ &= \overline{y}_{11} - \overline{y} - (\overline{y}_{1\cdot} - \overline{y}) - (\overline{y}_{\cdot 1} - \overline{y})\\ &= \overline{y}_{11} - \overline{y}_{1\cdot} - \overline{y}_{\cdot 1} + \overline{y}\\ &= 2 - 4 - 5 + 6 = -1\end{aligned}$$

Positive inflation:
$$\begin{aligned}\hat{\gamma}_{12} &= 6 - 6 - (-2) - 1\\ &= \overline{y}_{12} - \hat{\mu} - \hat{\alpha}_1 - \hat{\beta}_2\\ &= \overline{y}_{12} - \overline{y}_{1\cdot} - \overline{y}_{\cdot 2} + \overline{y} = 1\end{aligned}$$

Negative unemployment:
$$\begin{aligned}\hat{\gamma}_{21} &= \overline{y}_{21} - \hat{\mu} - \hat{\alpha}_2 - \hat{\beta}_1\\ &= \overline{y}_{21} - \overline{y}_{2\cdot} - \overline{y}_{\cdot 1} + \overline{y} = -1\end{aligned}$$

Negative inflation:
$$\begin{aligned}\hat{\gamma}_{22} &= \overline{y}_{22} - \hat{\mu} - \hat{\alpha}_2 - \hat{\beta}_2\\ &= \overline{y}_{22} - \overline{y}_{2\cdot} - \overline{y}_{\cdot 2} + \overline{y} = 1\end{aligned}$$

In general, the estimate of the interaction effect for the cell located in the i-th row and j-th column of the table is found by taking the cell mean and subtracting the means of the corresponding row and column and, finally, adding the overall mean. This gives us the formula

$$\hat{\gamma}_{ij} = \overline{y}_{ij} - \overline{y}_{i\cdot} - \overline{y}_{\cdot j} + \overline{y}$$

for the interaction effect. Note that the sum of the interaction effects equals zero for any column and any row.

The residual variable. Finally we can subtract the interaction effects from the remaining parts of the observations. The results are given in Table 15. By now the only thing left of the original observations are the effects due to the residual variable. The effect of the residual variable on the first observation in the cell for the positive unemployment story equals –1, 0 for the second observation, etc.

From the way the various effects have been subtracted, it follows that the residuals in Table 15 are obtained as deviations of the original observations from the means of the observations in the corresponding cells. This is not surprising, because if the only variables operating here were the valence of newscast, issue of newscast, and valence-issue interaction, then all the observations in a particular cell would be equal. The extent to which the observations in a cell differ from each other must be due to the residual variable.

One of the formal assumptions of analysis of variance is again that the residuals form a normal distribution. The numbers we have here are only the estimated values of the residual variable, but their distribution is approximately normal if the true residuals are normal. Figure 6 shows the frequency distribution of our residuals. The distribution is skewed, but it does not offer any strong evidence against normality, particularly because we have such a small number of observations.

The assumption of normality is needed for the F-tests. Experience has shown that the F-tests are not adversely affected by minor deviations from normality in the distribution of the residuals. But even though the F-tests have been found to be robust in this sense, one should still examine the distribution of the residuals. One should watch for skewness and single values that lie far away from the rest of the data. For a further discussion of the analysis of residuals, see Anscombe and Tukey (1963). For a similar discussion of decompositions of effects, see Cobb (1984).

Sums of squares from effects. The smaller the residuals are, the better the analysis of variance model fits. We would therefore like to have an overall sense of how large the residuals are. But the mean of the residuals is always equal to zero and gives no indication of the magnitude of the residuals. Instead we turn to the squared residuals, and the sum of the squared residuals in Table 15 becomes

$$(-1)^2 + 0^2 + \ldots + 2^2 = 12$$

This is the same sum of squared residuals we have in the analysis reported in Table 11.

The variance of the residuals can be thought of as the average squared residual, and it is found by dividing the sum of squared residuals by the residual degrees of freedom. Here we have 8 degrees of freedom, and in general there are n – rc degrees of freedom, where n is the total number of

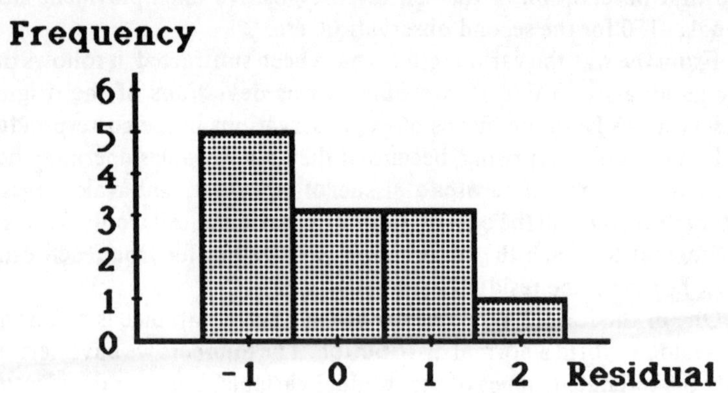

Figure 6: Histogram of Residuals in Table 15

TABLE 15
Rating Scores and Means of the Importance of the Economy by Issue and Valence after Subtracting Overall Mean, Row, Column, and Interaction Effects

Valence of Coverage	Economic Issue Covered in Newscast: Unemployment				Inflation				Mean
Positive	−1	0	1	(0.0)	−1	0	1	(0.0)	0.0
Negative	−1	0	1	(0.0)	−1	−1	2	(0.0)	0.0
Mean	0.0				0.0				0.0

observations, r the number of rows, and c the number of columns in the data table. In this case the variance becomes $s^2 = 12/8 = 1.5$, and the standard deviation $s = 1.2$. Thus a typical observation deviates 1.2 units from the mean in the cell in which it is located. Since the original observations range in values from 1 to 10, a deviation of 1.2 is quite small.

The other sums of squares in Table 11 can also be found from the effects we have identified. For valence we found that the effect of a positive story is −2 and a negative story is 2. Six people were given the −2 effect and the other six the 2 effect. Squaring the effects and adding them up for all twelve people gives the sum of squares

$$6(-2)^2 + 6(2)^2 = 48$$

for the valence variable. For the issue variable there are six people with a -1 effect and six others with a 1 effect. The overall effect of this variable then becomes

$$6(-1)^2 + 6(1)^2 = 12$$

Finally, the interaction sum of squares can be found from the four interaction effects -1, 1, -1, and 1 by squaring the effects, multiplying each square by the number of observations in the corresponding cell, and adding the products. That is,

$$3(-1)^2 + 3(1)^2 + 3(-1)^2 + 3(1)^2 = 12$$

which is the same interaction sum of squares we found in Table 11.

Formal model. This discussion started by focusing on the first observed value in the upper left cell of Table 7. Above we have found the effects that added together produce the observed value 1.0. This can be written, in words,

Observation = overall mean
+ effect of positive story
+ effect of unemployment story
+ effect of positive unemployment story
+ effect of residual variable

In numbers,

$$1 = 6 + (-2) + (-1) + (-1) + (-1)$$

and similarly for each of the eleven other observations. The magnitudes of these effects help us analyze the relative importance of the effects of the explanatory variables on the dependent variable, both directly for each of the categories of the explanatory variables and in an overall way for each variable by the corresponding sums of squares.

The decomposition above follows from the underlying theoretical model for a two-way analysis of variance. This model is an equation containing terms for the observed data and the different effects we have identified as the ones that together determine the data. The equation is written in such a way as to represent the actual real world process that produces the data. Two-way analysis of variance, as we discuss it here, makes use of an additive model, where the effects are added together to produce the data. That is, the k-th observed value located in the i-th row and j-th column of the data table can be written as the sum

$$y_{ijk} = \mu + \alpha_i + \beta_j + \gamma_{ij} + \epsilon_{ijk}$$

where μ is a constant

α_i is the effect of the i-th category of the row variable

β_j is the effect of the j-th category of the column variable

γ_{ij} is the effect of the (i, j)-th category of the interaction variable

ϵ_{ijk} is the effect of the residual variable

The mu, alphas, betas, and gammas are the parameters in this model. The formulas involving the various means we have for the effects are estimators of the model parameters. Numerical estimates of the parameters are obtained from our particular sample. The estimates are all found using the criterion that the sum of squared residuals should be as small as possible.

It is worth noting that the model we use is only one of many possible competing models. It could be, for example, that the effects act in a multiplicative way to generate the data or maybe in an exponential way. The advantage of the additive model is that it is much simpler to work with, but it should only be used if we think that the additive process is appropriate for the phenomenon we are studying.

Hypothesis testing. If the explanatory variables have any effect on the dependent variable, then the corresponding alphas, betas, and gammas are different from zero. While we do not have the true values of these parameters, we can use the observed data and the estimated parameter values to test hypotheses about the parameters and thereby reach conclusions about whether they are equal to zero or not.

One null hypothesis is that there are no row (valence) effects, i.e., that there is no difference between positive and negative stories and that the alphas are all equal to zero. This hypothesis can be expressed

$$H_0: \alpha_1 = \alpha_2 \; (= 0)$$

Because the estimated alphas are measured as deviations from the overall mean, some of the estimates will be negative and some will be positive. The weighted sum of the estimated effects, where the weights are the number of observations in each category, is equal to zero. Thus the only way the effects can be equal is for them all to be equal to zero. Another way of stating the same hypothesis is that the population means of the dependent variable are the same for all categories of the row variable.

This null hypothesis is tested by the F-value for valence in the analysis of variance table in Table 11, where F = 32.00. When we take the ratio of the row expected mean square and the residual expected mean square, we get the expression

$$1.00 + (6\alpha_1^2 + 6\alpha_2^2)/\sigma^2$$

where σ^2 is the variance of the residuals. The computed value of F is an estimate of the value of this expression. If the null hypothesis is true and the alphas really are equal to zero, then the value of this expression equals 1.00. In that case the observed sample value of F will be fairly close to 1.00.

On the other hand, if the null hypothesis is false, then the expression above has to be larger than 1.00. In that case the sample value of F will probably also be larger than 1.00 and approximately equal to whatever the true value is of the expression above. Thus a small value of F around 1.00 will lead us to conclude that the hypothesis of no effects is true, and a large value will make us conclude that the hypothesis is false. The specific cutoff value for F for which we reject the hypothesis is found in tables of the F-distribution. In our example, where there is 1 degree of freedom for valence and 8 for the residuals, we reject the null hypothesis if F is larger than 5.32 with a 5% significance level and 11.26 with a 1% significance level. Thus our observed F of 32.00 is significant at the 1% level.

In the general case, where there are r instead of 2 categories of the row variable, c categories of the column variable, and n observations altogether, the observed F has r–1 and n–rc degrees of freedom. The critical values of F are still found from the F-tables in the column headed by r–1 and the row headed by n–rc.

The null hypothesis that there are no differences between the categories that form the columns in the data table (here that there is no difference between stories on unemployment and inflation) is tested the same way. With c columns the null hypothesis states

$$H_0: \beta_1 = \beta_2 = \ldots = \beta_c (= 0)$$

It is tested by the F for the column variable (here economic issue) where F = 8.00. When we take the ratio of the column expected mean square and the residual expected mean square we get the expression

$$1.00 + (n_1\beta_1^2 + n_2\beta_2^2 + \ldots + n_c\beta_c^2)/(c-1)\sigma^2$$

where the n's are the numbers of observations in the various columns. The computed value of F is an estimate of the numerical value of this expression. As before, if the observed F is a good deal larger than 1.00, then the hypothesis is rejected. The critical value of F is found from the F-table, using c–1 and n–rc degrees of freedom. Rejecting the hypothesis means we conclude that at least some of the betas are different from zero. In our example F is so large that the hypothesis is rejected at the 5% but not at the 1% level.

Finally, it is possible to test whether all the interaction effects are equal to zero. The null hypothesis states that they are all equal, meaning that they all equal zero. In our example,

$$H_0: \gamma_{11} = \gamma_{12} = \gamma_{21} = \gamma_{22} \ (=0)$$

The hypothesis is tested by the F-ratio for interaction because that F is also an estimate of a quantity similar to the other two and involving the true gammas. In the general case the degrees of freedom for the F for interaction becomes (r–1)(c–1) and n–rc.

If the test for interaction reveals no significance, the formal model can take that into account and leave out the interaction effects. The model can then be expressed in the equation

$$y_{ijk} = \mu + \alpha_i + \beta_j + \epsilon_{ijk}$$

and this is a simpler, additive model than the one containing interaction effects. Any observation is here determined only by the effect of being in a particular row plus the effect of being in a particular column, plus the effect of the residual variable. In such a case the residual sum of squares is recomputed, as discussed in the section at the end of the chapter on pooling nonsignificant sums of squares.

The interpretation of the data is more troublesome if one or both main effects (row and column effects) are not significant while the interaction effect is significant. But we cannot remove a variable from the analysis without also removing any interaction variable which the variable helped create. This makes it hard to remove nonsignificant main effects.

We also have to keep in mind that even a very large and significant F-value only tells us that the corresponding effects differ from zero. It does not tell us anything about how much the effects differ from zero, and that is usually what is of interest. The larger the F, the stronger is the evidence that the effects are not equal to zero. The magnitudes of the differences can only be established by computing the effects for each category and interpreting them relative to the substantive topic we are studying.

Related Explanatory Variables

Related variables. One of the great advantages of experimental studies is that we can decide how many observations to make of the dependent variable for each combination of the various factors. This manipulation of the explanatory variables makes it possible to have those variables unrelated to each other. In the previous section the experimenter assigned the same number of subjects to each combination of categories of the explanatory variables. With such a design one can assess the unique effect of each explanatory variable and its interactions on the dependent variables.

This is not the case with observational studies. Here the investigator exercises no control over how many cases fall in the various categories or combinations of categories of the explanatory variables; any attempt to impose controls on the number of cases would immediately invalidate the research. With a random sample of the mass public we cannot stipulate, for example, that the proportion of blacks experiencing unemployment is the same as the proportion doing so among whites. More likely we are faced with a relationship between race and unemployment as shown in Table 16; the entries are realistic while contrived to keep the arithmetic simple.

The table shows 3 of 5 blacks (60%) to have suffered unemployment as opposed to 2 of 10 whites (20%). This means race and unemployment are correlated in the sample, and with phi equal to 0.40 the relationship is moderately strong.

Suppose we were interested in studying the effects of race and unemployment on how important the economy is rated as a problem. Table 17 lists the rating responses on a ten-point scale for the individuals

TABLE 16
Relationship Between Unemployment and Race
(hypothetical sample)

		Unemployment Last 12 Months		
		Yes	No	Total
Race	Black	3	2	5
	White	2	8	10
	Total	5	10	15

phi = 0.40

in Table 16. The correlation between unemployment and race will affect the analysis of variance of these data.

Formal model and plan for analysis. The equation for the formal model of a two-way analysis of variance with correlated explanatory variables is the same as for an analysis with uncorrelated variables. A particular observation is thought to be generated as a sum of an overall level, a row effect, a column effect, an interaction effect, and a residual effect. The effects are measured by sums of squares, as before, and the possible statistical significance of the effects are determined by F-ratios.

The major difference lies in the fact that a given variable does not necessarily have a unique sum of squares measuring the effect of that variable. The total sum of squares TSS is found as before, the sum of squared deviations of the observations from the overall mean. Similarly, the residual sum of squares RSS is found as the sum of squared deviations of the observations from their cell means. The difference TSS–RSS represents the combined effect of the row variable, column variable, and interaction variable. We would like to break this quantity into three parts, one for each of the three variables, but it is not possible to do that in a unique way.

The general approach is to deal with one of the variables at a time, find the sum of squares for that variable, and then allocate the remaining sum to the other variables. That way the sums of squares will depend on the order in which we let a variable enter the analysis. This is the same way collinearity is dealt with in stepwise regression.

Sums of squares. To show how the sums of squares for a two-way analysis of variance with unequal cell frequencies are computed, we use the data in Table 17 as an example. In order to simplify the discussion, this example is constructed such that there is no interaction effect

TABLE 17
Rating Scores and Means of the Importance of the Economy, by Race and Unemployment

		Unemployed Last 12 Months		
		Yes	No	Mean
Race	Black	7 8 9 (8.0)	2 6 (4.0)	6.4
	White	5 7 (6.0)	1 1 1 2 2 3 3 3 (2.0)	2.8
	Mean	7.2	2.4	4.0

present. We can see this from the four cell means because the difference between the means for blacks and whites equals 2.0 both in the yes and the no column.

The means in Table 17 suggest that blacks express more concern over the economy than do whites. The sum of squares due to race, reflecting this difference, can be found from the means in Table 17 and becomes

$$\text{RaceSS} = n_{1.}(\bar{y}_{1.} - \bar{y})^2 + n_{2.}(\bar{y}_{2.} - \bar{y})^2$$
$$= 5(6.4 - 4.0)^2 + 10(2.8 - 4.0)^2 = 43.20$$

There is also a difference in the means between those unemployed and not. The effect of the unemployment variables can be measured by the sum of squares

$$\text{UnemplSS} = n_{.1}(\bar{y}_{.1} - \bar{y})^2 + n_{.2}(\bar{y}_{.2} - \bar{y})^2$$
$$= 5(7.2 - 4.0)^2 + 10(2.4 - 4.0)^2 = 76.80$$

Adding these two effects gives a total of 120.00. At the same time, the computation of the total sum of squares results in TSS = 106.00. Since the sum of the effects cannot exceed the total sum of squares, we must modify the estimation of the effects of race and unemployment in some way.

It is possible to find the combined effect of race and unemployment just as we did for two unrelated variables in Table 9. We can string out the two variables in a combined variable with four categories and do a one-way analysis on the data when they are arranged that way. This gives the following sum of squares for the combined variable:

$$\begin{aligned}\text{Race\&UnemplSS} &= 3(8.0-4.0)^2 + 2(4.0-4.0)^2 \\ &\quad + 2(6.0-4.0)^2 + 8(2.0-4.0)^2 \\ &= 88.00\end{aligned}$$

Thus the whole is smaller than the sum of the parts. The sum of squares for both variables taken together equals 88.0, while the sum of the two separate sums of squares equals 120.0. The reason for this is that race and unemployment are correlated with each other, and this correlation stands in the way of our attempt to measure the separate effects of the two variables.

There are two options available for solving this problem. One, we can measure the effect of race first and then measure the effect of unemployment after race has been permitted to explain what it can. On the other hand, we can do the reverse and measure the effect of unemployment first and then allocate the remaining part of the combined effect to race. SPSS allows for both these arrangements.

The results are shown in Table 18. In both cases the sums of squares for race and unemployment add up to 88.00, but we use the separate sums of squares above as the first entry in the analysis of variance table. As is to be expected, the total and residual sums of squares are not affected by the way in which we divide the sums of squares for race and unemployment.

The importance of order. The example shows the importance of the order in which the variables are introduced. When an analysis like this is done on a computer, it is important that the output specifies in which order the variables have been entered in the analysis.

Which of these two results one chooses depends on reasoning that cannot be supplied by the analysis of variance. Instead, it must come from the substantive theory concerning the causal connections among the variables. For this example one might want to consider which of the two explanatory variables is exogenous. Clearly, race is not something that could be caused by unemployment, while it is possible to argue that race affects one's employment opportunities. Hence one could consider the effect of race first and then measure the effect of unemployment with the race effect removed. These are the results in the upper table in Table 18.

TABLE 18
Analysis of Variance Tables for Example with Correlated Explanatory Variables

Source	Sum of Squares	Degrees of Freedom	Mean Square	F-ratio	Significance
Option 1					
Race	43.20	1	43.20	28.80	0.0002
Unemployment, after Race	44.80	1	44.80	29.90	0.0001
Residual	18.00	12	1.50		
Total	106.00	14			
Option 2					
Unemployment	76.80	1	76.80	51.20	0.00001
Race, after Unemployment	11.20	1	11.20	7.50	0.018
Residual	18.00	12	1.50		
Total	106.00	14			

Another approach consists of taking whatever variable has the largest sum of squares as the first variable and allocating the remaining effect to the next variable. This corresponds to the usual stepwise regression, which chooses the explanatory variables in the order of their sums of squares. In our example that argues for unemployment as the first variable with an effect of 76.80. After unemployment, race has only a small additional effect of 11.20. These are the results shown in the lower table in Table 18.

Not only do the sums of squares change when the order of the variables is changed. From the changing sums of squares we get changing mean squares and thereby changing F-ratios. In our example all the F-ratios are significant, but it is very possible to imagine cases where a variable is found to be significant if it is included first in the analysis and not significant if it enters the analysis later.

One way to interpret the differing sums of squares is to say that there is a part of the combined sum of squares of 88.00 that is shared by the two explanatory variables. The sum of squares for race drops from 43.20

to 11.20 when the variable is entered first versus when it is entered as the second variable. This is a drop of 32.00. Similarly, the sum of squares for unemployment drops from 76.80 to 44.80, and this is also a drop of 32.00.

This shared part and the other sums of squares are illustrated in Figure 7. The area in the middle represents the portion of the variation in the dependent variable shared by both variables. The two outside areas illustrate those parts of the variation that each variable explains alone, after the other variable has entered the analysis first. Each of the explanatory variables loses a sizable share of its sum of squares when it is entered after the other variable. This is so because the two explanatory variables are related to each other as well as to the dependent variable.

Interaction. In order to keep the example simple, there was no

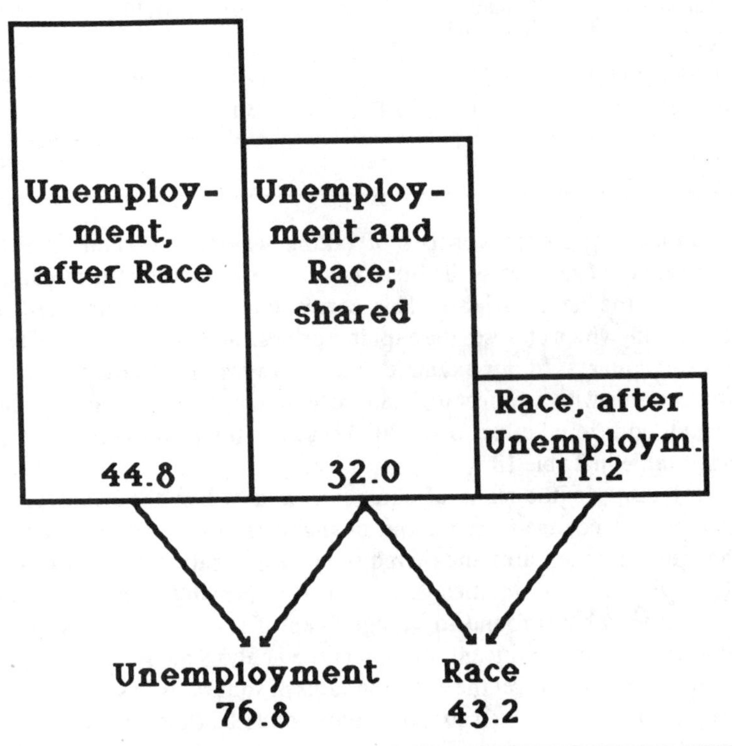

Figure 7: Partitioning of Variation Due to Unemployment and Race

interaction effect built into the data. The presence or absence of interaction has nothing to do with the correlation or lack thereof between the explanatory variables. Interaction is an effect on the dependent variable over and beyond the separate effects of the explanatory variables, and it can exist whether or not the explanatory variables themselves are correlated.

The presence of an interaction effect is seen in the patterns of the cell means; and when there is interaction, we must also include an interaction sum of squares. In that case the computations get considerably more cumbersome, and we do not include the necessary formulas here. The interaction sum of squares is always computed in such a way that the explanatory variables themselves are allowed to explain as much of the variation in the dependent variable as possible before the interaction variable is entered.

Special Topics

One observation per cell. There are times when each combination of the explanatory variables has only one observation of the dependent variable. That is, there is only one observation in each cell in the data table. This situation cannot be handled by the methods discussed so far. The two nominal variables would be uncorrelated in this case, since the number of observations is the same in each cell. But another problem arises instead, and it would not be possible to compute any F-ratios and thereby test any hypotheses about the presence of effects.

It would not be possible to do any testing because we do not have any way of getting the denominator for the F-values. As we have seen, the denominator for the F's is the mean square for the residuals, obtained from the residual sum of squares. But each residual in that sum of squares is obtained from the difference between the observed score and the mean in the corresponding cell in the data table. With only one observation in the cell, the mean is equal to that observation, and the residual would be zero. With the residuals all equal to zero, the residual sum of squares and mean square become zero, and we cannot divide by zero.

The case with only one observation in each cell does not occur that often, but it is useful to consider this case for another reason. If we want to get some preliminary ideas of whether row and column effects are present or not without performing all the computations necessary for a complete analysis, we can first compute the mean of the dependent variable for the observations in each cell. By replacing the original observations with the cell means, we then have the case in which there is only one value in each cell. These means can then be analyzed for the presence of row and column effects as outlined below.

The way to do an analysis of variance with one observation in each cell is to make the assumption that there are no interaction effects present. This limits the analysis; but if this assumption is true, we can get a good sense of the row and column effects. Even when the assumption of no interaction is true, we can still compute an interaction sum of squares using the same formulas as before. This sum of squares can then be thought of as containing random effects, and it can be used as the residual sum of squares. By dividing this sum of squares by the proper degrees of freedom we get a mean square for the denominators of the F's for the row and column effects.

When we have unequal cell frequencies and correlated explanatory variables, this approach suggests reducing the data to the case with one observation in each cell and basing the analysis on the reduced data. That way we do not have to worry about the explanatory variables being related, and there is no problem with the order in which the variables are brought into the analysis.

The analysis is based on the assumption of nonsignificant interaction effects. Had we started with only one observation in each cell, it would not have been possible to determine whether the interaction effects are present or not. The worst that can happen is that there are significant interaction effects present, unknown to us. What we here have taken as the residual mean square would then have been the effect of the residual variable plus the effect of the interaction variable. That makes the denominator in the F-values too large, since it should only represent the effect of the residual variable. If the denominators are too large, then the F's are too small. The result of this is that we may not be able to detect that the row and column effects are significant, even if they really are significant. But if we still find significant F-values using a denominator that is too large, then we know that the significance level is on the conservative side.

As a small numerical example we return to Table 7 and take the cell means in that table as the single observations in the various cells. Thus we have the data shown in the top part of Table 19. A two-way analysis of variance of these four observations gives us the results shown in the lower part of Table 19. The results from the original analysis of variance are shown in Table 11.

TABLE 19

Two-Way Analysis of Variance with One Observation in Each Cell

Valence of Coverage	Economic Issue Covered in Newscast		
	Unemployment	Inflation	Mean
Positive	2.0	6.0	4.0
Negative	8.0	8.0	8.0
Mean	5.0	7.0	6.0

Source	*Sum of Squares*	*Degrees of Freedom*	*Mean Square*	*F-ratio*	*Significance*
Valence	16.0	1	16.0	4.00	0.295
Issue	4.0	1	4.0	1.00	0.50
Residual	4.0	1	4.0		
Total	24.00	3			

Several comments can be made about the analyses in Tables 11 and 19. In both cases valence emerges as the more important variable. Using all the observations, valence has an eta square of 48/84 = 57%; using only the cell means, it has an eta squared of 16/24 = 75%. While the two percentages are different, they are still in the same ball park. The F-ratios for valence and issue are both smaller in Table 19 than they are in Table 11, but they are not excessively different.

The major difference between the two analyses lies in the degrees of freedom for the residual. When we use all the observations, the degrees of freedom for the residual is mainly determined by the number of observations in the data. When we use the means as single observations, the degrees of freedom are determined by the size of the table. Because each variable has only two categories, we end up with as little as 1 degree of freedom for the residual in this example. The major drawback of a very small number of degrees of freedom for the residuals is that in order to be called significant, the F-ratio has to be very large. With a 5% significance the critical value for F on 1 and 1 degrees of freedom equals as much as 161.4. Thus the largest difference between the results in Tables 11 and 19 are found in the last column, where we see that the results in Table 11 are much more significant than the results in Table 19.

Thus it is possible to do analysis of variance with only one observation in each cell, whether that is a single observation or a mean; but the analysis works better if the explanatory variables have more than just two categories. With more categories we get more degrees of freedom for the residual sum of squares and smaller critical values of F.

Pooling nonsignificant sums of squares. There are times when the F-value for the interaction variable is not significant. We are then faced with the question of what produced the interaction sum of squares. One answer is that in this case, the interaction sum of squares is due to randomness in the data coming from the effect of other variables not included in the analysis. But that effect is already identified as the effect of the residual variable, and we also have the residual sum of squares as a measure of that effect. This means we now have two measures of the effect of the residual variable. When that is the case, it is better to combine the two effects of the residual variable into one.

The interaction and residual sums of squares are added together, and the sum is used as the new residual sum of squares. This is known as pooling of the sums of squares. We get the degrees of freedom for the new residual sum of squares by adding (r–1)(c–1) from the interaction effect to n–rc from the old residual effect. This equals n–r–c+1. By dividing the new residual sum of squares by its degrees of freedom, we get the new residual mean square; and it is usually smaller than the old residual mean square, resulting in larger values of F for the row and column effects.

In addition, a larger number of degrees of freedom for the F's means that the critical values from the F-table for the rejection of the null hypotheses get smaller. Thus, by pooling the sums of squares, we get larger F-values, and at the same time we need smaller values of F in order to find our results significant. These two advantages can make it very worthwhile pooling insignificant sums of squares.

Interaction as nonparallel lines. The interaction variable has been introduced as the joint effect of the two explanatory variables over and beyond the separate effects of the two variables. One way to display the presence of interaction is to draw a picture like Figure 8. The information in that graph is taken from the data in Table 7.

The picture is made the following way. The categories for one of the explanatory variables are marked off along the horizontal axis. It makes no difference which of the two is chosen. The dependent variable is marked off along the vertical axis. Next, each of the cell means is plotted in its appropriate place. Finally, connecting lines are drawn between the means that have the same category of the second explanatory variable.

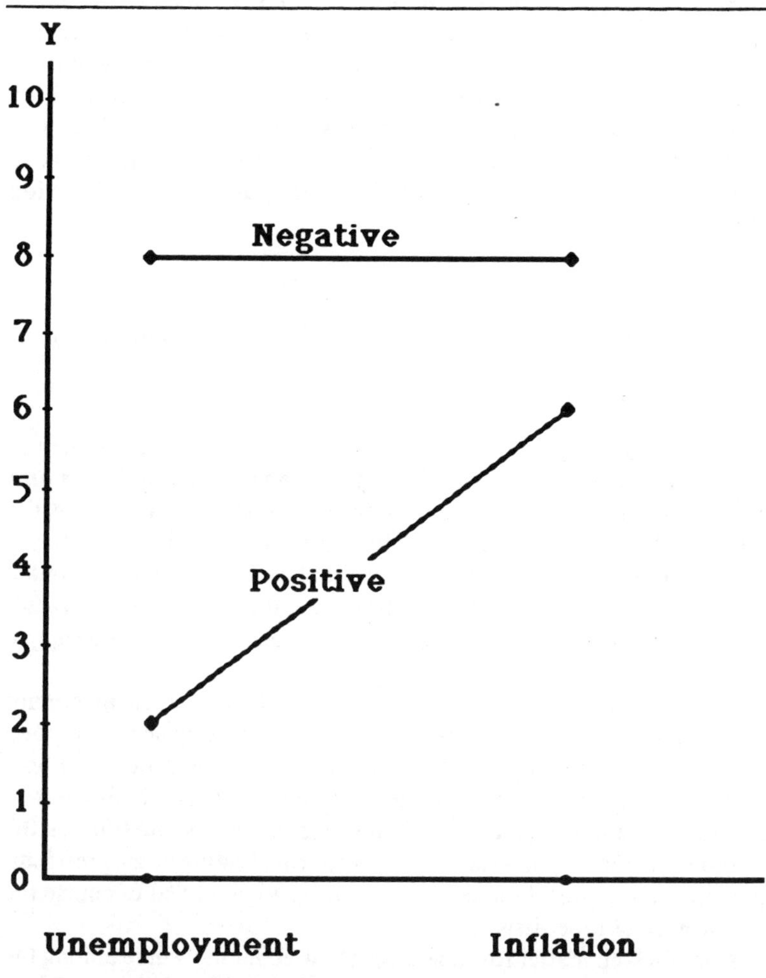

Figure 8: Means in Four Groups Pairwise Connected by Lines, Showing Presence of Interaction

In our graph unemployment and inflation are chosen as two points on the horizontal axis, the negative means are connected by one line and the positive means are connected by another line.

The important feature of the two lines is that they are not parallel. That tells us there is an interaction effect present in the data. The fact that the lines are not parallel means that it makes a difference for the dependent variable whether we are dealing with unemployment or inflation stories. The figure shows that for unemployment there is a change of 6 units when we go from positive to negative stories. But for inflation there is only a change of 2 units from positive to negative stories. In other words, it makes a difference whether we are dealing with unemployment or inflation when we compare positive and negative stories. This is only another way of stating that we have interaction effects in these data.

4. ANALYSIS OF VARIANCE, SAMPLE OF CATEGORIES

One-Way Analysis

Sample of categories. The type of analysis of variance outlined in Chapters 2 and 3 is called model I type analysis. That model is also known as a fixed model. We now turn to model II, also called the random effect model. The main difference between the two models is that model II does not require observations on the dependent variable for every one of the categories of the explanatory variable(s). Instead, model II handles situations where data are collected only for a sample of categories.

Such a situation occurs in research trying to determine whether or not the order of presentation makes a difference to the way people respond to questions in an interview. Let us continue with the problem of how important an issue individuals rate the economy. This is a broad area, and the entire interview consists of more than just one question on the economy. There might be questions on approval rating of the president, partisanship, political interest, economic well-being, and of course the importance of other issues.

It might well matter for the rating of the economy where among the other items this question is placed in the interview. Suppose we are concerned with the ordering of six particular questions in the interview schedule. These questions can be ordered in a staggering 720 different ways. This number is so large that there is no way we could use all of them in an experiment on the ordering of questions. The only possibility is to draw a sample of orderings and restrict our experiment to those particular orderings. Thus we are prepared to take a random sample from the 720 permutations and assign subjects randomly to each of those permutations of questions. Say we sample 5 such question orders and assign 4 subjects to each order.

Table 20 presents the rating responses furnished by those 20 subjects. Since these 5 orderings, numbered 1 through 5, form a randomly chosen sample of orderings selected from the larger population of all 720 orderings, we are no longer as interested as before in the specific effect of each ordering on the rating of the economy. We can still find the effect of each ordering by taking the difference between the ordering mean and the overall mean, but these effects now form a random sample from a larger set of effects. In other words, these five values have been sampled from a random variable that would have provided different values if other orderings had been selected instead. Because of this, a model II analysis is also called a random effect model as opposed to a fixed effect model.

We are interested in the question of whether the ordering a subject was exposed to has an effect on the rating score. This implies a null hypothesis which states that all the ordering effects are equal to zero. Analysis of variance model II offers a test of this hypothesis by determining whether the variance of all the effects equals zero. The only way a variance can equal zero is for all the values (taken as deviations from the mean) to equal zero themselves.

Formal model and computations. The formal structures of models I and II look very similar for a one-way analysis, and the computations are identical. But, in addition, a random model permits the estimation of the new concept of the variance of the effect for all the elements in the population.

The formal model for a model II analysis states that the j-th observation in the i-th group, y_{ij}, is equal to the overall mean μ, plus the effect of being in the i-th group, plus the effect of all other variables. This is expressed in the equation

$$y_{ij} = \mu + a_i + \epsilon_{ij}$$

where a_i is the effect of the explanatory variable in the i-th group (here ordering), and ϵ_{ij} is the effect of the residual variable on this particular observation.

The model also specifies that the distribution of the a's in the population of all the a's forms a normal distribution with mean zero and variance σ_a^2. In principle this requires an infinitely large population of a's, even though our example is restricted to a population of 720 a-values. Similarly, the residual variable is assumed to have a normal distribution with mean zero and variance σ^2. A random model like the one we are dealing with here also requires the same number of

TABLE 20

Hypothetical Data for an Example of One-Way Analysis of Variance, Model II and the Resulting Analysis of Varaince Table

	Question Ordering				
	1	2	3	4	5
	8	5	7	9	6
	7	4	6	8	5
	6	3	5	7	4
	5	2	4	6	3
Mean	6.5	3.5	5.5	7.5	4.5
Overall mean = 5.5					

Source	*Sum of Squares*	*Degrees of Freedom*	*Mean Square*	*F-ratio*	*Significance*
Between orderings	40.00	4	10.00	6.00	0.004
Within orderings	25.00	15	1.67		
Total	65.00	19			

$s^2 = 1.67$; $s_a^2 = 2.08$.

observations in each group; a requirement not encountered in a model I type of analysis. In our example each group has n = 4 observations.

The hypothesis we want to test is that ordering has no effect on the dependent variable. When ordering has no effect, then all the a's are equal to zero. In that case the variance of the a's is also equal to zero. The null hypothesis of σ_a^2 equal to zero can be tested by the same F-ratio used for the model I type of analysis in Chapter 2.

First we find the total sum of squares by computing the difference between each observation and the overall mean, squaring all the differences, and adding up the squares. That is,

$$\begin{aligned} TSS &= \Sigma(y_{ij} - \overline{y})^2 \\ &= (8 - 5.5)^2 + (7 - 5.5)^2 + \ldots + (3 - 5.5)^2 = 65.00 \end{aligned}$$

Similarly, the between-group sum of squares for ordering is found by taking the difference between each group mean and the overall mean, squaring all the differences, multiplying each square by the number of observations in each group, and adding all the products. That is,

$$\begin{aligned} BSS &= \Sigma n(\bar{y}_i - \bar{y})^2 \\ &= 4(6.5 - 5.5)^2 + \ldots + 4(4.5 - 5.5)^2 = 40.00 \end{aligned}$$

Finally, the within group sum of squares for the residual variable can be found as the difference of the total sum of squares and the between-group sum of squares, here WSS = 65.00 – 40.00 = 25.00.

The degrees of freedom are the same as for a model I analysis. The degrees of freedom for the total sum of squares equals the number of observations minus one, for the between-group sum of squares the number of groups minus one, and for the within-group sum of squares the number of observations minus the number of groups. For our examples these numbers are 19, 4, and 15, respectively.

The mean squares are found by dividing the sums of squares by their degrees of freedom. It can then be shown that for a random model the between-group mean square, here equal to 10.00, is an estimate of the quantity $\sigma^2 + n\sigma_a^2$, where σ^2 is the population variance of the residuals and σ_a^2 the population variance of the a's. This quantity is also known as the group expected mean square. It can also be shown that the residual mean square is an estimate of σ^2, also known as the residual expected mean square. These two estimates now make it possible to draw conclusions about σ_a^2.

Dividing the between-group mean squares by the residual mean square gives us an F-ratio estimating the quantity $1.00 = n\sigma_a^2/\sigma^2$. If the variance of the a's really is equal to zero, the observed ratio calculated from our sample data should lie in the neighborhood of 1.00. On the other hand, if σ_a^2 really is not equal to zero, then the observed ratio ought to be larger than 1.00. This means that the observed value of the F-ratio can give us a clue about whether the null hypothesis is true or not. For values of F around 1.00 the null hypothesis is not rejected, and for values somewhat larger than 1.00 it is rejected. In our example the observed value of F becomes F = 10.00 / 1.67 = 6.00, which is considerably larger than 1.00. In order to decide whether a particular value of F is large enough for the null hypothesis of a zero variance of the a's to be rejected, we consult tables for the F distribution. The F-table tells us that when the hypothesis of a zero variance is true, the probability is only 0.05 of observing an F-value of 3.06 or larger. Since we observed F equal to 6.00, we reject the null hypothesis. Thus ordering does affect the rating scores of the economy, and this goes for the population of all orderings, not just the five orderings in the sample.

Estimating variance components. The rejection of the null hypothesis establishes that the explanatory variable has an effect on the dependent variable. The next question is how to measure how large this effect is.

One such measure is provided by the proportion of the between sum of squares to the total sum of squares, which in our example is 40.00/65.00 = 0.62. The ordering variable, therefore, explains 62% of the total variation in the ratings of the economy. Another, and related, way of measuring the effect of the ordering variable would be to estimate the effects (the a's) for each of the five orderings in the sample. These a's can be estimated by the differences between the ordering means and the overall mean; that is, $\hat{a}_1 = 6.5 - 5.5 = 1.0$, $\hat{a}_2 = 3.5 - 5.5 = -2.0$, and so on.

One difficulty with these numbers is that they do not tell us anything about the magnitudes of the a's for all the other orderings in the population. Also, their magnitudes cannot be summarized by their mean, since their sum is always equal to zero. Instead of measuring how large the effect is of the ordering variable this way, we turn to the variance of the a's instead. Since the mean of the a's is zero, we know that the larger the variance is, the larger are the a's.

In order to estimate the variance of the a's we make use of the group and residual mean squares. Since the group mean square equals 10.00 and the residual mean square equals 1.67, we have the following expressions,

$$10.00 \cong \sigma^2 + 4\sigma_a^2 \qquad \text{and} \qquad 1.67 \cong \sigma^2$$

where the quantities on the left are only estimates of and not exactly equal to the expected mean squares on the right. Now we can solve the two expressions for the two variances and get the following estimated variance components

$$s^2 = 1.67 \qquad \text{and} \qquad s_a^2 = (10.00 - 1.67)/4 = 2.08$$

Since the variance of the a's exceeds the variance of the residuals, on the average the a-values are larger than the residuals. Another way to measure the effects is to take the square roots of the estimated variances and consider the standard deviations. The standard deviation of the a's becomes 1.44, and this is a number that can be taken as the average ordering effect. Thus a typical ordering differs by almost one and a half rating points from the overall mean for all orderings.

There is little difference between a fixed and a random one-way analysis of variance. The computations and the F-ratios are the same, and the only differences are that the random model requires the same number of observations in each group and that it permits the computations of variance components. The two models differ more when there are two explanatory variables rather than just one.

Two Explanatory Variables

Formal model and computations. A random effects model of analysis of variance with two explanatory variables is based on the same ideas as the random model with only one explanatory variable. The categories of both explanatory variables are samples from much larger populations of categories, and the aim of the analysis is to assess the effects of the explanatory variables on the dependent variable.

Let us continue the example from the previous section and add one more explanatory variable. In addition to the order of the questions, we suspect the probing of the importance of other issues may affect the rating subjects provide for the importance of the economy. Again, the number of possible items is large enough to defeat any reasonable effort to probe them all. To keep the example simple we draw a sample of two issues, denoted A and B, from an exhaustive list of issues on the political agenda. We cross this sample of two issues with the sample of five orderings and end up with ten experimental conditions. In other words, each of the five selected question orders is prefaced with the question regarding the importance of one of the two issues A or B. Table 21 displays the rating scores provided by the subjects, who were randomly assigned to each of the ten conditions.

The formal model for the analysis of data of this kind specifies that the k-th observation in the cell defined by the i-th row and the j-th column, y_{ijk}, can be written as the sum

$$y_{ijk} = \mu + a_i + b_j + c_{ij} + \epsilon_{ijk}$$

The various terms in this sum have very much the same interpretations as the corresponding terms in the fixed model for a two-way analysis of variance in Chapter 2. The parameter μ is a constant that centers the effects around zero. The next term, a_i, measures the effect of the i-th category of the row variable (issue), and the two issue effects are denoted

a_1 and a_2. These two quantities have been sampled from a large population of a-values, and it is assumed that the distribution of the a-values in the population is normal with mean zero and variances σ_a^2. In order to assess the effect of issue, we are not as concerned with the two values a_1 and a_2 as we are with the entire population of a-values. One way to specify in a null hypothesis that the variable has no effect is to specify that the population variance of the a's equals zero, because this implies that all the a-values in the population are equal to zero.

Similarly, the term b_j refers to the effect of the j-th category of the column variable (ordering). The five columns give rise to the five effects denoted b_1, b_2, b_3, b_4, and b_5. We assume, again, that the population of b's from which these five were sampled has a normal distribution with mean zero and variance σ_b^2. The null hypothesis that ordering has no effect gets translated into the statement that the variance of the b's equals zero.

The interaction effect, produced by the combination of the i-th row and the j-th column is captured by the term c_{ij}. With 10 cells in the data table there are 10 interaction terms. They are assumed to have been sampled from a population of interaction terms following a normal distribution with mean zero and variance σ_c^2. The null hypothesis of no interaction effect translates into the statement that the variance of the c's equals zero.

The residual term in the model, ϵ_{ijk}, measures the effect on rating scores stemming from all other variables. We assume that the 20 residuals in our example come from a population of residual terms with a normal distribution with mean zero and variance σ^2.

The five sums of squares, degrees of freedom, and mean squares are computed in the same way for a random model as they are for a fixed model. The results for our example are shown in the analysis of variance table in Table 21. The total sum of squares is the same for this analysis as it is for the one-way analysis above, and the ordering sum of squares is also unchanged in comparison with the results in Table 20 for the one-way analysis. But the old residual sum of squares of 25.00 on 15 degrees of freedom has visibly declined since the issue and interaction variables have been extracted. It now stands only at 11.00 on 10 degrees of freedom.

The major difference between a model I and a model II two-way analysis of variance lies in the computations of the F-ratios. Recall that for the model I type of analysis in Chapter 3, the F-ratios for the row variable, the column variable, and the interaction variable were each obtained by dividing the corresponding mean square by the mean

TABLE 21
Hypothetical Data for an Example of Two-Way Analysis of Variance, Model II, and the Resulting Analysis of Variance Table

	Question Ordering					
	1	2	3	4	5	Mean
Issue						
A	8	5	7	9	6	5.9
	7	4	6	8	5	
B	6	3	5	7	4	5.1
	5	2	4	6	3	
Mean	5.5	4.5	3.5	6.5	7.5	5.5

Source	*Sum of Squares*	*Degrees of Freedom*	*Mean Square*	*F-ratio*	*Significance*
Issue	3.2	1	3.20	1.18	0.30
Ordering	40.0	4	10.00	3.70	0.04
Interaction	10.8	4	2.70	2.45	0.11
Residual	11.0	10	1.10		
Total	65.0	19			

F(issue) = 3.20/2.70 = 1.18.
F(ordering) = 10.00/2.70 = 3.70.
F(int) = 2.70/1.10 = 2.45.

square for the residual variable. This is no longer the case with a model II analysis.

Here the mean square for the row variable (issue) must be divided by the mean square for interaction in order to give an F-ratio for the row variable. Similarly, the F-ratio for the column variable (ordering) is obtained by dividing the column mean square by the interaction mean square. Finally, the interaction F is found by dividing the interaction mean square by the residual mean square. The reason the F-ratios are different in the random model has to do with the various mean squares estimates, as seen in the next section.

In the example the F-ratio for the row variable (issue) becomes 3.20/2.70 = 1.18, and for the column variable (ordering) it becomes 10.00/2.70 = 3.70. The interaction F becomes 2.70/1.10 = 2.45. Only the F for the column variable is significant at a 5% significance level.

It could make quite a difference whether a set of data is analyzed according to a random or a fixed model. If the row and column mean squares had been divided by the residual mean square instead, as required for a fixed model, we would have gotten F's of 2.91 and 9.09. Compared to the F's we got for the random model, we see that the fixed model would have shown the effects to be much more significant. But it is not that we have a choice between fixed and random model. It should always be clear from the way the data were collected which way the data should be analyzed.

Estimating variance components. In addition to seeing whether any of the variances of the effects equal zero, we often want to estimate the numerical values of the variances. These variances tell us how large the effects are, and they give a better sense of how well the substantive model explains the data than the results of the hypothesis tests.

In order to estimate the unknown variances, we need to know something about how they relate to quantities we can compute from the data. From the model for the two-way random model, it is possible to derive that the various mean squares and population variances are related in the following way:

The row mean square is an estimate of	$\sigma^2 + n\sigma_c^2 + nc\sigma_a^2$
The column mean square is an estimate of	$\sigma^2 + n\sigma_c^2 + nr\sigma_b^2$
The interaction mean square is an estimate of	$\sigma^2 + n\sigma_c^2$
The residual mean square is an estimate of	σ^2

where n is the number of observations in each cell, r the number of rows, and c the number of columns in the data table. The expressions on the right are the expected mean squares.

These expressions show why we compute the F-ratios the way we do. For example, by dividing the row mean square by the interaction mean square, we see from the estimates that we get something which estimates the quantity 1.00 + a ratio with σ_a^2 in the numerator. If the null hypothesis of no row effect is true, then that ratio is equal to 1.00, and F is just an estimate of 1.00. If this null hypothesis is not true and σ_a^2 is different from zero, then F is an estimate of something larger than 1.00. We see that the interaction mean square is used in the denominators for the row and column F's because both row and column mean squares estimate quantities that contain the interaction variance σ_c^2.

These expressions can be used to estimate the unknown effect variances. We replace the population variances by their sample estimates, using the letter s for estimates, and then we set the resulting expressions equal to the observed mean squares. That gives the four equations

$$3.2 = s^2 + 2s_c^2 + 10s_a^2$$

$$10.0 = s^2 + 2s_c^2 + 4s_b^2$$

$$2.7 = s^2 + 2s_c^2$$

$$1.1 = s^2$$

These equations can now be used to solve for the four estimated variances. The last equation shows that the variance of the residuals equals 1.10, and the standard deviation of the residuals becomes s = 1.05. From the next to the last equation we get, for the interaction effects,

$$s_c^2 = (2.7 - 1.1)/2 = 0.8 \qquad s_c = 0.89$$

Now we can use the first two equations to find the row and column estimated variances,

$$s_a^2 = (3.2 - 2.7)/10 = 0.05 \qquad s_a = 0.22$$

$$s_b^2 = (10.0 - 2.7)/4 = 1.82 \qquad s_b = 1.35$$

These estimates confirm our impressions from the F-values. The column variable emerges with the largest effect; an average column mean deviates from the overall mean by a value of 1.35 points. An average row mean deviates only by 0.22 points from the overall mean. Also, there is a noticeable interaction effect of 0.89 points.

5. OTHER MODELS

Mixed Models

The choice between a fixed or a random model depends on whether we have data on all the categories of the explanatory variables or not. If we have data for all the categories, we use a fixed model; and if we have data for a sample of categories, we use a random model. The choice is most often determined by how easy or difficult it is to collect the data, and it is usually not very difficult to determine which model to use.

However, one difficulty arises when we have two or more explanatory variables and when we have data for all categories of some of them and data on a sample of categories for others. Thus some of the explanatory variables argue for a fixed model while others argue for a random model. The correct model in a case like this is the so-called mixed model, which allows for some fixed and some random effects.

We do not discuss mixed models here, but they are commonly treated in more extensive discussions of analysis of variance.

Three Explanatory Variables

Analysis of variance models generalize directly to three or more categorical, explanatory variables. The main difficulty is that with more variables, there are more effects to keep track of; in particular, the number of interaction effects goes up rapidly. Suppose we have three explanatory variables denoted A, B, and C. Besides three main effects, one for each variable, there are several possible interaction effects. First, each pair of variables gives rise to an interaction effect, resulting in the AB, AC, and BC interactions. Moreover, another interaction effect emerges from the combination of all three variables taken together, called the ABC interaction. That makes a total of four different interaction effects in addition to the three main effects.

The problem is not so much keeping track of the many interaction effects as it is trying to figure out what they mean for the substantive problem under study. Our theories are often not developed well enough for us to know what to make of the higher-order interaction effects among many variables. It is usually desirable to have these interaction effects to be statistically nonsignificant, since they then can be dropped from the model and their sums of squares pooled with the residual sum of squares.

As with the analysis involving two variables, the analysis of more variables requires the explanatory variables to be unrelated if we want separate, unique effects for each of the variables. This is most easily achieved if there are the same numbers of observations for each combination of the explanatory variables. This is only seldom the case for observational data, while it is much easier to achieve for experimental situations.

Latin Square Design

Basic ideas. As we increase the number of explanatory variables, we are faced with the problem of measuring our data under increasingly complex circumstances. In order to make the data gathering less cumbersome and less costly, and perhaps at all feasible, we can avail ourselves of more specialized designs, one of which is called the latin square design.

Suppose the effects of three variables A, B, and C on a dependent variable Y are to be examined, and that each explanatory variable has the same number of categories. In a psychological perception experiment, for example, the color of an object may be one of the explanatory variables, its four categories being red, blue, yellow, and white. The other two variables may be shape and texture, each with four categories. Taken together, the three variables define (4)(4)(4) = 64 different combinations of categories. In order to investigate whether these three variables have any effect on the dependent variable Y, we could set up an experiment to be analyzed by a three-way analysis of variance. With 64 distinct combinations, a minimum of 64 observations would be required, giving only one observation for every combination. A full analysis would require more than one observation for every combination of the explanatory variables. Gathering data under these conditions may be expensive and cumbersome, perhaps making it too difficult to conduct the research.

A latin square design provides a solution to this dilemma. Such a design permits the investigator to study the effects of A, B, and C on Y using only (4)(4) = 16 instead of 64 observations as a minimum for analysis. This reduction is made possible by the assumption that all four interaction effects AB, AC, BC, and ABC are equal to zero. The interaction terms capture the lion's share of degrees of freedom, in this example AB, AC, and BC each being responsible for (4–1)(4–1) = 9 degrees of freedom, and the ABC interaction takes up (4–1)(4–1)(4–1) = 27 degrees of freedom. This adds up to 54 out of a grand total of 63. Only 9 degrees of freedom are used for the effects of the three variables themselves. Once we ignore the interaction effects, we can proceed with a far smaller number of degrees of freedom and, thus, number of observations. If the assumption of no interaction effects is tenable, the use of a latin square design offers great savings in time and effort.

This kind of a saving is obtained by carefully selecting the combinations of the three explanatory variables for which the dependent variable Y is observed. We choose combinations of categories that are balanced in such a way that the effects of A, B, and C can actually be assessed.

Design and analysis. Suppose the categories for variable A are denoted A_1, A_2, A_3, and A_4, and similarly for the other two variables B and C. One possibility is to observe Y for the following set of combinations:

Combinations of A, B and C	Value of Y
$A_1B_1C_1$	y_{111}
$A_1B_2C_4$	y_{124}
$A_1B_3C_3$	y_{133}
$A_1B_4C_2$	y_{142}
$A_2B_1C_2$	y_{212}
$A_2B_2C_1$	y_{221}
$A_2B_3C_4$	y_{234}
$A_2B_4C_3$	y_{243}
$A_3B_1C_3$	y_{313}
$A_3B_2C_2$	y_{322}
$A_3B_3C_1$	y_{331}
$A_3B_4C_4$	y_{344}
$A_4B_1C_4$	y_{414}
$A_4B_2C_3$	y_{423}
$A_4B_3C_2$	y_{432}
$A_4B_4C_1$	y_{441}

The notation for the three subscripts for Y is such that the first subscript refers to the category of the A variable, the second subscript to the category of the B variable, and the third subscript to the category of the C variable.

This list of combinations is not as random as it may seem, and there is a system underlying the selection. The system is such that each category of A occurs once with each category of B and of C; that is, A_1 occurs together with each of the four categories of B as well as with each of the four categories of C, and the same for A_2, A_3, and A_4. The same principle also holds true for the other two variables B and C. It is this kind of balancing of the categories that will make it possible to extract separate and unique sums of squares for the variables A, B, and C. Note that this particular way of combining the categories of the three variables is only one of several ways the categories can be combined.

Another way of displaying the combinations of categories is shown in Table 22. Variable A determines the rows of the table, variable B the columns, and the cells of the table are reserved for variable C. A close look at the table shows that a particular category of C occurs once in each row and each column of the table. This assures that each category of a variable occurs only once with each of the categories of the other variables.

The bottom part of the table shows numerical values of the dependent variable Y for each of the 16 cells of the design, here one observation per cell. We now turn to the question of how to assess the effects of the three variables A, B, and C on Y. The values of Y are not alike because they have been affected by A, B, C, and the residual variable, and the degree to which the observations are different is measured by the total sum of squares, TSS. Here we have

$$\text{TSS} = \Sigma(y_{ijk} - \overline{y})^2 = 271.42$$

with 15 degrees of freedom, since there are 16 observations.

In order to find how much A, B, and C have contributed to this sum, we must first find the mean of Y for each of the categories of A, B, and C. Since each of the three variables has four categories, we must compute 12 different means. Let us start with the mean of Y for the first category of A. The category A_1, occurs with the four observations in the first row of the table, and their mean is

$$\begin{aligned}\overline{y}_{1\cdot\cdot} &= (y_{111} + y_{124} + y_{133} + y_{142})/4 \\ &= (12.0 + 10.5 + 10.7 + 11.2)/4 = 11.10\end{aligned}$$

Since the first subscript refers to the A variable and we are finding the mean for the first category of A, we denote this mean $\overline{y}_{1\cdot\cdot}$, with dots placed in the second and third subscript to indicate that we have added up over those subscripts for B and C. Similarly, we find

$$\overline{y}_{2\cdot\cdot} = 12.22 \qquad \overline{y}_{3\cdot\cdot} = 12.15 \qquad \overline{y}_{4\cdot\cdot} = 4.52$$

These means are different, indicating that A has an effect. To measure that effect we subtract the overall mean of 10.00 from each of the four group means, square the differences, multiply each difference by the number of observations in the group (4), and add these products. That gives the following sum of squares for the A variable,

$$\begin{aligned}\text{SSA} &= 4(11.10 - 10.00)^2 + 4(12.22 - 10.00)^2 \\ &\quad + 4(12.15 - 10.00)^2 + 4(4.52 - 10.00)^2 \\ &= 163.04\end{aligned}$$

TABLE 22
Combinations of Categories Used in a Latin Square Design, with Data

	B_1	B_2	B_3	B_4	
A_1	C_1	C_4	C_3	C_2	
A_2	C_2	C_1	C_4	C_3	
A_3	C_3	C_2	C_1	C_4	
A_4	C_4	C_3	C_2	C_1	
					Means
	12.0	10.5	10.7	11.2	11.10
	15.9	10.3	15.2	7.5	12.22
	12.7	11.2	13.6	11.1	12.15
	7.7	0.1	8.6	1.7	4.52
Means	12.08	8.02	12.02	7.88	10.00

The sum of squares for B is found in a similar way. B has an effect if the means for the four categories of B are different. These means are found as the four column means, and they are different. The magnitude of the differences is measured by subtracting the overall mean from each of the four group means, squaring each difference, and multiplying each square by 4. The sum of squares for B is found by adding these products, that is,

$$SSB = \Sigma 4(\bar{y}_{.j.} - \bar{y})^2 = 67.29$$

The sum of squares for C is more cumbersome to find because the means for the different categories of C are not as apparent in the data table as the means for A and B. In order to find the mean of the four observations for C_1, we see that this category occurs for the observations that are located on the diagonal in the table running from the upper left to the lower right. The mean of these observations gives us $\bar{y}_{..1} = 9.40$. Similarly, for $\bar{y}_{..2}$ we collect the four observations that refer to C_2, and the same procedure is followed for the other two means. The effect of variable C is measured the same way as for A and B, and we get

$$SSC = \Sigma 4(\bar{y}_{..k} - \bar{y})^2 = 38.66$$

The residual sum of squares is found by subtracting the sums of squares for A, B, and C from the total sum of squares. The various sums of squares with their degrees of freedom, mean squares, and F-ratios are shown in Table 23. All three variables have significant effects, and together they account for almost all the variation in Y.

The advantage of a latin square design is that it makes it possible to assess the effects of several explanatory variables by observing a smaller number of observations than the total number of combinations of the explanatory variables. In this example we need only 16 observations, even though the three variables define a total of 64 possible combinations. But this procedure is only permitted if all the interaction effects can be assumed to be insignificant. Violations of this assumption call the use of a latin square design into question (Winer, 1971: 514-538).

Nested Designs

A variety of designs for collecting and analyzing data exist beyond those discussed above. From among the remaining designs we mention the nested design, sometimes also called hierarchical design. In its most simple form the nested design is an incomplete two-way design. It is incomplete in the sense that not all the data are available which would allow for a two-way analysis the way such an analysis is discussed in Chapters 3 and 4.

As an example of data calling for a nested design, take congressional districts organized within those states with more than one district. If we were to assess the effect of district versus the effect of state level forces on some dependent variable, we would construct a design in which the districts were nested within their respective states. Since a given district is located only in one state, the two explanatory variables district and state cannot be completely crossed the way the two explanatory variables were crossed in Chapter 3. Table 24 presents a fragment of the nested design, listing three states S_1, S_2, and S_3 with three congressional districts nested within each state. Within each district n individuals are observed on the dependent variable Y. The notation for y_{ijk} is such that the first subscript refers to state, the second to district, and the third to individual.

A nested design in conjunction with a random model was employed by Stokes (1965, 1967) in his study of electoral effects. Voting turnout as well as the party division in congressional elections were observed across

TABLE 23
Analysis of Variance Table for Latin Square Example

Source	*Sum of Squares*	*Degrees of Freedom*	*Mean Square*	*F-ratio*	*Significance*
A	163.04	3	54.34	509.80	0.0000
B	67.29	3	22.43	55.15	0.0001
C	38.66	3	12.88	31.69	0.0004
Residual	2.44	6	0.41		
Total	271.43	15			

TABLE 24
Form of the Data for a Nested Design

	Congressional District								
State	C_1	C_2	C_3	C_4	C_5	C_6	C_7	C_8	C_9
S_1	y_{111} y_{112} ⋮ y_{11n}	y_{121} y_{122} ⋮ y_{12n}	y_{131} y_{132} ⋮ y_{13n}						
S_2				y_{241} y_{242} ⋮ y_{24n}	y_{251} y_{252} ⋮ y_{25n}	y_{261} y_{262} ⋮ y_{26n}			
S_3							y_{371} y_{372} ⋮ y_{37n}	y_{381} y_{382} ⋮ y_{38n}	y_{391} y_{392} ⋮ y_{39n}

time for districts, states, and the nation as a whole. The purpose of the analysis was to separate out the effects due to district, state, and national forces as they bear on voting turnout and the partisan division of the vote. Stokes presents the variance components for the three effects and compares their sizes across a long historical span, noting striking trends in the variations of these effects over time.

Analysis of Variance and Regression

A final comment is devoted to the relationship between analysis of variance and regression analysis. These models are closely related because they are both special cases of the so-called general linear model. Regression is treated in more detail in several other papers in this series, and we merely intend to hint at two aspects of the interface between the two models.

Both regression and analysis of variance. The first issue we raise is the question of what happens if we apply both methods to the same data. When there are several values of the dependent variable Y for each value of the independent variable X and X is a metric variable, then it is possible to do analysis of variance as well as regression. An illustration of data of this kind is shown in the top of Table 25, where there are five different values of X and for each X there are from two to five values of Y. As an example, let X measure media use on a scale from 1 to 5, and Y is the rating score of the importance of the economy.

Since X is a metric variable, regression analysis would seem like the proper model for the analysis of the relationship between X and Y. The results of such a regression analysis are shown just below the data in Table 25. The slope is positive, the relationship is fairly strong, and the relationship is very significant. Since there is only one X variable, the degrees of freedom split up with 1 for the regression and as many as 13 for the residual, measuring how well the regression model fits.

It is also possible to do a one-way analysis of variance on these data. In that case we look at these data as simply arranged in five different groups. We make no use of the fact that X is a metric variable, which provides a strong ordering of the groups from small to large values of X. By giving up this fact we are not using all the information in the data, and the penalty for this turns out to be that we must use more degrees of freedom for the model, leaving fewer for the residual.

The results from the analysis of variance are shown in the middle of Table 25. The total sums of squares and degrees of freedom are the same as for the regression analysis, but they are allocated differently. In

TABLE 25
Both Regression and Analysis of Variance

Data:	X:	1	2	3	4	5
	Y:	4	5	6	6	8
		3	4	5	7	10
		2	3	4	8	
				3		

Regression analysis: $Y = 1.03 + 1.45X$ $R^2 = 52.35/70.40 = 0.75$

Source	*Sum of Squares*	*Degrees of Freedom*	*Mean Square*	*F-ratio*	*Significance*
Regression	52.35	1	52.35	33.95	0.00006
Residual	20.05	13	1.54		
Total	70.40	14			
Analysis of variance:				$eta^2 = 59.40/70.40 = 0.84$	
Groups	59.40	4	14.85	11.42	0.001
Residual	13.00	10	1.30		
Total	70.40	14			
Combined:					
Regression	52.35	1	52.35	40.27	0.0001
Deviation from line	7.05	3	2.35	1.81	0.21
Residual	13.00	10	1.30		
Total	72.40	14			

particular, the residual sum of squares is smaller for the analysis of variance, indicating that the analysis of variance model fits better than the regression model. On the other hand, the regression model requires only 1 degree of freedom, while the analysis of variance model requires 4 degrees of freedom. The net effect of the different sums of squares and degrees of freedom is that the F for the regression is much more significant than the F for analysis of variance. Thus, if the analysis is done for the purpose of seeing whether a relationship is significant, regression is the better model to use.

But since the analysis of variance fits better, it gives the stronger relationship. Measuring the strength of the relationship, we find that with regression we get R^2 equal to 0.75, while for analysis of variance we get eta^2 equal to 0.84. The fact that the relationship is stronger using analysis of variance is simply a reflection of the fact that analysis of variance uses 4 degrees of freedom and regression only 1. In general, the more degrees of freedom a model uses for the study of a relationship between two variables, the better the model fits and the stronger the relationship becomes. But the fewer degrees of freedom a model uses, the more parsimonious it is and the better it helps us understand the nature of the relationship.

Aside from comparing the two methods, there is another reason for doing both analyses. Together they permit us to examine whether the relationship between X and Y is linear or not. The regression model assumes a linear relationship, but many times we do no more than casually look at a scatterplot to see if the assumption is true. The reason we now can do more has to do with the residuals. In regression they are measured as deviations from the regression line, whereas in analysis of variance they are measured as deviations from the group means. If the regression line passes through all the group means, then the residuals will be the same for the two analyses. But when the relationship is not linear, the regression line will not pass through the group means, and the two sets of residuals will be different. In particular, the residuals around the regression line will produce a larger sum of squares than the residuals around the group means.

By comparing the results from the two analyses, we find that the two residual sums of squares differ by 7.05. They differ because the group means do not lie on the regression line. In the bottom part of Table 25 this difference is entered as "deviation from line" sum of squares along with the residual sum of squares from the analysis of variance and the regression sum of squares from the regression analysis. The 4 degrees of freedom from the analysis of variance have been allocated with 1 for the linear relationship, as found by the regression analysis, and 3 for the nonlinear part of the relationship. That gives us the mean squares and F-ratios in the combined table, showing a very significant linear relationship and a nonsignificant deviation from linearity.

Regression instead of analysis of variance. Data studied by analysis of variance can always be studied using regression analysis with suitably constructed dummy variables. Any categorical variable can be represented by a set of dummy variables; and even though it may be cumbersome to set up the dummy variables, the regression software may be easier to use than analysis of variance software. For a much more

TABLE 26
Dummy Variables for Data in Table 3

Group	Y	D_1	D_2	D_3	D_4
A	6	1	0	0	0
	6	1	0	0	0
	6	1	0	0	0
	8	1	0	0	0
	9	1	0	0	0
B	7	0	1	0	0
	8	0	1	0	0
	8	0	1	0	0
	8	0	1	0	0
	9	0	1	0	0
C	4	0	0	1	0
	4	0	0	1	0
	5	0	0	1	0
	6	0	0	1	0
	6	0	0	1	0
D	5	0	0	0	1
	5	0	0	0	1
	6	0	0	0	1
	6	0	0	0	1
	8	0	0	0	1
E	3	0	0	0	0
	4	0	0	0	0
	4	0	0	0	0
	4	0	0	0	0
	5	0	0	0	0

extensive discussion of the correspondence between the two sets of models, see Edwards (1979).

As an illustration, let us go back to the data in Table 3 used for the comparison of several groups in the one-way analysis of variance and do a regression analysis instead. Since there are 5 groups of observations, we need 4 dummy variables for the analysis. The assignment of zeros and ones for the dummy variables are shown in Table 26.

A multiple regression of Y on the four variables D_1, D_2, D_3, and D_4 results in the estimated regression equation

$$Y = 4.0 + 3.0D_1 + 4.0D_2 + 1.0D_3 + 2.0D_4$$

The sums of squares and degrees of freedom for this analysis are identical to those shown for the analysis of variance in Table 5. Since there are four explanatory variables in this regression analysis, we get four degrees of freedom for the regression sum of squares of 12.50. Since the sums of squares are the same in the two analyses, we also get that eta square is equal to R square. In short, there are no differences between the results of the two analyses. The use of dummy variables works equally well for two-way analyses of variance.

The choice of method of analysis comes down to a question of convenience. Depending on how the data file is set up or the availability of computer software, one analysis may be easier to perform than another. The choice may also depend on personal preference, some people find regression analysis more appealing while others prefer analysis of variance.

6. CONCLUSIONS

Review

We entered into the discussion of the method known as analysis of variance (ANOVA) by way of a substantive question. The question dealt with the effect the mass media may have on the public's concern with the economy. Let us now review to what extent ANOVA has helped us answer that basic question. The data came from hypothetical experiments.

One-way ANOVA, employing what is called a fixed model, has applied a test of the (null) hypothesis that television newscasts have no effect on how important people rate the economy as an issue. An experimental group viewed a newscast containing a story on the economy, while a control group viewed the same newscast minus the economy story; participants of both groups were randomly assigned to the groups. The results showed a highly significant F-ratio, which meant that the null hypothesis was rejected. We conclude that television newscasts raise the public's concern with the economy.

But do they do equally so for the key economic issues, namely unemployment and inflation, and does it matter whether the news is good or bad for each of these issues? These questions call for an extension on the one-way to a two-way ANOVA. Now, the economic issue (unemployment, inflation) forms one explanatory variable, while the valence of the news coverage (positive, negative) forms the other. By randomly assigning the subjects to one of the four conditions created by crossing the two variables, we are able to eliminate the systematic effect of all other variables. Moreover, by assigning the same number of subjects to each condition, we make certain that the two explanatory variables are uncorrelated with each other. Only with equal, or unequal but proportional, cell frequencies can we proceed in a straightforward fashion to estimate the unique effect of each explanatory variable on the dependent variable, test for the significance of each, and estimate the proportion of the overall variation due to each explanatory variable.

Two-way ANOVA also introduces a concept not known in a one-way analysis: the concept of interaction. This refers to the way in which a category of one explanatory variable combines with a category of the other explanatory variable to produce an effect on the dependent variable that goes beyond the sum of the separate effects. In this example the analysis shows that when the news is negative, unemployment and inflation stories create the same concern in the public with the economy. But when the news is positive, only unemployment stories create little concern, while inflation stories still generate moderate levels of concern.

Interaction is a feature common in both experimental and observational studies. In addition, observational studies typically confront the researcher with correlated explanatory variables. This correlation complicates two-way ANOVA, which was not designed with that condition in mind. In using two-way ANOVA on data with correlated explanatory variables, the analyst must decide which of the explanatory variables is to be entered into the analysis first. As in royal families, being first carries considerable privilege. In ANOVA it bestows the shared explanatory variation to the variable entered first, with the result that the variable entered second will prove less significant than if it came first; at worst, its effect is no longer statistically significant. With correlated variables two-way ANOVA leaves us out on a limb with two sets of estimated effects to choose from. To decide we must reach for metastatistical considerations.

These considerations are illustrated with data from a hypothetical sample survey on the salience of the economy among blacks and whites and depending on whether one personally suffered unemployment or not. Neither of these conditions lends itself to experimental manipulation, and they are plainly correlated with each other. The sums of squares, as estimates of the effects of race and unemployment, are shown to change sharply depending on which of the two takes the first crack at explaining the importance ratings of the economy.

Having grappled with the intricacies of correlated variables, also known as a nonorthogonal design, we took on what is known as the random model. Whatever the differences of ANOVA considered so far, all those versions conform to the fixed model, where data are available for all categories of the explanatory variable. In research situations where this is not feasible, the random model comes to the rescue. Now the researcher has to obtain a random sample of categories, and then for each of the chosen categories a random sample of respondents is chosen. The need for a sample of categories arises in studies of the effect of something that occurs in almost limitless permutations, such as orderings of questions in a questionnaire. Salience ratings of the economy, for example, may very well depend on where among other items this question is placed, with possibly damaging consequences for the substantive conclusions.

Both the fixed and random models make certain assumptions which we noted on several occasions. These assumptions, however, need not always be met in the strictest sense of their meanings. Sometimes they can be moderately violated without the results losing their theoretical justification.

The assumption of a normal distribution of the residuals for each category or combination of categories of the explanatory variable(s) is one of them. This assumption need not bother us greatly as long as the sample of observations for each category is relatively large. This goes for both the fixed and the random model, as far as they were presented, although departures from normality are to be taken more seriously in the latter case. The random model, moreover, also requires the effects to be normally distributed. To secure large sample sizes of respondents would seem an easier job for survey studies than for experiments.

A second assumption worth our attention concerns the variance of the residual term. This variance is supposed to be constant for all categories or combination of categories of the explanatory variable(s). This assumption can be explicitly tested; but even when it is found lacking, the analysis is not necessarily doomed. This holds true, for example, in one-way analysis employing a fixed model as long as the number of observations is approximately equal for all categories. Whereas the planning of experiments typically can assure such equality, survey studies are less equipped to do so.

Other Topics

This short introduction to analysis of variance covers the major issues and leaves other topics to further studies. Throughout the discussion we have stated what assumptions the data have to satisfy in order to do the analysis, but we have left out a more detailed treatment of what happens if the assumptions are not satisfied. We have not discussed what is known as multiple comparison procedures, which enable us to compare subsets of group means after the null hypothesis of equal means has been rejected. Furthermore, with unequal number of observations in the groups, we have correlated explanatory variables, and we give only a brief introduction to the solution of this problem. We do not explicitly discuss the so-called repeated measurement designs, where several observations have been made on a single unit (individual). These observations can be taken together as a block of observations, and the variations in the individuals can be taken out of the residual sum of squares. It is also worth mentioning that we give only a limited discussion of the treatment of interactions. For a more detailed discussion of these and other issues, we refer to the textbooks in the references or other texts on analysis of variance.

REFERENCES

ANSCOMBE, F. J. and J. W. TUKEY (1963) "The examination and analysis of residuals." Techometrics 5, no. 2 (May): 141-160.

BLOOM, H. S. and H. D. PRICE (1975) "Voter response to short-run economic conditions: The asymmetric effect of prosperity and recession." American Political Science Review 69: 1240-1254.

COBB, G. (1984) "An algorithmic approach to elementary ANOVA." The American Statistician 38 (May): 120-123.

COCHRAN, W. G. (1965) "The planning of observational studies of human populations." J. of the Royal Statistical Society, series A, 128, part 2: 234-265.

———(1983) Planning and Analysis of Observational Studies. New York: Wiley

COCHRAN, W. G. and G. COX (1957) Experimental Designs. New York: Wiley.

EDWARDS, A. F. (1979) Multiple Regression and the Analysis of Variance and Covariance. San Francisco: W. H. Freeman.

HAYS, W. J. (1981) Statistics, 3rd ed. New York: Holt, Rinehart & Winston.

IYENGAR, S. and D. R. KINDER (1987) News that Matters: Television and American Opinion. Chicago: Chicago University Press.

KERNELL, S. (1977) "Presidential popularity and negative voting." American Political Science Review 71: 44-66.

LANOUE, D. (1986) Understanding Presidential Popularity in the United States: Prosperity and Partisanship. Ph.D. dissertation, SUNY at Stony Brook.

PETERSEN, R. G. (1986) Design and Analysis of Experiments. New York: Marcel Dekker.

SCHEFFÉ, H. (1959) The Analysis of Variance. New York: Wiley.

SNEDECOR, G. W. and W. G. COCHRAN (1967) Statistical Methods. Ames: Iowa State Univ. Press.

STOKES, D. E. (1965) "A variance components model of political effects," in J. M. Claunch (ed.). Mathematical Applications in Political Science. Dallas: Arnold Foundation, 61-85.

———(1967) "Parties and the nationalization of electoral forces," in W. N. Chambers and W. D. Burnham (eds.). The American Party Systems. New York: Oxford Univ. Press, 182-202.

WINER, B. J. (1971) Statistical Principles in Experimental Design. New York: McGraw-Hill.

PART IV

ANALYSIS OF COVARIANCE

ALBERT R. WILDT
OLLI T. AHTOLA

1. INTRODUCTION

Overview of Analysis of Covariance

Numerous situations arise in the social sciences where interest centers on the relationship or association between two variables or among a number of variables. For example, a political scientist may wish to contrast voting frequency by sex and/or income, or a sociologist may be concerned with the relationship between mobility and the age of the head of the household. In cases where such measurement of association is of concern, the statistical procedure employed by the researcher is, in part, determined by the nature of the variables under consideration.

Considering only instances involving a single dependent variable, a number of different cases may be constructed according to whether the independent and dependent variables are quantitative or qualitative in nature. Quantitative variables are interval- or ratio-scaled (e.g., age expressed in years or income expressed in dollars), and qualitative variables are categorical and include both nominal- and ordinal-scaled measures (e.g., sex or religion). Those cases in which the dependent variable is qualitative or categorical are not of primary concern to the following discussion and are not considered.

Instances involving a single quantitative dependent variable may be classified into one of three cases. Case 1 involves one or more qualitative (categorical) independent variables. In this context the researcher is usually investigating the possibility of differences in the average value of the dependent variable over the various categories of the independent variable(s). An analysis procedure appropriate for case 1 is analysis of variance. (The reader is referred to Iverson and Norpoth [1976] for a discussion of analysis of variance.) Case 2 involves quantitative independent variables. In this context the researcher is usually investigating for possible changes in the dependent variable which may accompany changes in the independent variable(s). Correlation and regression analysis are appropriate procedures here. Case 3 involves both quantitative and qualitative independent variables. This case is of primary concern for the present discussion, and two alternate (though statistically similar) procedures are available for analyzing situations which meet this condition. They are analysis of covariance and regression analysis with dummy variables. It is analysis of covariance which is of concern in the discussion to follow.

Analysis of covariance is a special case of the linear model, just as are the regression and the analysis of variance models. Traditionally, regression analysis has been used in conjunction with survey designs or observational data, and analysis of variance with experimental designs. Analysis of covariance, which is a combination of the two techniques, can be discussed as either an extension of regression analysis or as an extension of analysis of variance. This is quite natural because the technique is useful whether the underlying design is experimental, quasi-experimental or purely observational—without any experimental control or manipulation.

Because of the relationship of analysis of covariance to regression analysis and analysis of variance, an understanding of the basic concepts of these two procedures is essential to the understanding of analysis of covariance. Accordingly, in the discussion presented in this paper it is assumed that the reader possesses this necessary basic knowledge of analysis of variance and regression analysis.

Alternate Problem Perspectives with Analysis of Covariance

Within the class of problems involving a quantitative dependent variable and both quantitative and qualitative independent variables, there are three different problem perspectives which are commonly encountered. Analysis of covariance may be used with each of these perspectives. The first perspective, which we designate as the experimental perspective, involves those instances when interest centers on the differences occurring in the dependent variable over the categories, or levels of the qualitative independent variable(s). In these cases it is assumed that one or more quantitative independent variables, referred to as covariates, influence the dependent variable in a linear fashion, and independently of the level or category of the qualitative independent variable(s); but this relationship is *not of primary concern* to the researcher (the covariate is considered a nuisance variable). The quantitative independent variable (covariate) is included in the analysis either to remove extraneous variation from the dependent variable, and thereby, increase the precision of the analysis, or to remove bias due to the groups not being matched on that quantitative independent variable. The analysis procedure in this case can be viewed as adjusting the dependent variable for differences in the covariate and then investigating the relationship between the qualitative independent variable(s) and the adjusted values of the dependent variable. This type of situation arises in the case of both observational studies and designed experiments. It is this case which is covered in considerable detail in succeeding sections.

The second problem perspective is exemplified by those situations in which primary concern centers upon the relationship between the dependent variable and the quantitative independent variable(s) or covariate(s). In these cases one or more categorical, or qualitative, independent variables represent the nuisance factor, included in the specification of the model in order to make it more realistic. In this type of application, the analysis of covariance technique extends the study of regression analysis to data of more complex structure in which the nature of the regression might be obscured by the effects of the categorical independent variable. In analyzing data in this context, the researcher first removes the effects of the categorical independent variable, and then examines the nature of the relationship between the quantitative variables.

With the third perspective, which we designate as the regression perspective, the covariate(s) and the categorical independent variable(s) are of equal interest and there is often no reason to suspect any causal priority. In cases such as this, the researcher may wish to examine the effect or contribution of each independent variable (both quantitative and qualitative), after adjusting or correcting for the effects of all other independent variables. This perspective is most commonly taken in cases involving observational, rather than experimental data. This analysis is equivalent to regression analysis where the qualitative independent variables are represented by dummy variables.

The perspective adopted by the researcher will usually depend upon the problem context, the type of data employed and, in some cases, the background of the researcher. The two most commonly used perspectives are the experimental and the regression perspectives. Also, it should be noted that the name applied to the analysis may vary depending upon the perspective taken. Those researchers trained in an experimental design tradition usually employ the experimental perspective and label the procedure, analysis of covariance. On the other hand, researchers exposed more often to problems which are not amenable to experimentation usually assume the regression perspective and label the procedure regression analysis with dummy variables.

With this background, a brief discussion of some applications of analysis of covariance is presented before entering into a more technical discussion of the procedure itself.

2. APPLICATIONS OF ANALYSIS OF COVARIANCE

Four applications of analysis of covariance are presented below. The discussion is nontechnical in nature, and intended to provide a sense for the type of situations in which analysis of covariance has been and can be utilized. The applications discussed include both observational and experimental studies.

Application One: Coerciveness and Change

Feierabend and Feierabend (1972) report on an observational study relating the rate of social change to the level of permissiveness-coerciveness of a political regime. The final analysis of the study is a one-way analysis of covariance utilizing data from seventy-six countries over the post World War II period. The dependent variable is the rate of socioeconomic change, a combined rate of change index based on the pooled standard scores of annual measures of change on selected variables (caloric intake, urbanization, radios, and primary education). The categorical independent variable is the degree of permissiveness-coerciveness; three levels based on the composite ratings of three factors (presence of civil rights, toleration of political opposition, and democracy in government) intended to measure the extent to which political and social freedoms are present in a society.

Analysis of covariance was utilized in an effort to adjust the rate of socioeconomic change for the level of development of each country (the covariate), expressed in a modernity index (computed by averaging standard scores on the following indicators: urbanization, gross national product, caloric intake, physicians, newspapers, radios, and telephones). The rationale for this adjustment is the assumption that the more highly developed a country is, the lower the relative change is apt to be. This adjustment is made so as to allow the measurement of the degree to which differences between groups are significant when each case is set statistically equal to every other case on the controlled variable (level of development). This particular application represents an attempt to remove the effects of a disturbing variable (i.e., the bias introduced because the groups were not matched on level of development) in an observational study.

Application Two: Partitioning and Perceived Crowding in a Public Space

Stokols, Smith, and Prostor (1975) report on a field experiment to examine the potential utility of behavioral research for architectural design. They investigated the relationship between a specific aspect of architectural design (method of aerial partitioning) and the perception of crowding. The setting for the research was the waiting area in a southern California office of the Division of Motor Vehicles. Three experimental trials were conducted on successive Mondays, each employing one of three levels of partitioning. The first level involved minimal partitioning in which the floor area was uncluttered and persons waiting for service could form a line in any manner they chose. The second involved a series of ropes and standings which partitioned the area in a maze-like fashion so as to direct the movement of individuals waiting in line. The third method was similar to the second with the exception that five foot high portable partitions were used in place of ropes. The main dependent measures considered in the study were the degree to which subjects felt crowded or uncrowded, and relaxed or tense while waiting in line.

It was suspected that individual differences in subjects would influence reaction to the experimental variable. Therefore, specific characteristics most likely to moderate subjects' reactions were identified. They included items pertaining to the subjects perception of crowding and noise at home, their friendliness towards roommate or family members and the number of persons with whom they shared a bedroom.

Upon exit from the waiting area each subject was asked to complete a questionnaire, which included a series of seven-point bi-polar scales pertaining to the dependent variables. Information on subject characteristics was also obtained. The data were anlayzed using analysis of covariance in the context of a two-way (two variable: method of partitioning and sex) design. A separate analysis was conducted for each dependent variable.

In this application, covariance analysis was employed in conjunction with a field experiment in an effort to statistically control or adjust for individual subject differences. By inclusion of the covariates, the researcher can adjust for those behavioral differences attributable to subject characteristics. This reduces the variability of response within levels of the experimental variable, and therefore, achieves a more accurate experiment.

Application Three: Comparison of Alternate Teaching Methods

Some experimental studies employ existing (intact) groups which may differ in some important respects. In many instances intact groups offer a more practical approach to a given problem. In such instances, analysis of covariance may be a useful device for performing the statistical analysis because it provides a means both to remove bias attributable to the experimental groups not being matched on some important subject characteristic, and to increase the precision of the experiment. Pasternack and Charen (1969) illustrated the use of analysis of covariance in the comparison of the relative effectiveness of two methods of presenting laboratory experiments to (intact) classes of high school students. The classes differed in previous knowledge of the subject matter and in level of intelligence. It was suspected that these differences might influence the achievement of the students on the evaluative instruments used. Therefore, the scores of the students were statistically adjusted for differences in the auxiliary variables by analysis of covariance.

Operationally, the study consisted of a pretest followed by the experimental manipulation with the same test being given at the completion of the experiment. Also, IQ scores of the students in the classes were obtained. In this case, the posttest score was the dependent variable, type of instruction was the independent categorical variable of primary concern, and the two other independent variables, pretest and IQ scores, were employed as covariates. This particular instance illustrates the use of analysis of covariance in an effort to remove bias which would result because the intact groups were not matched on some relevant variable.

Application Four: American Occupational Structure

Blau and Duncan (1967), in their study *American Occupational Structure*, illustrate the use of analysis of covariance in the context of an observational study. They considered the problem of relating present occupational status to occupational status of the first job, where occupational status is measured on an interval scale. However, the researchers were concerned that educational level will have an effect on the relationship under investigation. For this specific case, analysis of covariance may be employed to investigate whether or not the slopes (i.e., the nature of the linear relationship between present occupational status and status of first job) are the same for all educational levels. The problem is formulated with present occupational status as the dependent variable, educational level as the categorical independent variable, and occupational status on first job as the continuous independent variable or covariate. Analysis of covariance may be used in this application to detect major patterns of interaction that may be present in the three variable problem. If no interaction is detected, then it will be assumed that the slope, the coefficient relating present occupational status to occupational status of the first job, is constant over occupational levels; in which case, the data may be pooled and a common slope employed. In this particular problem, interest centers on the relationship of the dependent variable and the covariate.

3. PRINCIPAL USES OF ANALYSIS OF COVARIANCE

Problem applications in which analysis of covariance is appropriate are characterized by the presence of a quantitative dependent variable, and both quantitative and qualitative independent variables. A large number of experimental and observational studies meet this criterion. And, even though it has not been frequently applied to problems in the social sciences, analysis of covariance has numerous potential applications for social science research.

The principal uses of analysis of covariance are:

(1) to increase precision in randomized experiments,
(2) to remove bias which may result when test units cannot be assigned at random to experimental conditions,
(3) to remove the effects of disturbing variables in observational studies, and
(4) to fit regressions in the context of multiple classifications.

Increase Precision of Randomized Experiments

In experimental settings considerable effort is usually expended in an attempt to increase the accuracy of the experiment by controlling extraneous variability. Extraneous variability in experiments is typically controlled in one of two ways. The experimenter either applies experimental (direct) control or statistical (indrect) control. Direct control includes such methods as maintaining extraneous variables at constant levels, grouping the objects under study into homogeneous groups (blocks), increasing the uniformity of conditions under which the experiment is run, and increasing the accuracy of the measurements. This type of control is incorporated through the design of experimental procedures.

Indirect (statistical) control relates to the analysis of the experiment rather than its design. Statistical control may be achieved by measuring one or more concomitant variables in addition to the independent variable(s) of primary interest. By partitioning out the amount of variability in the dependent variable accounted for by the concomitant variables, the experimenter is able to more accurately assess the influence of the other independent (experimental) variable(s).

In randomized experiments, the dependent variable, in addition to being influenced by the experimental variable(s), may be subject to the influence of a quantitative independent variable, often reflecting some characteristic of the test unit. In these cases, covariance analysis serves to increase the precision of the experiment by removing the effect of an extraneous source of variance that would otherwise inflate the experimental error. This is similar to the reduction obtained by paring or matching test units.

The gain in precision from the use of the covariance adjustment depends upon the degree of correlation between the covariate and the dependent variable. The higher this correlation, the larger the variation attributable to the covariate, and the more effective the analysis of covariance procedure will be in reducing the error variance.

Remove Bias Due to Nonrandom Assignment of Experimental Test Units

Numerous situations arise in which the researcher finds it unfeasible to randomly assign individual test units to treatment conditions. In these cases a common procedure is to utilize preexisting (intact) groups and to randomly assign treatment levels to these groups. The utilization of analysis of covariance under these conditions may result in two benefits. First, analysis of covariance provides a method to adjust for preexisting differences among the intact groups employed in the experiment. In this respect, analysis of covariance may remove bias attributable to the fact that the intact groups are not similar, or matched, on certain important test unit characteristics. Second, the use of analysis of covariance in these situations may result in the same benefit as in a completely randomized experiment, that is, increase the precision of the experiment by reducing the error variance.

While the use of the analysis of covariance to adjust for preexisting differences among intact groups is very useful in certain instances, it should be used with caution. This caution stems from the fact that when random assignment is not used in forming experimental groups, the results may be subject to difficulties in interpretation. Whereas, in a properly randomized experiment all uncontrolled variables are distributed among the groups in such a way that they can be taken into account with the test of significance employed; this is not necessarily true when intact groups are employed. Therefore, there remains the possibility that some variable has been overlooked that will bias the evaluation of the experiment. The fact that the use of intact groups removes certain safeguards which are assured due to randomization, is pointed out by Lord (1967 and 1969). Lord concludes that when the test units are not randomly assigned to treatment groups, there is no logical nor statistical procedure that can be counted on to make proper allowances for uncontrolled preexisting differences between groups. Also, an inconvenience which often arises with the use of intact groups is that an unequal number of test units are assigned to the various treatment groups. This results in an unbalanced design which may complicate the analysis procedures in certain cases.

When to Use Analysis of Covariance in Experimental Settings

It should be understood that statistical control (e.g., covariance adjustment) and direct experimental control are alternate approaches to achieving the same goal of increasing the precision of an experiment. In some cases it may be convenient to control some variables by direct experimental control and some by statistical control (as is done in the randomized block analysis of covariance to be discussed later). This leads to the question of how to determine when to use covariance analysis.

Analysis of covariance is usually considered appropriate when the following conditions prevail: (1) there are one or more extraneous sources of variation believed to affect the dependent variable; (2) this extraneous source of variation can be measured on an interval (or ratio) scale; (3) the functional form of the relationship between the dependent variable and the extraneous variable(s) is known (a linear relationship is usually assumed); (4) direct experimental control of extraneous sources of variation is either not possible or not feasible; and (5) it is possible to obtain a measure of extraneous variation that does not include effects of the treatment. The fifth criterion is met when; (a) the observations on the covariate are obtained prior to the presentation of the treatments, or (b) the observations on the covariate are obtained after the presentation of the treatments but before the treatments have had an opportunity to affect the covariate, or (c) it can be assumed that the covariate is unaffected by the treatment. If this fifth condition is not satisfied and the covariate is influenced by the treatment, the adjustment made on the dependent variable is biased because some effects attributable to the treatment are eliminated from the dependent variable.

If measurements on the covariate(s) are obtained prior to presentation of treatments, an alternative research strategy is to use the covariate to form homogeneous groups of test units (blocks), and to analyze the data with the appropriate (randomized block design) analysis of variance procedure. In general, direct experimental control is considered preferable to analysis of covariance if an experimenter's principal interest is in reducing the experimental error, rather than removing bias from estimates of treatments effects caused by the use of intact groups. It is important to note that randomized block analysis of variance requires less restrictive assumptions than does covariance analysis. Analysis of covariance assumes that the correct form of regression equation has been fitted, and that the within treatment regression coefficients are homogeneous (the effect of the covariate does not vary over treatment groups). But the randomized block design is essentially a function-free regression that is appropriate even though the relationship between the dependent variable and the extraneous variable is nonlinear. Consequently, if homogeneous blocks can be formed, one need not worry about knowing the functional relationship between the blocking variable and the dependent variable. However, the interaction of blocks and treatment levels is assumed to be zero in most randomized block designs. This assumption is analogous to the assumption of homogeneity of regression coefficients in a covariance analysis.

Remove Bias in Observational Studies

In observational studies, naturally occurring groups are analyzed. With these groups it is recognized that differences in the dependent variable may occur due to differences in certain characteristics (variables) of the groups which are not of primary concern to the analysis. If analysis of variance is conducted without considering these characteristics, the results may be biased. In those cases where the disturbing variables are quantitative (interval- or ratio-scaled), analysis of covariance may be employed in an effort to remove the bias introduced because the groups have not been matched on these disturbing variables. In other words, differences may exist in these disturbing variables from group to group, and covariance analysis provides a means to statistically adjust the dependent variable for these preexisting differences. Also, in cases where the groups do not differ on the disturbing variables and there is no danger of bias, the covariance adjustment may act to increase the precision of the analysis in the same manner as in a randomized experiment.

Observational studies have a similarity to experimental studies employing intact groups. With experimental studies and intact groups, one is unable to randomly assign test units to treatments, however, one typically insures that treatments are randomly assigned into experimental groups. Observational studies utilize natural intact groups in which no random assignment may be made by the researcher. Therefore, the problems that may exist when using intact groups in experimental settings are also present and possibly compounded in observational settings. Typically, the way to ascertain whether these problems exist or not, is to investigate the degree of multicollinearity (amount of linear association among the independent variables) which exist within the observational data. If this collinearity is high it may be difficult or impossible to statistically separate the impact of the various independent variables on the dependent variable.

Regression with Multiple Classifications

In other situations, usually nonexperimental, interest of the researcher centers on the relationship between two or more quantitative variables; but concern exists with regard to the possible effects of some qualitative (categorical) variable upon this relationship. That is, the group to which the test units belong, or the classification of which they are a part, may moderate the nature of the relationship between the quantitative variables so that it will differ across groups or classifications. In cases such as this, analysis of covariance may be employed. In this analysis the researcher must first establish that there is no interaction between the covariate and the categorical independent variable. If an interaction is shown to exist, it warns the researcher that the relationship between the covariate and dependent variable varies over the levels of the categorical independent variable and that separate, individual analyses must be conducted for each level of the categorical independent variable. If the interaction is not statistically significant, it supports the assumption of constant slope, and the data for all levels of the categorical independent variable may be analyzed together within the context of the analysis of covariance model.

4. STATISTICAL PROCEDURES FOR ANALYSIS OF COVARIANCE FOR A ONE-WAY LAYOUT

Introduction

A one-way layout describes any context involving a single qualitative independent variable, with any number of levels, and one or more covariates (quantitative independent variables). The one-way layout is common to both experimental and observational studies. In randomized experiments, the one-way layout is analogous to the completely randomized design, where test units are randomly assigned to treatment levels of a single qualitative independent variable. Random experiments provide a strong basis for hypothesis testing, that is, they allow the rigorous testing of causal hypotheses, and represent the most desirable, though sometimes unattainable, conditions for hypothesis testing. In other experiments, where random assignment of test units is not feasible, preexisting groups are used and the treatment levels are randomly assigned to these intact groups. This type of experimental design is also a one-way layout, as long as it includes a single qualitative independent variable; but it does not, in general, lend itself to as strong a basis of hypothesis testing as does the completely randomized experiment. Observational studies, involving multiple groups, also come under the heading of the one-way layout. With observational studies, the test units are not randomly assigned to groups nor are the treatments randomly assigned to groups by the researcher, and this type of study is not as rigorous as experimental designs in establishing causal relationships between variables. Furthermore, as in experiments with intact groups, it is more difficult to eliminate the possibility that the group membership of a test unit has been influenced by the covariate or vice versa, which would bias the results.

As previously mentioned, three distinct problem perspectives may be employed in conjunction with analysis of covariance. Here we address the analysis procedures for one-way layouts associated with all three perspectives. However, primary consideration is given to the experimental perspective, which includes those cases, both observational and experimental, in which primary interest is in the effect of a single qualitative independent variable on the dependent variable and the covariates are considered nuisance variables. (It is noted that in this and subsequent sections of this paper a basic knowledge of analysis of variance and regression analysis is assumed. Also, all discussion of experimental designs that follows considers only fixed effects models. Consequently, it is *not* assumed that the treatment levels are a random selection of all possible treatment levels, so findings cannot be generalized to treatment levels other than those particular levels included in the analysis.)

Covariance Model

For the one-way layout, the covariance model considers the observed value of the dependent variable to be influenced by the effect of the particular treatment level or group from which the observation comes, and the values of the concomitant variables (covariates). Verbally, an additive model representing this situation is:

$$\begin{bmatrix}\text{Observed value}\\ \text{of dependent}\\ \text{variables}\end{bmatrix} = [\text{constant}] + \begin{bmatrix}\text{effect of}\\ \text{treatment}\\ \text{level or group}\end{bmatrix} + \begin{bmatrix}\text{effect}\\ \text{of}\\ \text{covariate}\end{bmatrix} + \begin{bmatrix}\text{resi-}\\ \text{dual}\\ \text{effect}\end{bmatrix}$$

Algegraically, the analysis of covariance model for the one-way layout with one covariate is represented as:

$$Y_{ij} = u + \tau_i + \beta(X_{ij} - \bar{X}) + e_{ij};\ i=1, \ldots, k;\ j=1, \ldots, n_i; \qquad [1]$$

where Y_{ij} is the observed value of the dependent variable for the jth observation within the ith group or treatment level, u is the true mean effect, τ_i is the effect due to the ith group or level of the categorical independent variable (treatment) with $\Sigma n_i \tau_i = 0$, β is the (regression) coefficient representing the average effect of a one unit change in the covariate on the dependent variable, X_{ij} is the observed value of the covariate, $\bar{X}$ is the general mean of the covariate, e_{ij} is a random error which is normally and independently distributed with mean zero and variance σ^2, k is the number of groups, and n_i is the number of observations in group i. The term $(X_{ij}-\bar{X})$ is used rather than X_{ij} so that the constant term of the model will be the grand mean of the dependent variable.

An explicit examination of the assumptions underlying the analysis of covariance model and the consequences of violating those assumptions is presented in the Appendix. Also, it is noted that the above model and the discussion that follows are applicable whether there are an equal or unequal number of observations in each group. However, for convenience of exposition the subscript on n_i will usually be dropped and $\sum_{i=1}^{k} n_i$ will be designated as N.

Completely Randomized Design

The term "completely randomized design" is used here in a broad sense and refers to those contexts, both experimental and observational, where interest centers on detecting differences in the dependent variable over the various levels of a single qualitative independent variable, which may represent distinct naturally occurring groups of observations or levels of an experimental treatment. The problem perspective assumed here is that which has previously been labled the experimental perspective, in which interest centers on the relationship between the qualitative independent variable and the dependent variable with the covariate, or quantitative independent variable, considered as a nuisance variable. Under this perspective, covariance analysis provides a means to adjust the dependent variable for the value of the covariate for each observation. This should allow more precise information on the treatment or group effects to be obtained. This is accomplished by reducing the error variance (i.e., subtracting out the effect of the covariate) and/or by adjusting the group means on the dependent variable for differences in the mean values of the covariate for the respective groups.

The adjustment for the covariate may be made in any of several different ways. In given instances the appropriate form of the adjustment is determined from prior knowledge about the relationship between the dependent variable and the covariate. However, in a large number of applications no strong evidence exists to indicate the form of the adjustment, in these cases the adjustment is usually assumed to amount to some scalar multiple of the covariate. Although the form of the adjustment need not be linear, only the linear case will be considered here. Furthermore, only one covariate will be considered in the following discussion. (For a discussion of multiple covariates refer to Kirk [1968] or Winer [1971].)

Considering equation 1, the dependent variable may be adjusted for the covariate as follows:

$$Y_{ij(adj)} = Y_{ij} - \beta(X_{ij} - \bar{X}) = u + \tau_i + e_{ij} \qquad [2]$$

where $Y_{ij(adj)}$ is the value of the dependent variable adjusted for the covariate. Since, as in analysis of variance, the usual purpose of analysis of covariance within the experimental perspective is to test the hypothesis that group means are equal, an obvious approach would be to conduct analysis of variance on the adjusted scores, $Y_{ij(adj)}$. If β were known, this would be an appropriate approach to the problem. However, β must be estimated from the data and that estimate is made by utilizing all data observed under all treatment levels. Under these conditions, the adjusted treatment means are not independent of each other, and the assumptions necessary for establishing the ratio of mean squares as an F-distribution are violated. Therefore, some alternative approach must be employed. Consistent with the above rationale, this alternate approach should yield the appropriate sum of squares and mean square terms (necessary for the F-test), which are adjusted for the covariate. One such approach is described below.

If one wishes to predict the value of a particular observation on the dependent variable with knowledge of the sample mean for the dependent variable and the value of the associated covariate, but with no knowledge of which group or treatment is associated with each observation, how would one proceed? A reasonable approach would be to use the value of the sample mean adjusted by the value of the covariate. Specifically, the model used to yield this estimate would be,

$$Y'_{ij} = \bar{Y} + b_T(X_{ij} - \bar{X}) \qquad [3]$$

where;

Y'_{ij} = the predicted score for observation j in group i,

$\bar{Y}$ = the grand (sample) mean of the dependent variable,

X_{ij} = the value of the covariate for observation j in group i,

$\bar{X}$ = the grand (sample) mean of covariate, and

b_T = the estimated coefficient for the covariate.

It is noted that the predicted score, Y'_{ij}, represents that portion of the dependent variable accounted for by the covariate, i.e., with knowledge of only the value of the covariate.

At this point a question may arise as to how one might obtain an estimate for the coefficient of the covariate term. A close look reveals that equation 3 can be viewed as a simple regression model with $(Y_{ij} - \bar{Y})$ as a dependent variable and $(X_{ij} - \bar{X})$ as the independent variable. It is a relatively easy matter to obtain b_T by the method of least squares. b_T will be referred to as the overall regression coefficient and is computed:

$$b_T = \frac{\sum_{i=1}^{k}\sum_{j=1}^{n} (X_{ij} - \bar{X})(Y_{ij} - \bar{Y})}{\sum_{i=1}^{k}\sum_{j=1}^{n} (X_{ij} - \bar{X})^2} \qquad [4]$$

With this estimate of b_T, the total sum of squares of Y adjusted for the covariate (and grand mean), which is also the sum of squared residuals about the regression line, may be computed. It is designated as $T_{yy(adj)}$ and is computed as follows:

$$T_{yy(adj)} = \sum_{i=1}^{k}\sum_{j=1}^{n} (Y_{ij} - Y'_{ij})^2$$

$$= \sum_{i=1}^{k}\sum_{j=1}^{n} [Y_{ij} - \bar{Y} - b_T(X_{ij} - \bar{X})]^2$$

$$= \sum_{i=1}^{k}\sum_{j=1}^{n} (Y_{ij} - \bar{Y})^2 + b_T^2 \sum_{i=1}^{k}\sum_{j=1}^{n} (X_{ij} - \bar{X})^2$$

$$- 2b_T \sum_{i=1}^{k}\sum_{j=1}^{n} (X_{ij} - \bar{X})(Y_{ij} - \bar{Y}).$$

But from equation 4,

$$\sum_{i=1}^{k}\sum_{j=1}^{n}(X_{ij}-\bar{X})(Y_{ij}-\bar{Y}) = b_T \sum_{i=1}^{k}\sum_{j=1}^{n}(X_{ij}-\bar{X})^2$$

therefore,

$$T_{yy(adj)} = \sum_{i=1}^{k}\sum_{j=1}^{n}(Y_{ij}-\bar{Y})^2 - b_T^2 \sum_{i=1}^{k}\sum_{j=1}^{n}(X_{ij}-\bar{X})^2. \quad [5]$$

This sum of squares represents variation among the values of the dependent variable attributable to the group or treatment effect and the residual effect, but which is *not* associated with the linear regression of Y on X.

It is noted that the right hand side of equation 5 consists of two terms. The first, $\Sigma\Sigma\,(Y_{ij} - \bar{Y})^2$, is the total sum of squares of Y (adjusted for the grand mean) not adjusted for the covariate. This term is designated T_{yy} and is referred to as the total sum of squares of Y. The second term; $b_T^2\,\Sigma\Sigma\,(X_{ij} - \bar{X})^2$ or $b_T^2\,T_{xx}$, where $T_{xx} = \Sigma\Sigma\,(X_{ij} - \bar{X})^2$ is the total sum of squares of X; represents an adjustment that is made to the unadjusted total sum of squares of Y which removes linear effects of the covariate. This adjustment will always reduce the sum of squares for Y as long as b_T does not equal 0. Consequently, the total adjusted sum of squares of Y, $T_{yy(adj)}$, is sometimes called the reduced sum of squares. By defining $T_{xy} = \Sigma\Sigma\,(X_{ij} - \bar{X})\,(Y_{ij} - \bar{Y})$, the sum of squares for the cross product of X and Y, the adjusted total sum of squares is expressed, using abbreviated notation, as,

$$T_{yy(adj)} = T_{yy} - b_T^2\,T_{xx} = T_{yy} - T_{xy}^2/T_{xx} \quad [6]$$

The degrees of freedom for $T_{yy(adj)}$ are $N - 2$. One additional degree of freedom, as compared to completely randomized analysis of variance, has been lost because of the linear restriction imposed on the sum of squares, i.e., deviations from the regression line rather than from the sample mean are used to compute the adjusted total sum of squares.

The variation in Y associated with the error term in the covariance model is specified by the adjusted within group sum of squares, $E_{yy(adj)}$, and is the sum of the squared deviations of the observed value of the dependent variable from the value predicted with knowledge of the associated group or treatment level and the covariate. This predicted value is computed as follows:

$$Y'_{j|i} = \bar{Y}_i + b_w(X_{ij} - \bar{X}_i) \qquad [7]$$

where $\bar{Y}_i$ and $\bar{X}_i$ are the means of Y_{ij} and X_{ij}, respectively for group i, and b_w is an estimate of β in equation 1 obtained by estimating the simple regression model with $(Y_{ij} - \bar{Y}_i)$ as the dependent variable and $(X_{ij} - \bar{X}_i)$ as the independent variable. Computationally, b_w is expressed:

$$b_w = \frac{\sum_{i=1}^{k}\sum_{j=1}^{n} (X_{ij} - \bar{X}_i)(Y_{ij} - \bar{Y}_i)}{\sum_{i=1}^{k}\sum_{j=1}^{n} (X_{ij} - \bar{X}_i)^2} \qquad [8]$$

and is referred to as the pooled within class regression coefficient.

With this estimate of b_w, $E_{yy(adj)}$ is computed as follows:

$$E_{yy(adj)} = \sum_{i=1}^{k}\sum_{j=1}^{n} (Y_{ij} - Y'_{i/j})^2$$

$$= \sum_{i=1}^{k}\sum_{j=1}^{n} [Y_{ij} - \bar{Y}_i - b_w(X_{ij} - \bar{X}_i)]^2$$

$$= \sum_{i=1}^{k}\sum_{j=1}^{n} (Y_{ij} - \bar{Y}_i)^2 + b_w^2 \sum_{i=1}^{k}\sum_{j=1}^{n} (X_{ij} - \bar{X}_i)^2$$

$$- 2b_w \sum_{i=1}^{k}\sum_{j=1}^{n} (X_{ij} - \bar{X}_i)(Y_{ij} - \bar{Y}_i).$$

But from equation 8,

$$\sum_{i=1}^{k}\sum_{j=1}^{n} (Y_{ij} - \bar{Y}_i)(X_{ij} - \bar{X}_i) = b_w \sum_{i=1}^{k}\sum_{j=1}^{n} (X_{ij} - \bar{X}_i)^2$$

therefore,

$$E_{yy(adj)} = \sum_{i=1}^{k}\sum_{j=1}^{n} (Y_{ij} - \bar{Y}_i)^2 - b_w^2 \sum_{i=1}^{k}\sum_{j=1}^{n} (X_{ij} - \bar{X}_i)^2. \qquad [9]$$

This sum of squares represents variation among the values of the dependent variable attributable to the residual effect *only.*

It is noted that, as with the adjusted total sum of squares of Y, the adjusted within group sum of squares consists of two components: $E_{yy} = \Sigma\Sigma\ (Y_{ij} - \bar{Y}_i)^2$, the unadjusted within group sum of squares of Y; and, $b_w^2\ E_{xx}$, where $E_{xx} = \Sigma\Sigma\ (X_{ij} - \bar{X}_i)^2$ is the within group sum of squares of X, which represents an adjustment that removes the linear effect of the covariate. By defining $E_{xy} = \Sigma\Sigma\ (X_{ij} - \bar{X}_i)\ (Y_{ij} - \bar{Y}_i)$, the within group sum of squares for the cross product of X and Y, the adjusted within group sum of squares is expressed:

$$E_{yy(adj)} = E_{yy} - b_w^2\ E_{xx} = E_{yy} - E_{xy}^2/E_{xx}. \qquad [10]$$

The degrees of freedom for $E_{yy(adj)}$ are N-k-1. Again, one degree of freedom has been lost because of the linear restriction imposed, which results in the deviations being computed from the regression line.

The adjusted total sum of squares, $T_{yy(adj)}$, represents variation due to the treatment or group effect plus the residual effect; and the adjusted within group sum of squares, $E_{yy(adj)}$, represents variation due to only the residual effect. Therefore, the adjusted between group sum of squares of Y, $B_{yy(adj)}$, which represents variation due only to the treatment or group effect may be computed by subtraction,

$$B_{yy(adj)} = T_{yy(adj)} - E_{yy(adj)}. \qquad [11]$$

The degrees of freedom associated with $B_{yy(adj)}$, which are equal to the difference in the degrees of freedom of the terms in equation 11, are (N−2)−(N−k−1) = k−1.

At this point, the reader may be curious as to why the adjusted between group sum of squares is computed by subtraction rather than by a procedure analogous to that used in computing the adjusted total and adjusted within group sums of squares. The reason is that in cases where group effects exist the use of this second method would result in a covariance adjustment which would also remove a portion of the variation attributable to the treatment or group effect. This would be unsatisfactory, and therefore, the approach given by equation 11 is used.

With the computation of the three adjusted sums of squares, the null hypothesis of no group effects, i.e., $\tau_i = 0$ for all i, can be tested. As in analysis of variance, an F-statistic is computed. It is of the form,

$$F = \frac{B_{yy(adj)}/(k-1)}{E_{yy(adj)}/(N-k-1)} \qquad [12]$$

Under the null hypothesis (and the model assumptions) this ratio has an F-distribution with degrees of freedom k-1 and N-k-1. In terms of predicted scores, this test is equivalent to testing the hypothesis that scores predicted using equation 3 fit the data as well as scores predicted using equation 7. That is, the test examines whether knowledge of group membership significantly adds to the prediction of the dependent variable. (Refer to pages 45-49 for a more detailed discussion of the correspondence between hypothesis testing and comparison of alternate models.)

A summary of the computational formulae associated with the analysis of covariance for the completely randomized design is presented in Table 1.

The F-statistic given by equation 12 is only a summary measure which indicates if any significant group differences in the dependent variable exist. If significant differences are present, one naturally wants to investigate the nature of these differences. Therefore, when the F-ratio is significant it is customary to compute the group means adjusted for the covariate to aid in the interpretation of the results. The adjusted group means are computed as follows:

$$\bar{Y}_{i(adj)} = \bar{Y}_i - b(\bar{X}_i - \bar{X}); \quad i=1, \ldots, k, \qquad [13]$$

where $b = b_w$, is the unbiased estimate of β in equation 1 calculated from the error sums of squares and cross products, as shown in equation 8. What this adjustment does is eliminate the effect of the covariate from the group means which allows for more meaningful interpretation.

The comparison of group means and the interpretation of the statistical analysis are considered in more detail immediately following the next section.

TESTING β

Accompanying the covariance model are certain implicit assumptions concerning the coefficient of the covariate. Two of these assumptions,

TABLE 1
Analysis of Covariance for Completely Randomized Design

Source of Variation	Sum of Squares and Cross Products			Adjusted Sum of Squares	Degrees of Freedom	Adjusted Mean Square	Expected Mean Square	F-Ratio
	XX	XY	YY					
Treatment/ Group	--	--	--	$B_{YY(ADJ)}$	K-1	$\frac{B_{YY(ADJ)}}{K-1}$	$\sigma^2_{\varepsilon\mid\beta} + \frac{\Sigma N_I \tau^2_I}{K-1}$	$\frac{MST_{(ADJ)}}{MSE_{(ADJ)}}$
Error	E_{XX}	E_{XY}	E_{YY}	$E_{YY(ADJ)}$	N-K-1	$\frac{E_{YY(ADJ)}}{N-K-1}$	$\sigma^2_{\varepsilon\mid\beta}$	
Total	T_{XX}	T_{XY}	T_{YY}	$T_{YY(ADJ)}$	N-2			

$E_{xx} = \Sigma\Sigma(X_{ij} - \bar{X}_i)^2$

$E_{xy} = \Sigma\Sigma(X_{ij} - \bar{X}_i)(Y_{ij} - \bar{Y}_i)$

$E_{yy} = \Sigma\Sigma(Y_{ij} - \bar{Y}_i)^2$

$T_{xx} = \Sigma\Sigma(X_{ij} - \bar{X})^2$

$T_{xy} = \Sigma\Sigma(X_{ij} - \bar{X})(Y_{ij} - \bar{Y})$

$T_{yy} = \Sigma\Sigma(Y_{ij} - \bar{Y})^2$

$E_{yy(adj)} = E_{yy} - E^2_{xy}/E_{xx}$

$T_{yy(adj)} = T_{yy} - T^2_{xy}/T_{xx}$

$B_{yy(adj)} = T_{yy(adj)} - E_{yy(adj)}$

$b_w = E_{xy}/E_{xx}$

which should be verified before the results of the covariance analysis are used, are:

(1) the effect, or impact, of the covariate on the dependent variable is the same for all levels of the categorical independent variable, and

(2) the coefficient is nonzero.

Sufficient information is available through the computations associated with the analysis of covariance model to test each of these assumptions. (Some consequences of violating the above and other assumptions are discussed in the Appendix.)

In analysis of covariance, an assumption underlying the adjustment of the within group sum of squares is that the within group regression coefficients are equal for all groups. Consequently, before the analysis of covariance results are interpreted one should test the hypothesis that these coefficients are equal. An analogy might be drawn here to two-way analysis of variance. In two-way analysis of variance the first test made is usually the test for an interaction effect. The reason for making this test first, is that, if the two independent variables produce different results, when acting in combination, than would be expected on the basis of the separate effects, then it makes very little sense, theoretically, to study the effects of one independent variable while not controlling for the other. In other words, the relationship between one independent variable and the dependent variable differs according to the value of the other independent variable; consequently, the relationships should be studied separately within each category of the other independent variable. A similar problem is faced in analysis of covariance. If the slopes, within group regression coefficients, differ significantly across groups, it is inappropriate to use the covariance model (equation 1) which assumes a constant slope. We should, in that case, consider a more complex model having a unique slope for each group.

A test for the homogeneity of regression coefficients is given by

$$F = \frac{(E_{yy(adj)} - S_1)/(k-1)}{S_1/(N-2k)}, \qquad [14]$$

where $E_{yy(adj)}$ has been previously defined as the adjusted within group sum of squares (i.e., the sum of squared deviations about the regression line assuming a common regression coefficient over all groups), and S_1 is the sum of squared deviations about the within class regression lines, each with unique slope depending upon the particular treatment level. Algebraically,

$$S_1 = E_{yy} - \sum_{i=1}^{k} b_{w_i}^2 E_{xx_i}, \qquad [15]$$

where $b_{w_i} = E_{xy_i}/E_{xx_i}$ is the within class regression coefficient for group i, $E_{xy_i} = \Sigma_j(X_{ij} - \overline{X}_i)(Y_{ij} - \overline{Y}_i)$ is the within group sum of squares for the cross product of X and Y for group i, and $E_{xx_i} = \Sigma_j (X_{ij} - \overline{X}_i)^2$ is the within group sum of squares of X for group i. Making substitutions, equation 14 becomes:

$$F = \frac{\left(\sum_{i=1}^{k} b_{w_i}^2 E_{xx_i} - b_w^2 E_{xx}\right)/(k-1)}{\left(E_{yy} - \sum_{i=1}^{k} b_{w_i}^2 E_{xx_i}\right)/(N-2k)}., \qquad [16]$$

which, under the hypothesis of homogeneity of the within class regression, is distributed as the F-distribution with k-1 and N-2k degrees of freedom. In this test one must be especially worried about committing a type II error, i.e., accepting the null hypothesis of no difference when it is false, so a numerically large level of significance (α = .10 or larger) is recommended.

It is evident from the formulation of the covariance model that the coefficient of the covariate is assumed to be nonzero. If this were not the case, there would be no benefit to complicating the analysis by the inclusion of the covariate. In certain instances the researcher may wish to test this assumption. In testing this assumption, the null hypothesis is that β equals zero. The validity of this null hypothesis is tested using the F-ratio,

$$F = \left[\frac{E_{xy}^2}{E_{yy}E_{xx} - E_{xy}^2}\right](N-k-1), \qquad [17]$$

which , under the null hypothesis, is distributed as the F-distribution, with 1 and N-k-1 degrees of freedom.

COMPARISONS AMONG MEANS

Many studies involve more than two groups or treatment levels. In such studies, a significant F-ratio for group or treatment effects indicates that at least one of the groups differs from another, but not which one or ones. Therefore, additional analysis is usually undertaken to determine which pairs or combinations of group means are significantly different. With analysis of covariance these comparisons are made with the adjusted group means as calculated by equation 13.

A comparison between two group means is made by considering the differences between them, e.g., $\overline{Y}_1 - \overline{Y}_2$, and testing whether that difference is significantly different from zero. A comparison may also involve more than two means. This can be done, for example, by averaging two means and then comparing this average with a third mean. This procedure could give rise to the difference, $(\overline{Y}_1 - \overline{Y}_2)/2 - \overline{Y}_3$. It is evident that the number of possible pairwise and nonpairwise comparisons among group means increases markedly as the number of groups increase.

In general, a comparison among k means takes the form of a linear combination, or weighted sum of means (referred to as a contrast) for which the coefficients, or weights, sum to zero but are not all equal to zero. Algebraically, a contrast is expressed:

$$C = \sum_{i=1}^{k} c_i \overline{Y}_i = c_1 \overline{Y}_1 + c_2 \overline{Y}_2 + \ldots + c_k \overline{Y}_k., \qquad [18]$$

where

$$\sum_{i=1}^{k} c_i = 0.$$

In terms of this algebraic formulation, the comparison between the two group means, $\overline{Y}_1$ and $\overline{Y}_2$, mentioned in the preceding paragraph is equivalent to setting c_1 equal to +1, c_2 equal to −1, and all other c_i equal to zero.

Mean comparisons may be classified as orthogonal or non-orthogonal, and as a priori or a posteriori. Two comparisons among k means are said to be orthogonal to each other if they utilize nonoverlapping pieces of information. A maximum of k−1 mutually orthogonal comparisons are possible in the analysis containing k groups or treatment levels, though the k−1 comparisons are not unique. Another way of viewing orthogonal comparisons is that any treatment/group sum of squares with k−1 degrees of freedom can be divided into k−1 orthogonal components which are additive, i.e., sum to equal the treatment/group sum of squares, and correspond to an orthogonal comparison. Mathematically, two contrasts, C_1 and C_2, are considered orthogonal if

$$\sum_{i=1}^{k} c_{1i} c_{2i}/n_i = 0,$$

where c_{ji} is the coefficient of the ith group mean in the jth contrast and n_i is the number of observations in group i.

A priori or planned comparisons are those which are specified prior to conducting the anlaysis. In experimental studies these usually involve a specific set of hypotheses that the experiment is designed to test. Those comparisons developed *after* conducting the initial analysis, for "exploring" the data, are referred to as a posteriori or post hoc comparisons. While it is usually considered "nice" to use a priori orthogonal comparisons, the choice should be dictated by the type and purpose of the study. The remainder of this section considers a limited number of statistical comparisons. For further discussion the reader is referred to Kirk (Ch. 3, 1968).

A Priori Orthogonal Comparisons. The preceding discussion considered the form of mean comparisons but not the statistical testing of these comparisons. In testing a comparison, the null hypothesis is that the value of the contrast is zero. For example, in the previously considered comparison involving two means, $C = 1\overline{Y}_1 - 1\overline{Y}_2$, the null hypothesis is that the population mean for group one (u_1) minus the population mean for group two (u_2) is zero. (The alternate hypothesis for this test is $u_1 - u_2 \neq 0$.) Within the context of the completely randomized analysis of covariance model, the null hypothesis, in case of planned orthogonal comparisons, may be tested using the t-statistic,

$$t = \frac{\Sigma c_i \overline{Y}_{i(adj)}}{\sqrt{MSE_{(adj)}[\Sigma(c_i^2/n_i) + [\Sigma c_i(\overline{X}_i - \overline{X})]^2/E_{xx}]}}, \qquad [19]$$

with N−k−1 degrees of freedom.

It is noted that when a large number of mean comparisons (multiple comparisons) are made, the probability of obtaining at least one significant comparison, due strictly to chance, can become large. Many researchers have investigated this problem and, as a result, various procedures have been devised which provide for a given α-level over a collection of comparisons. This naturally results in a much lower α-level on any given comparison within the collection. However, according to Kirk (1968: 78), "for planned orthogonal comparisons, contemporary practice in the behavioral sciences favors setting the type I error probability level at α for each comparison. For planned and unplanned nonorthogonal comparisons it is suggested that the type I error probability should be set at α for the collection of comparisons."

A Posteriori Nonorthogonal Comparisons. In many situations the researcher is not sufficiently knowledgeable concerning the effect of the independent variable to a priori specify the appropriate mean comparisons. However, if the overall F-test leads to the rejection of the null hypothesis of no treatment/group effects, the researcher is usually interested in further "exploring" the data in an effort to uncover the sources of the treatment/gorup effect. In such cases of unplanned mean comparisons it is usually recommended that a procedure be employed which maintains a specified α-level for the entire collection of comparisons. Two such procedures are discussed here (Kirk, 1968:472): Tukey's HSD (honestly significant difference) test, sometimes referred to as the "w" procedure, and Scheffe's test.

Tukey's HSD test was designed for making *all pairwise* mean comparisons. The test statistic, in the case of an equal number of observations per group is computed

$$q = \frac{c_i \bar{Y}_{i(adj)} + c_j \bar{Y}_{j(adj)}}{\sqrt{\frac{MSE_{(adj)}}{n}\left[1 + \frac{B_{xx}}{(k-1)E_{xx}}\right]}}, \qquad [20]$$

where q is compared to q-critical, for k means and N−k−1 degrees of freedom, obtained from the distribution of the studentized range statistic (tables for q are reproduced in Kirk [1968]). In the case of unequal cell sizes an approximate statistic can be obtained by substituting n^* for n where,

$$n^* = k/\Sigma(1/n_i).$$

Scheffe's test is recommended for *only nonpairwise* mean comparison's since it is less sensitive for pairwise comparisons than Tukey's test. The test statistic is computed:

$$F = \frac{[\Sigma c_i \bar{Y}_{i(adj)}]^2}{MSE_{(adj)} \left[1 + \frac{B_{xx}}{(k-1)E_{xx}}\right] \left[\Sigma(c_i^2/n_i)\right]} \cdot \frac{1}{(k-1)}, \qquad [21]$$

and compared to the tabulated F value with k and N−k−1 degrees of freedom.

NUMERIC EXAMPLE FOR COMPLETELY RANDOMIZED DESIGN

The country of Finland is divided into a large number of political subdivisions called municipalities. The State owned liquor company has a monopoly on wholesale and package store liquor sales, and has the sole authority to grant liquor licenses for restaurants. For centuries there has been a law that liquor can be sold and/or commercially served only in the urban municipalities. This law, however, was recently (at least temporarily) repealed, and the State liquor monopoly wished to determine whether selling liquor in rural municipalities would have a negative impact.

A key consideration for decision makers was whether the establishment of a liquor store, either alone or with a licensed restaurant, would significantly affect the number of traffic accidents in the rural municipalities. New liquor stores and licensed restaurants were established in rural municipalities at approximately the same time during early summer. Twelve rural municipalities, four where only a package store was licensed, four where both a restaurant and package store were licensed and four where no store or restaurant was licensed, were included in the study. Traffic accident records were obtained for the twelve months prior to the establishment of the liquor stores, and for the twelve months after the establishment of the stores.

The study, as described above, could be either an observational or experimental study depending upon the amount of control the State liquor monopoly had in deciding which municipalities would be licensed. An experimental study would have resulted if the twelve rural municipalities were randomly assigned to the three groups. On the other hand, it would be an observational study if applications for the various types of licensing were processed in the normal manner and, after the appropriate licensing had been obtained, four municipalities with each type of licensing were selected for inclusion in the study.

It was not considered appropriate to use the change (algebric difference between the before and after measures) in traffic accidents as the dependent

TABLE 2
Data for Completely Randomized Design: Traffic Accidents During the Test Period (Y) and Traffic Accidents During Preceding Year (X)

	Type of Liquor Licensing (Treatments or Groups)					
	Control (Group 1)		Package Store Only (Group 2)		Restaurant and Package Store (Group 3)	
	X	Y	X	Y	X	Y
Observed Values	190	177	252	226	206	226
	261	225	228	196	239	229
	194	167	240	198	217	215
	217	176	246	206	177	188
Mean	215.50	186.25	241.50	206.50	209.75	214.50

Sample Means X = 222.25 Y = 202.42

variable, because it was well known that there was a decreasing trend in traffic accidents due to less driving per resident, caused by a substantial increase in gasoline prices during this time period. Consequently, it was decided that the after measure would be used as the dependent variable and the before measure as a covariate.

The setting described above represents a completely randomized design with the number of traffic accidents per ten thousand population during the test period as the dependent variable, the number of traffic accidents per ten thousand population during the preceding period as the covariate, and the type of liquor licensing as the categorical independent variable. This categorical independent variable has three levels; (1) no liquor available (control level), (2) package store only, and (3) restaurant licensing and package store. The data resulting from this study are presented in Table 2.

The primary purpose of the study is to determine the impact of liquor licensing on traffic accidents in the rural municipalities. In a statistical framework, the objective is to test the hypothesis that $\tau_i = 0$ for all i, i.e., all three levels of liquor licensing have equal impact on the dependent variable. An α-level of .05 is selected for this test and most subsequent tests. This hypothesis is tested with an F-ratio (equation 12). The F-ratio requires the calculation of $B_{yy(adj)}$ and $E_{yy(adj)}$, the adjusted between group sum of squares of Y, and the adjusted within group sum of squares of Y, respectively. But $B_{yy(adj)}$ is obtained by subtraction (equation 11) and requires calculation of $T_{yy(adj)}$, the adjusted total sum of squares of Y.

The formulae for computing $T_{yy(adj)}$ and $E_{yy(adj)}$ are given by equations 6 and 10, respectively, and require the calculation of the following six terms:

$$T_{xx} = \sum_{i=1}^{3}\sum_{j=1}^{4} (X_{ij} - \bar{X})^2 = \text{total sum of squares of X}$$

$$= (190 - 222.25)^2 + (261 - 222.25)^2 + \ldots + (177 - 222.25)^2$$

$$= 7784.25,$$

$$T_{xy} = \sum_{i=1}^{3}\sum_{j=1}^{4} (X_{ij} - \bar{X})(Y_{ij} - \bar{Y}) = \text{total sum of squares for the cross product of X and Y}$$

$$= (190 - 222.25)(177 - 202.42) + (261 - 222.25)(225 - 202.42)$$

$$+ \ldots + (177 - 222.25)(188 - 202.42)$$

$$= 4153.75,$$

$$T_{yy} = \sum_{i=1}^{3}\sum_{j=1}^{4} (Y_{ij} - \bar{Y})^2 = \text{total sum of squares of Y}$$

$$= (177 - 202.42)^2 + (225 - 202.42)^2 + \ldots + (188 - 202.42)^2$$

$$= 5366.92,$$

$$E_{xx} = \sum_{i=1}^{3}\sum_{j=1}^{4} (X_{ij} - \bar{X}_i)^2 = \text{within group sum of squares of X}$$

$$= (190 - 215.50)^2 + (261 - 215.50)^2 + \ldots + (177 - 209.75)^2$$

$$= 5494.75,$$

$$E_{xy} = \sum_{i=1}^{3}\sum_{j=1}^{4} (X_{ij} - \bar{X}_i)(Y_{ij} - \bar{Y}_i) = \text{within group sum of squares for the cross product of X and Y}$$

$$= (190-215.50)(177-186.25) + (261-215.50)(225-186.25)$$

$$+ \ldots + (177 - 209.75)(188 - 214.50)$$

$$= 4005.67,$$

$$E_{yy} = \sum_{i=1}^{3}\sum_{j=1}^{4} (Y_{ij} - \bar{Y}_i)^2 = \text{within group sum of squares of Y}$$

$$= (177 - 186.25)^2 + (225 - 186.25)^2 + \ldots + (188 - 214.50)^2$$

$$= 3670.75.$$

Given these six terms, the adjusted total, within and between group sums of squares ($T_{yy(adj)}$, $E_{yy(adj)}$ and $B_{yy(adj)}$, respectively), are computed as follows:

$$T_{yy(adj)} = T_{yy} - T_{xy}^2/T_{xx} = 5366.92 - (4153.75)^2/7784.25 = 3150.44,$$

$$E_{yy(adj)} = E_{yy} - E_{xy}^2/E_{xx} = 3670.75 - (4005.67)^2/5494.75 = 748.68,$$

$$B_{yy(adj)} = T_{yy(adj)} - E_{yy(adj)} = 3150.44 - 748.68 = 2401.76.$$

The F-ratio is then computed:

$$F = [B_{yy(adj)}/(k-1)] / [E_{yy(adj)}/(N-k-1)]$$

$$= [2401.76/(3-1] / [748.68/(12-3-1)]$$

$$= 12.83.$$

This F-ratio is significant at the $\alpha = .05$ level ($F_{.05;2,8} = 4.46$), and the null hypothesis is rejected. This implies that the type of licensing does have differential effect, the exact nature of which has yet to be examined. The results of the above computations are summarized in Table 3.

Before initiating a detailed analysis of the exact nature of the group effects, it is appropriate to test the assumptions that have been made

TABLE 3
Analysis of Covariance for Completely Randomized Design with Data From Illustrative Example

Source of Variation	Sum of Squares and Cross Products			Adjusted Sum of Squares	Degrees of Freedom	Adjusted Mean Square	F-ratio
	XX	XY	YY				
Treatment	---	---	---	2401.76	2	1200.88	12.83
Error	5494.75	4005.67	3670.45	748.68	8	93.59	
Total	7784.25	4153.75	5366.92	3150.44	10		

concerning the covariance model. The first assumption to be tested is the equality of the within group regression coefficients. The covariance model assumes homogeneity of the within class regression. Therefore, if the null hypothesis of no difference in regression coefficients is rejected, the covariance model is inappropriate. This test (equation 14 requires the computation of the within group sum of squares for the cross product of X and Y for each group:

$$E_{xy_1} = \sum_{j=1}^{4} (X_{1j} - \bar{X}_1)(Y_{1j} - \bar{Y}_1)$$

$$= (190 - 215.50)(177 - 186.25) + \ldots$$
$$+ (217 - 215.50)(176 - 186.25)$$
$$= 2397.50$$

$$E_{xy_2} = \sum_{j=1}^{4} (X_{2j} - \bar{X}_2)(Y_{2j} - \bar{Y}_2)$$

$$= (252 - 241.50)(226 - 206.50) + \ldots$$
$$+ (246 - 241.50)(206 - 206.50)$$
$$= 357.00,$$

$$E_{xy_3} = \sum_{j=1}^{4} (X_{3j} - \bar{X}_3)(Y_{3j} - \bar{Y}_3)$$

$$= (206 - 209.75)(266 - 214.50) + \ldots$$
$$+ (177 - 209.75)(188 - 214.50)$$
$$= 1252.50,$$

and the within group sum of squares of X for each group:

$$E_{xx_1} = \sum_{j=1}^{4} (X_{1j} - \bar{X}_1)^2$$

$$= (190 - 215.50)^2 + \ldots + (217 - 215.50)^2$$

$$= 3185.00,$$

$$E_{xx_2} = \sum_{j=1}^{4} (X_{2j} - \bar{X}_2)^2$$

$$= (252 - 241.50)^2 + \ldots + (246 - 241.50)^2$$

$$= 315.00,$$

$$E_{xx_3} = \sum_{j=1}^{4} (X_{3j} - \bar{X}_3)^2$$

$$= (206 - 209.75)^2 + \ldots + (177 - 209.75)^2$$

$$= 1994.75.$$

With these values, the within class regression coefficients for each group are calculated:

$$b_{w_1} = E_{xy_1}/E_{xx_1} = 2397.50/3185.00 = 0.7527,$$

$$b_{w_2} = E_{xy_2}/E_{xx_2} = 357.00/315.00 = 1.1333,$$

$$b_{w_3} = E_{xy_3}/E_{xx_3} = 1252.50/1994.75 = 0.6279.$$

Given these terms, S_1 (equation 15) is computed:

$$S_1 = E_{yy} - \sum_{i=1}^{k} b_{w_i}^2 E_{xx_i}$$

$$= 3670.75 - (.7527^2 \text{ x } 3185.00 + 1.1333^2 \text{ x } 315.00 + .6278^2 \text{ x } 1994.75)$$

$$= 674.996.$$

And finally, the F-ratio is computed:

$$F = [(E_{yy(adj)} - S_1)/(k-1)] / [S_1/(N-2k)]$$

$$= [(748.680 - 674.996)/(3-1)] / [674.996/(12-6)]$$

$$= .3275$$

Given this F-value, there is no reason to reject the hypothesis of homogeneity of regression (at $\alpha = .10$, $F_{2,6} = 3.46$). Therefore, the observed data appear to be consistent with the assumption of a common coefficient for the covariate.

The second assumption to be tested is that the regression coefficient is nonzero. The covariance model assumes that the covariate is associated with the dependent variable and, therefore, its coefficient is nonzero. The test of the null hypothesis (equation 17) is given by:

$$F = E_{xy}^2(N-k-1)/(E_{yy}E_{xx} - E_{xy}^2)$$

$$= (4007)^2\,(12-3-1)/[(3670.75)\,(5494.75) - (4007)^2]$$

$$= 31.2237.$$

Given this F-value, the hypothesis that $\beta = 0$ is rejected (at $\alpha = .05$, $F_{1,8} = 5.32$) and the hypothesized model is consistent with the observed data.

To assist in the interpretation of the results, the adjusted group means are calculated (equation 13). These computations require the pooled within class regression coefficient:

$$b_w = E_{xy}/E_{xx} = 4005.67/5494.75 = 0.729.$$

The adjusted group mean for the control group (group 1) is:

$$\bar{Y}_{1(adj)} = \bar{Y}_1 - b_w(\bar{X}_1 - \bar{X}) = 186.25 - .729\,(215.50 - 222.25)$$

$$= 191.17.$$

For the group where only the package store was established (group 2), the adjusted mean is:

$$\bar{Y}_{2(adj)} = \bar{Y}_2 - b_w(\bar{X}_2 - \bar{X}) = 206.50 - .729\,(241.50 - 222.25)$$

$$= 192.46.$$

And for the group with both the package store and the licensed restaurant (group 3), the adjusted mean is:

$$\bar{Y}_{3(adj)} = \bar{Y}_3 - b_w(\bar{X}_3 - \bar{X}) = 214.50 - .729\,(209.75 - 222.25)$$

$$= 223.62.$$

In this study, the researchers were mostly interested in comparing group 3 (both package store and licensed restaurant) with the control group (group 1). Group 2 (package store only) was included in the study for exploratory reasons, since it was considered a possible alternative if it turned out not to be feasible to establish both the package store and the licensed restaurant. The a priori comparison of group 1 with group 3 is tested with the t-statistic (equation 19),

$$t = \sum_{i=1}^{3} c_i \bar{Y}_{i(adj)} \Bigg/ \sqrt{MSE_{(adj)} \left[\sum_{i=1}^{3} c_i^2/n_i + \left[\sum_{i=1}^{3} c_i(\bar{X}_i - \bar{X}) \right]^2 / E_{xx} \right]}$$

$$= \frac{(+1)(191.17) + (0)(192.46) + (-1)(223.62)}{\sqrt{93.59 \left[\frac{1}{4} + \frac{1}{4} + \frac{[(1)(215.50-222.25) + (-1)(209.75-222.25)]^2}{5494.75} \right]}}$$

$$= -4.7155$$

Given this calculated t-value, the null hypothesis, that the value of the contrast is zero, is rejected ($t_{.05;8} = 2.306$). Consequently it is concluded that the mean accident rate was higher in group 3 than in the control group.

If the researchers, after obtaining a significant overall F-ratio, wanted to compare all means to each other, Tukey's test for a posteriori, non-orthogonal comparisons is appropriate. The first comparison between the control group (group 1) and group 3 (both package store and licensed restaurant) is given by (equation 20):

$$q = [c_1 \bar{Y}_{1(adj)} + c_3 \bar{Y}_{3(adj)}] \Bigg/ \sqrt{\frac{MSE_{(adj)}}{n} \left[1 + \frac{B_{xx}/(k-1)}{E_{xx}} \right]}$$

$$= \frac{(+1)(191.17) + (-1)(223.62)}{\sqrt{\frac{93.585}{4} \left[1 + \frac{2289.5/2}{5494.75} \right]}}$$

$$= -6.103.$$

Given this calculated q-value the null hypothesis, that the two group means are equal, is rejected at the $\alpha = .05$ level ($q_{8,3} = 4.04$). The researchers would conclude that group 3 has higher mean accident rate than the control group. The second comparison between the control group and group 2 (package-store only) is given by:

$$q = [c_1 \bar{Y}_{1(adj)} + c_2 \bar{Y}_{2(adj)}] \Bigg/ \sqrt{\frac{MSE_{(adj)}}{n}\left[1 + \frac{B_{xx}/(k-1)}{E_{xx}}\right]}$$

$$= \frac{(+1)(191.17) + (-1)(192.46)}{5.317}$$

$$= -.243.$$

This difference is not significant ($q_{.05,8,3} = 4.04$) and the researchers would conclude that no difference exists between these two groups. The third comparison between groups 2 and 3 is given by:

$$q = [c_2 \bar{Y}_{2(adj)} + c_3 \bar{Y}_{3(adj)}] \Bigg/ \sqrt{\frac{MSE_{(adj)}}{n}\left[1 + \frac{B_{xx}/(k-1)}{E_{xx}}\right]}$$

$$= \frac{(+1)(192.46) + (-1)(223.62)}{5.317}$$

$$= -5.860$$

For this calculated q-value the null hypothesis is rejected and the researchers would conclude that group 3 (package store and licensed restaurant) has a higher mean accident rate than group 2 (package store only).

GEOMETRIC REPRESENTATION

In order to make it easier for those who are not mathematically oriented to see what is done in analysis of covariance, a graphical representation of the numeric example is provided.

In Figure 1, the data for the three groups, with four observations in each group, are shown. The horizontal axis gives the values of the covariate, traffic accident rate during the previous year, and the vertical axis gives

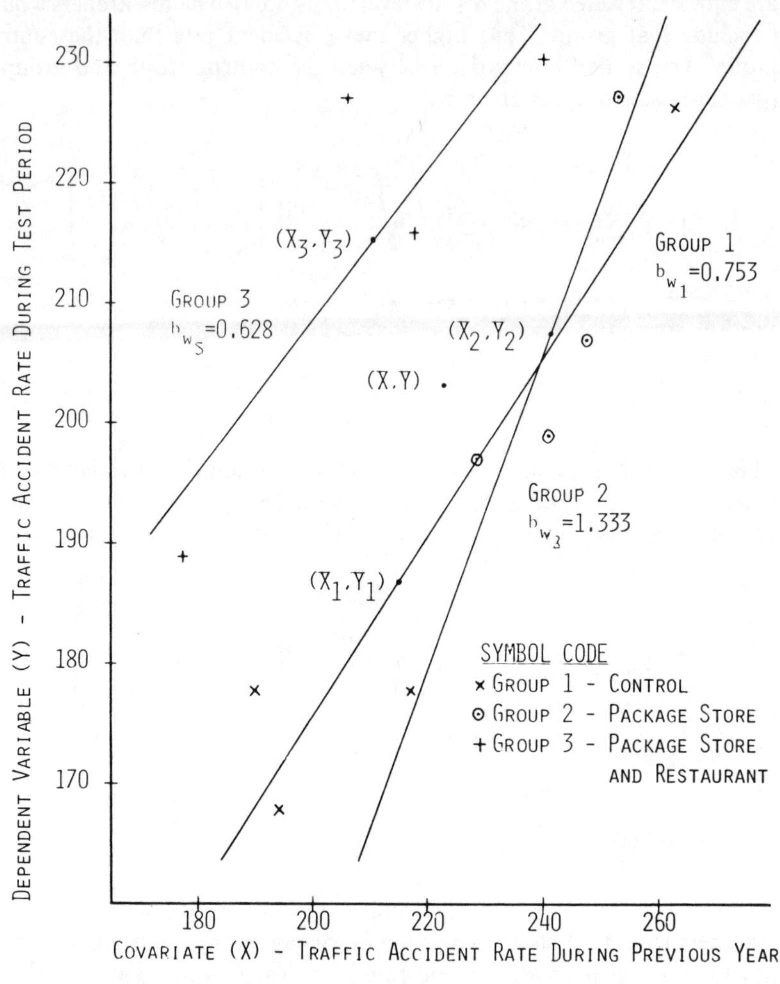

Figure 1: Within Class Regression Lines (Unique Slopes)

the values of the dependent variable, traffic accident rate in the test year. Also, regression lines computed separately for each group are indicated. As can be seen in Figure 1, the separate regression lines have slopes which are fairly close (parallel) to each other. In the previous section the test statistic for the homogeneity of these regression slopes was calculated, and it was found that the null hypothesis of homogeneity of regression could not be rejected.

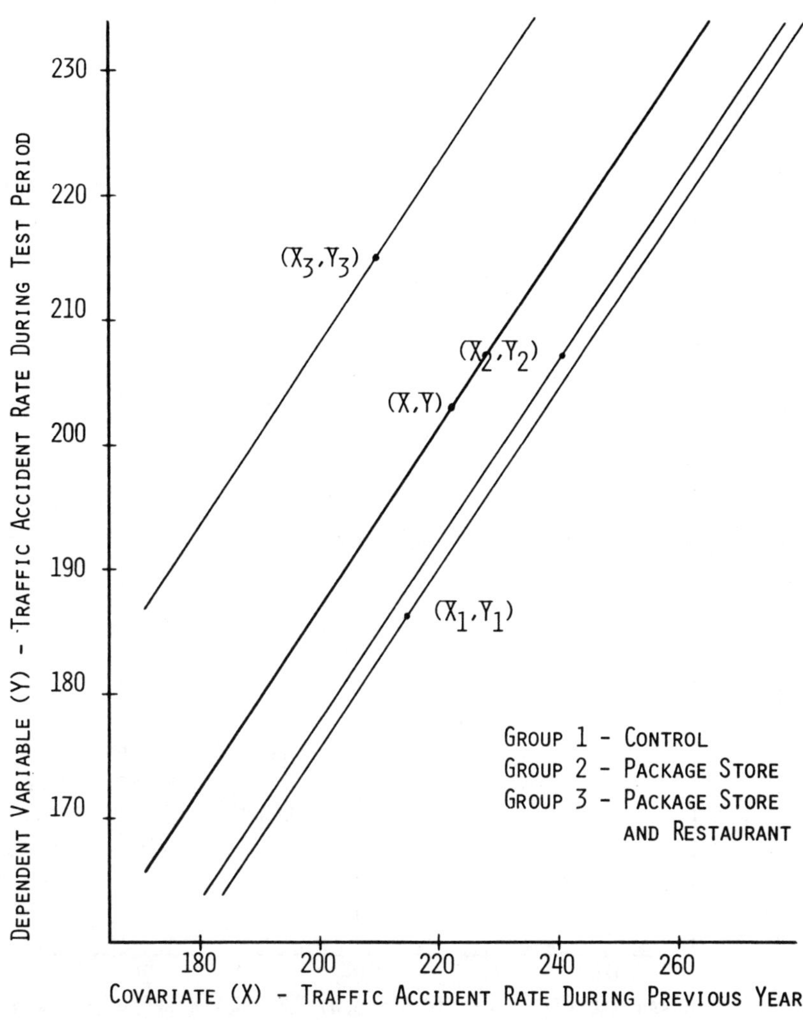

Figure 2: Lines of Common Slope (b_w = 0.729) Through Group Centroids

In Figure 2, lines with common slope are drawn through each group centroid ($\overline{X}_i$, $\overline{Y}_i$) and through the centroid of all observations ($\overline{X}$, $\overline{Y}$). The slope (b_w = .729) of these lines is derived by pooling all observations and adjusting for mean differences among groups. (One would get this regression slope by superimposing the group centroids on top of each other, i.e., adjusting so that all groups have the same mean value for both

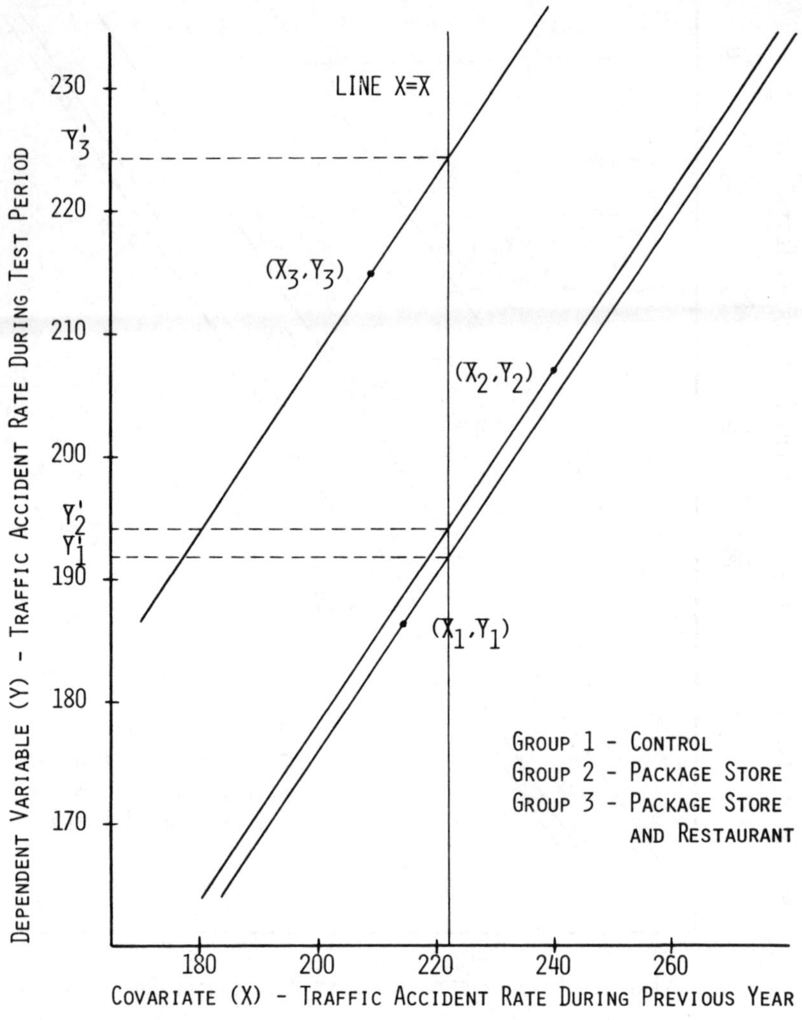

Figure 3: Graphical Representation of Adjusted Group Means

X and Y, and conducting a regular regression analysis.) Group effects are represented by the vertical differences (measured on the Y axis) between the lines going through group centroids and the line going through the centroid of all observations.

The adjusted group means, $\overline{Y}_i'$, are shown in Figure 3. The adjusted means are obtained from the intersection of the within group regression lines (with common slope) and the line, $X = \overline{X}$. Thus, a group mean is adjusted by moving it along the line which passes thorugh the group centroid and has slope b_w so that its value on the X axis is equal to the sample mean, $\overline{X}$. The adjusted treatment means are read from the Y axis. From Figure 3, it can be seen that groups 1 and 2 (control group and package store only, respectively) have considerably different unadjusted group means, but when adjusted for the value of the covariate the means of these two groups are very close to each other. Also, it is observed that for group 3 (both package store and licensed restaurant) the adjusted mean is much higher than for the two other groups. (The regression line going through group 3 centroid is considerable above the other two lines, i.e., it has a considerably higher intercept).

ALTERNATE PERSPECTIVE OF TESTING WITH ANALYSIS OF COVARIANCE

In the preceding discussion, mention has been made of a number of statistical tests, e.g., test for homogeneity of regression coefficients and test for absence of group or treatment effects. It is often helpful to view these tests as a comparison of alternate models. Figure 4 presents five alternate statistical models within the context of a completely randomized design. Model 1 considers the observed value of the dependent variable to be a function of two components: the overall mean and an error term. Model 2, the usual analysis of variance model for the completely randomized design, considers the observed valued of the dependent variable to be a function of three components: the overall mean, the group or treatment effect and an error term. With the analysis of variance model, testing that all group effects are identically zero is equivalent to comparing Model 1 to Model 2. If Model 1 explains the variability of the dependent variable as well as Model 2, it can be concluded that the inclusion of the group effect component contributes nothing to the explanatory power of Model 2, and the null hypothesis that all group effects are identically zero may not be rejected.

Let SS_1 be the variation (sum of squares) in the dependent variable explained by the explanatory terms (excluding the error term) in Model 1, and SS_2 be the variation explained by the explanatory terms in Model 2. The difference, $SS_2 - SS_1$, is the "extra sum of squares" due to the inclusion of the extra terms (τ_i's) in Model 2. Since the total sum of squares, T_{yy}, is the same in both models, the difference in the explained variation may be expressed as the difference in the unexplained, or error, variation. Therefore, the extra sum of squares is equal to $E_{yy1} - E_{yy2}$,

MODEL 1: $Y_{ij} = \mu + \varepsilon_{ij}$

MODEL 2: $Y_{ij} = \mu + \tau_i + \varepsilon_{ij}$

MODEL 3: $Y_{ij} = \mu + \beta(X_{ij} - \bar{X}) + \varepsilon_{ij}$

MODEL 4: $Y_{ij} = \mu + \tau_i + \beta(X_{ij} - \bar{X}) + \varepsilon_{ij}$

MODEL 5: $Y_{ij} = \mu + \tau_i + \beta_i(X_{ij} - \bar{X}) + \varepsilon_{ij}$

Y_{ij}	=	OBSERVED VALUE OF THE DEPENDENT VARIABLE
μ	=	OVERALL MEAN
τ_i	=	EFFECT DUE TO iTH LEVEL OF CATEGORICAL INDEPENDENT VARIABLE
β_i	=	COEFFICIENT OF COVARIATE FOR GROUP i
β	=	COEFFICIENT OF COVARIATE, COMMON FOR ALL GROUPS
X_{ij}	=	OBSERVED VALUE OF THE COVARIATE
$\bar{X}$	=	MEAN OF THE COVARIATE
ε_{ij}	=	RANDOM ERROR

Figure 4: Alternate Statistical Models Under Completely Randomized Design

where E_{yyk} is the error sum of squares of Y for Model k. The degrees of freedom associated with this extra sum of squares is equal to the difference in the degrees of freedom of the component parts, or (N−1) − (N−k) = k−1. *If* all group effects are identically zero, this difference (extra sum of squares) will be due strictly to sampling error, and it can be shown that the expected value of $(E_{yy1} - E_{yy2})/(k-1)$ is equal to σ^2_ε, the variance of the error term. Irrespective of the existence of group effects the expected value of $E^{yy2}/N-k)$ is equal to σ^2_ε. With the added assumption that the errors are normally distributed, the ratio

$$F = \frac{(E_{yy1} - E_{yy2})/(k-1)}{E_{yy2}/(N-k)} \qquad [22]$$

is distributed as the F-distribution, with k−1 and N−k degree of freedom, under the null hypothesis of no group effects. This F-ratio provides a means to statistically test the significance of the "extra" terms included in Model 2.

This same extra sum of squares principle may be applied to the analysis of covariance model. In the discussion to follow, three hypotheses are considered:

(1) homogeneity of regression coefficients,
(2) zero value of β, and
(3) absence of group or treatment effects.

Testing the homogeneity of regression coefficients is equivalent to comparing Model 4, with a common value of β over all groups or treatment levels, to Model 5, having unique values of β for each group. Under the null hypothesis of homogeneity, the extra sum of squares explained by the inclusion of separate β values should not be statistically significant. The test used here is similar to that mentioned above, and considers the ratio,

$$F = \frac{(E_{yy4} - E_{yy5})/[(N-k-1) - (N-2k)]}{E_{yy5}/(N-2k)} \qquad [23]$$

which under the null hypothesis, H_0: $\beta_1 = \beta_2 = \ldots \beta_k = \beta$, is distributed as the F-distribution with k-1 and N-2k degrees of freedom. It is noted that

$$E_{yy4} = E_{yy(adj)} = E_{yy} - b_w^2 E_{xx}$$

(recall equation 10), and

$$E_{yy5} = E_{yy} - \Sigma b_{w_i}^2 E_{xx_i}.$$

Therefore, equation 23 may be restated as,

$$F = \frac{[(E_{yy} - b_w^2 E_{xx}) - (E_{yy} - \Sigma b_{w_i}^2 E_{xx_i})]/[(N-k-1) - (N-2k)]}{(E_{yy} - \Sigma b_{w_i}^2 E_{xx_i})/(N-2k)}$$

$$= \frac{(\Sigma b_{w_i}^2 E_{xx_i} - b_w^2 E_{xx})/(k-1)}{(E_{yy} - \Sigma b_{w_i}^2 E_{xx_i})/(N-2k)}. \qquad [24]$$

The reader will note that this is the same F-ratio (see equation 16) presented in an earlier section for testing this same hypothesis.

Likewise, testing the hypothesis, H_0: $\beta = 0$, under the assumption of homogeneity of regression coefficients is equivalent to comparing Model 2 to Model 4. The appropriate F-ratio for this test is,

$$F = \frac{(E_{yy2} - E_{yy4})/[(N-k) - (N-k-1)]}{E_{yy4}/(N-k-1)} \qquad [25]$$

which under the null hypothesis is distributed as the F-distribution with 1 and N-k-1 degrees of freedom. Since $E_{yy2} = E_{yy}$, equation 25 may be restated as,

$$F = \frac{(E_{yy} - E_{yy(adj)})/[(N-k) - (N-k-1)]}{E_{yy(adj)}/(N-k-1)}$$

$$= \frac{b_w^2 E_{xx}}{(E_{yy} - b_w^2 E_{xx})/(N-k-1)}$$

$$= \frac{E_{xy}^2}{(E_{yy}E_{xx} - E_{xy}^2)/(N-k-1)} . \qquad [26]$$

The reader will note that equation 26 is identical to the previously mentioned F-ratio for testing this hypothesis given in equation 17.

Lastly, testing the hypothesis that all group effects are identically zero under the assumption of homogeneous regression coefficients is equivalent to comparing Model 3 to Model 4. The appropriate F-ratio for this test is

$$F = \frac{(E_{yy3} - E_{yy4})/[(N-2) - (N-k-1)]}{E_{yy4}/(N-k-1)} \qquad [27]$$

which under the null hypothesis, H_0: $\tau_i = 0$ for all i, is distributed as the F-distribution with k-1 and N-k-1 degrees of freedom. But from the development of equation 5, it is noted that $E_{yy3} = T_{yy(adj)}$. Therefore, equation 27 may be restated as,

$$= \frac{[T_{yy(adj)} - E_{yy(adj)}]/[(N-2)-(N-k-1)]}{E_{yy(adj)}/(N-k-1)}$$

$$= \frac{B_{yy(adj)}/(k-1)}{E_{yy(adj)}/(N-k-1)} \qquad [28]$$

which is equivalent to the overall F-test in the completely randomized analysis of covariance model (equation 12).

Other Problem Perspectives

Earlier, it was mentioned that analysis of covariance could be utilized under three alternate problem perspectives. From the viewpoint of the statistical model all three perspectives are quite similar. But, in conducting the analysis, the method of partitioning the sum of squares is different. Statistical testing, within the context of analysis of covariance, is accomplished through mean square comparisons, where the mean squares are computed by dividing sums of squares by the appropriate degrees of freedom. The problem perspective taken by the researcher will influence the method of partitioning the total sum of squares into its various components and, therefore, may affect the outcome of the statistical testing.

In all cases, the total sum of squares, not adjusted for the covariate (i.e., sum of squared deviations of the dependent variable from its mean) is partitioned into the sum of squares explained collectively by the independent variables (including the covariate) and the sum of squares error. Since the error term is assumed independent of the explanatory variables, the sum of squares error plus sum of squares explained will always add to equal the total sum of squares. The explained sum of squares must then be partitioned into components associated with each of the independent variables. The method employed in this partitioning is conditional upon the analysis perspective taken.

With the experimental perspective, which has been extensively considered up to this point, the sum of squares explained by the covariate is computed without giving consideration to the categorical independent variable. The sum of squares associated with the categorical independent variable is then computed by subtracting the sum of squares explained by the covariate from the sum of squares explained by the independent variables collectively. This is a hierarchical, or sequential, procedure whereby the sum of squares assigned to the categorical independent variable is the residual of the explained sum of squares left after the covariance adjustment is taken.

With the second perspective the adjustment is first made for the categorical independent variable rather than the covariate. The sum of squares associated with the categorical independent variable is computed first, and the sum of squares associated with the covariate is the residual which is left after subtracting the sum of squares due to the categorical independent variable from the sum of squares explained by the independent variables collectively. That is, the sum of squares attributable to the covariate represents the explained variation remaining after removing the effects of the categorical independent variable. This is also a hierarchical, or sequential, procedure but the order in which the variables are treated is opposite of that of the experimental perspective.

With the third, or regression perspective, both variables are of equal interest and a nonhierarchical procedure, sometimes referred to as a "partial" procedure, is used. The sum of squares for the covariate is the explained variation attributable to the covariate after the adjustment is made for the categorical independent variable, and the sum of squares attributable to the categorical independent variable is that portion of the explained variation after adjustment has been made for the covariate. (With the regression perspective, the sum of squares of the covariate and the categorical independent variable need not necessarily add up to the total explained sum of squares.)

The degree to which the sum of squares in each of these analyses will differ is a function of the relationship between the covariate and the other independent variable. Ideally, the mean value of the covariate will be equal over all levels of the categorical independent variable, in which case all three analyses will yield the same results. However, since direct control is usually not imposed, the mean value of the covariate over the various levels of the categorical independent variable is not likely to be identical. (This is particularly true for observational and experimental studies where intact groups are employed.) This will result in some degree of correlation, or overlap in the explanatory power of covariate and the categorical independent variable. Therefore, depending upon the nature of the relationship, the computed mean squares and associated F-ratios may well vary depending upon the approach employed in the particular analysis. Analysis procedures under the second and regression perspectives are now considered.

ANALYSIS UNDER SECOND PERSPECTIVE

Under the second perspective, which is usually taken only in observational studies, interest centers on the relationship between the covariate and the dependent variable within distinct categorically defined groups. We call this design a "regression within groups design." In this design one tries to "partial out" the effect of the categorical variable from the error term and, hence, get more precise information on the relationship of the covariate with the dependent variable. The focus in this analysis is testing for significant within group correlation between the covariate and the dependent variable, and estimating the nature of this relationship while controlling for the differences among group means. This kind of design is only employed in observational studies, and the same warnings are applicable here as those given earlier in connection with observational studies.

The statistical model under the regression within groups design is the same as that under the completely randomized design and the computational procedures differ only slightly. As under all three perspectives, the computation of the total sum of squares of Y (adjusted only for the grand mean), T_{yy}, and the adjusted error sum of squares of Y, $E_{yy(adj)}$, remain unchanged. Under the regression within groups design the categorical independent variable is the nuisance variable, and the adjusted (for groups) total sum of squares of Y, $T_{yy(adj)}$ is obtained by subtracting the (unadjusted) between groups sum of squares of Y, $B_{yy} = \Sigma n(\overline{Y}_i - \overline{Y})^2$, from the total sum of squares of Y as follows:

$$T_{yy(adj)} = T_{yy} - \sum_{i=1}^{k} n\,(\overline{Y}_i - \overline{Y})^2; \qquad [29]$$

and the adjusted (for groups) covariate sum of squares, $C_{yy(adj)}$ is computed:

$$C_{yy(adj)} = T_{yy(adj)} - E_{yy(adj)}. \qquad [30]$$

The degrees of freedom for $C_{yy(adj)}$ is equal to the number of covariates.

The statistical test for the null hypothesis of no covariate effects (i.e., H_o: $\beta = 0$) is given by:

$$F = \frac{C_{yy(adj)}/1}{E_{yy(adj)}/(N-k-1)}. \qquad [31]$$

Under the null hypothesis this ratio has an F-distribution with 1 and (N-k-1) degrees of freedom.

Under this perspective, as with the others, the test of homogeneity of regression is given by equation 14 and b_w, given by equation 8, is an unbiased estimator of β. Also, a test for significant group effects can be made by using the ratio:

$$F = \frac{B_{yy}/(k-1)}{E_{yy(adj)}/(N-k-1)}, \qquad [32]$$

which under the null hypothesis of no group effects has an F-distribution with k-1 and N-k-1 degrees of freedom.

The analysis of covariance table for the regression within group design is presented in Table 4.

ANALYSIS UNDER REGRESSION PERSPECTIVE

Under the regression perspective, the covariate and categorical independent variable are of equal interest. The analysis under this problem perspective is identical to the least-squares regression analysis. The total sum of squares of Y (adjusted only for the grand mean), T_{yy}, and the adjusted error sum of squares of Y, $E_{yy(adj)}$, are computed as before. The between group (treatment) sum of squares of Y adjusted for the covariate is:

$$B_{yy(\text{adj for Co})} = T_{yy(\text{adj for Co})} - E_{yy(\text{adj})}, \qquad [33]$$

where

$$T_{yy(\text{adj for Co})} = T_{yy} - T_{xy}^2/T_{xx}. \qquad [34]$$

And the covariate sum of squares of Y adjusted for the group effect is:

$$C_{yy(\text{adj for Group})} = T_{yy(\text{adj for Group})} = E_{yy(\text{adj})}, \qquad [35]$$

where

$$T_{yy(\text{adj for Group})} = T_{yy} - \sum_{i=1}^{k} n\,(Y_i - Y)^2. \qquad [36]$$

In this case there are two null hypotheses of interest; the first is that the group effect is zero (H_o: $\tau_i = 0$, for all i), and the second is that the covariate

TABLE 4
Analysis of Covariance for Regression Within Groups Design

Source of Variation	Sum of Squares and Cross Products			Adjusted Sum of Squares	Degrees of Freedom	Adjusted Mean Square	F-ratio
	XX	XY	YY				
Covariate	--	--	--	$C_{YY(ADJ)}$	1	$C_{YY(ADJ)}$	$\frac{MSC(ADJ)}{MSE(ADJ)}$
Error	E_{XX}	E_{XY}	E_{YY}	$E_{YY(ADJ)}$	N-K-1	$\frac{E_{YY(ADJ)}}{N-K-1}$	
Total	--	--	T_{YY}	$T_{YY(ADJ)}$	N-K		

$E_{xx} = \Sigma\Sigma(X_{ij} - \bar{X}_i)^2$
$E_{xy} = \Sigma\Sigma(X_{ij} - \bar{X}_i)(Y_{ij} - \bar{Y}_i)$
$E_{yy} = \Sigma\Sigma(Y_{ij} - \bar{Y}_i)^2$
$T_{yy} = \Sigma\Sigma(Y_{ij} - \bar{Y})^2$

$E_{yy(adj)} = E_{yy} - E^2_{xy}/E_{xx}$
$T_{yy(adj)} = T_{yy} - \Sigma n(\bar{Y}_i - \bar{Y})^2$
$C_{yy(adj)} = T_{yy(adj)} - E_{yy(adj)}$
$b_w = E_{xy}/E_{xx}$

effect is zero (H_o: $\beta = 0$). The statistical test for group effect is given by:

$$F = \frac{B_{yy(adj\ for\ Co)}/(k-1)}{E_{yy(adj)}/(N-k-1)}, \qquad [37]$$

which, under the null hypothesis, has an F-distribution with k−1 and N−k−1 degrees of freedom. The test for covariate effect is given by:

$$F = \frac{C_{yy(adj\ for\ Group)}/1}{E_{yy(adj)}/(N-k-1)}, \qquad [38]$$

which, under the null hypothesis, has an F-distribution with 1 and N−k−1 degrees of freedom. The test for homogeneity of regression is unchanged and is given by equation 14; and b_w, given by equation 8, is an unbiased estimator of β.

The analysis of covariance table for the regression perspective is given in Table 5.

5. ANALYSIS OF COVARIANCE FOR MORE COMPLEX LAYOUTS

The preceding section considers only the one-way layout which is characterized by a single categorical independent variable with k levels and the covariate. In many situations, both observational and experimental, one may wish to consider two or more categorical independent variables. Situations such as these, which also involve quantitative independent variables (covariates), may be analyzed using an analysis of covariance model.

In considering two or more categorical independent variables in conjunction with covariates, a large number of model configurations are possible. However, the analysis procedures used for these models are in part influenced by the distribution of observations over the levels of the categorical independent variables. The analysis for the one-way layout generally is unaffected by the uneven distribution of observations over groups—unequal group or cell size. (The only modification needed to the analysis procedures already presented to handle unequal cell sizes is to replace n by n_i and define $N = \Sigma n_i.$) However, when two or more categorical independent variables are considered matters become more complicated.

TABLE 5
Analysis of Covariance for Regression Design

Source of Variation	Adjusted Sum of Squares	Degrees of Freedom	Adjusted Mean Square	F-Ratio
Treatment	$B_{YY(ADJ\ FOR\ COV)}$	K-1	$\frac{B_{YY(ADJ\ FOR\ COV)}}{K-1}$	$\frac{MST_{(ADJ)}}{MSE_{(ADJ)}}$
Covariate	$C_{YY(ADJ\ FOR\ GROUP)}$	1	$\frac{C_{YY(ADJ\ FOR\ GROUP)}}{1}$	$\frac{MSC_{(ADJ)}}{MSE_{(ADJ)}}$
Error	$E_{YY(ADJ)}$	N-K-1	$\frac{E_{YY(ADJ)}}{N-K-1}$	
Total	T_{YY}	N-1		

$B_{yy} = \Sigma n(\overline{Y}_i - \overline{Y})^2$

$E_{xx} = \Sigma\Sigma(X_{ij} - \overline{X}_i)^2$

$E_{xy} = \Sigma\Sigma(X_{ij} - \overline{X}_i)(Y_{ij} - \overline{Y}_i)$

$E_{yy} = \Sigma\Sigma(Y_{ij} - \overline{Y}_i)^2$

$T_{yy} = \Sigma\Sigma(Y_{ij} - \overline{Y})^2$

$E_{yy(adj)} = E_{yy} - E^2_{xy}/E_{xx}$

$T_{yy(adj\ for\ Cov)} = T_{yy} - T^2_{xy}/T_{xy}$

$T_{yy(adj\ for\ Group)} = T_{yy} - B_{yy}$

$B_{yy(adj\ for\ Cov)} = T_{yy(adj\ for\ Cov)} - E_{yy(adj)}$

$C_{yy(adj\ for\ Group)} = T_{yy(adj\ for\ Group)} - E_{yy(adj)}$

$b_w = E_{xy}/E_{xx}$

With more than one categorical independent variable, the ideal situation is to have what is referred to as "balanced" observations, that is, observations that occur with equal or proportional frequency in each level of every categorical independent variable. For such balanced designs available statistical procedures allow the analyst to partition the sum of squares associated with a particular categorical independent variable, so that it is independent of the sums of squares associated with each other categorical independent variable. However, if observations are not balanced, it becomes impossible to assign the sum of squares to a single categorical independent variable in such a way that it is not influenced by the other categorical independent variables.

The analysis procedures considered in this section are generally applicable to balanced designs. In cases where the data are not balanced, it is recommended that the effect or contribution of one categorical independent variable be measured in terms of its "partial" or marginal sum of squares. The partial sum of squares represents the sum of squares explained by the given variable after the impact of the other independent variables have been accounted for. The statistical procedure employed in these cases is the method of least squares (regression analysis with dummy variables).

The preceding discussion deals only with categorical independent variables. If in addition to categorical independent variables, the model has a covariate, the covariate may still be handled in any of three ways, as previously discussed (pages 49-54) under the three alternate problem perspectives. However, with unbalanced designs, since the categorical independent variables are analyzed using the least squares method, it is most often the case that the regression perspective is taken and all independent variables (categorical and covariates) are analyzed using least squares.

In observational studies the researcher has no direct control over the test units and, consequently, has no influence on the distribution of observations over the levels of the categorical independent variables. In other words, the researcher has no way to insure that each level of a given categorical independent variable has an equal (or proportional) number of observations, on each level of every other categorical independent variable. If the data from an observational study are such that they are balanced, then the analysis procedures discussed in this section are appropriate. But if the data are not balanced it is recommended that the data be analyzed using regression analysis with dummy variables.

In experimental settings the researcher can exert direct or experimental control over the assignment of treatments (categorical independent variables), and is able to achieve a balanced or near balanced design.

For cases such as these a number of designs and associated analysis procedures have been developed. In the remainder of this section a number of procedures for analysis of covariance with two or more categorical independent variables are discussed. These procedures are most commonly employed in the context of experimental studies and will be discussed accordingly.

Randomized Complete Block Design

In some experimental settings interest centers on a single categorical independent variable as in the one-way layout, but the researcher is able to identify one or more characteristics of the test units which will influence the value of the dependent variable. In such cases, it is sometimes possible to group similar test units (test units are grouped so that the variability of test units within any grouping, referred to as a block, is less than the variability among the groupings). This results in an experiment with two categorical independent variables: the initial variable of interst, and a second variable representing the groupings (blocks) of test units included in an effort to increase the precision of the experiment. If this second variable were not included, the design would be a completely randomized design and the variation in the dependent variable attributable to this second variable would be included in the error term. But by including the second variable, a portion of the error variance is accounted for by this variable (representing test unit characteristics). Therefore, the error variance is reduced, enabling the researcher to increase the accuracy of the experiment. Given this perspective, it is seen that blocking is a form of direct control which reduces experimental error by controlling variability due to the heterogeneity of test units.

Designs such as the one described above are called randomized block designs. When such designs include a quantitative independent variable in addition to the two categorical independent variables, they are analyzed using a randomized block analysis of covariance model.

An additional condition for the use of the randomized block design is that the treatment levels can be randomly assigned to the test units within each block. An exception is made to the randomization procedure when a block consists of one test unit which receives all treatment levels. In this case, the order of treatment levels is randomly determined for each test unit, given that the nature of the experiment allows this. The randomized block design is not applied to observational data.

While there are a number of different ways of blocking, the discussion to follow considers only the randomized complete block design with one observation per cell, i.e., every treatment level is assigned to one test unit from each block. Therefore, each block contains k (the number of treatment levels) test units and there are n blocks, where n is the number of replications desired for the experiment. (For an example of the randomized complete block analysis of covariance design refer to page 64.)

COVARIANCE MODEL

The linear model for the randomized complete block analysis of covariance with one covariate is,

$$Y_{ij} = u + \tau_i + R_j + \beta(X_{ij} - \bar{X}) + e_{ij}; \qquad [39]$$

$$i=1, \ldots, k; \quad j=1, \ldots, n;$$

where Y_{ij} is the observed value of the dependent variable for the *ith* treatment level and the *jth* block, u is the true mean effect, τ_i is the effect due to the *ith* level of the categorical independent variable (treatment) where $\Sigma\tau_i = 0$, R_j is the effect due to the *jth* block where $\Sigma R_j = 0$, β is the (regression) coefficient of the covariate, X_{ij} is the observed value of the covariate, $\bar{X}$ is the general mean of the covariate, and e_{ij} is the random error which is normally and independently distributed with mean zero and variance σ^2.

For the randomized block design, primary interest lies in examining the differences among treatment effects, and both the blocking variable and the covariate(s) are nuisance variables which are included to increase the precision of the experiment. As in the completely randomized design, the hypothesis of no treatment effects is tested using an F-ratio of adjusted mean squares. To conduct this test it is necessary to compute the adjusted treatment sum of squares of Y, $B_{yy(adj)}$ and the adjusted error sum of squares of Y, $E_{yy(adj)}$.

The rationale and the development of the computational procedure for the adjusted error sum of squares of Y, $E_{yy(adj)}$, for the randomized complete block design are directly analogous to those of the completely randomized design and are not repeated here. The computational equation for $E_{yy(adj)}$ is;

$$E_{yy(adj)} = E_{yy} - b_w^2 E_{xx} = E_{yy} - E_{xy}^2/E_{xx} \qquad [40]$$

where,

$$E_{yy} = \sum_{i=1}^{k} \sum_{j=1}^{n} (Y_{ij} - \bar{Y}_{i\cdot} - \bar{Y}_{\cdot j} + \bar{Y})^2,$$

$$E_{xy} = \sum_{i=1}^{k}\sum_{j=1}^{n} (X_{ij} - \bar{X}_{i\cdot} - \bar{X}_{\cdot j} + \bar{X})(Y_{ij} - \bar{Y}_{i\cdot} - \bar{Y}_{\cdot j} + \bar{Y}),$$

$$E_{xx} = \sum_{i=1}^{k}\sum_{j=1}^{n} (X_{ij} - \bar{X}_{i\cdot} - \bar{X}_{\cdot j} + \bar{X})^2, \text{ and}$$

$$b_w = E_{xy}/E_{xx}$$

with $\bar{Y}_{i\cdot}$ equal to the mean of the Y_{ij} for treatment i, $\bar{Y}_{\cdot j}$ the mean value for block j and corresponding definitions on $\bar{X}_{i\cdot}$ and $\bar{X}_{\cdot j}$. The degrees of freedom for $E_{yy(adj)}$ are $(n-1)(k-1)-1$.

In the completely randomized design the adjusted between group (treatment) sum of squares, $B_{yy(adj)}$, is computed by subtracting the adjusted within group sum of squares, $E_{yy(adj)}$, from the adjusted total sum of squares, $T_{yy(adj)}$. Following this procedure with the randomized block design will yield an adjusted sum of squares, which includes block effects as well as treatment effects. Therefore, an alternate procedure, described in the following paragraph, is utilized to compute the adjusted treatment sum of squares.

Assume that all treatment effects are zero, i.e., $\tau_i = 0$ for all i, then the adjusted within group sum of squares of Y would be computed as in the one-way layout (equation 10) as:

$$E^*_{yy(adj)} = E^*_{yy} - E^{*2}_{xy}/E^*_{xx} \qquad [41]$$

where;

$$E^*_{yy} = \sum_{i=1}^{k}\sum_{j=1}^{n} (Y_{ij} - \bar{Y}_{\cdot j})^2,$$

$$E^*_{xy} = \sum_{i=1}^{k}\sum_{j=1}^{n} (X_{ij} - \bar{X}_{\cdot j})(Y_{ij} - \bar{Y}_{\cdot j}), \text{ and}$$

$$E^*_{xx} = \sum_{i=1}^{k}\sum_{j=1}^{n} (X_{ij} - \bar{X}_{\cdot j})^2.$$

If this assumption that all treatment effects are zero is not valid, then $E^*_{yy(adj)}$ consists of both treatment effects and error effects. But the adjusted error sum of squares, $E_{yy(adj)}$ has been calculated (equation 40), therefore, the adjusted treatment sum of squares of Y, $B_{yy(adj)}$, may be obtained by subtraction as follows:

$$B_{yy(adj)} = E^*_{yy(adj)} - E_{yy(adj)}. \qquad [42]$$

Further, it can be shown that

$$E^*_{yy} = B_{yy} + E_{yy},$$

$$E^*_{xy} = B_{xy} + E_{xy}, \text{ and}$$

$$E^*_{xx} = B_{xx} + E_{xx}$$

where,

$$B_{yy} = n \sum_{i=1}^{k} (\bar{Y}_{i\cdot} - \bar{Y})^2,$$

$$B_{xy} = n \sum_{i=1}^{k} (\bar{X}_{i\cdot} - \bar{X})(\bar{Y}_{i\cdot} - \bar{Y}), \text{ and}$$

$$B_{xx} = n \sum_{i=1}^{k} (\bar{X}_{i\cdot} - \bar{X})^2.$$

Therefore, equation 42 is expressed:

$$B_{yy(adj)} = (B_{yy} + E_{yy}) - (B_{xy} + E_{xy})^2/(B_{xx} + E_{xx}) - E_{yy(adj)}. \qquad [43]$$

The degrees of freedom for $B_{yy(adj)}$ are (nk−n−1)−(n−1)(k−1)−1=k−1, the difference in the degrees of freedom of the terms in equation 42.

With the computation of the adjusted treatment and error sums of squares, the hypothesis of no treatment effects can be tested. This statistical test amounts to testing the null hypothesis that $\tau_i = 0$ for all i. The test statistic is the F-ratio,

$$F = \frac{B_{yy(adj)}/(k-1)}{E_{yy(adj)}/(N-n-k)} \qquad [44]$$

which, under the null hypothesis, has an F-distribution with k-1 and N-n-k degrees of freedom.

If one is interested in testing for block effects, an adjusted block sum of squares of Y, designated $S_{yy(adj)}$, is computed by a procedure analogous to that used in computing $B_{yy(adj)}$. The computational form is:

$$S_{yy(adj)} = (S_{yy} + E_{yy}) - (S_{xy} + E_{xy})^2/(S_{xx} + E_{xx}) - E_{yy(adj)} \qquad [45]$$

where;

$$S_{yy} = k \sum_{j=1}^{n} (\bar{Y}_{\cdot j} - \bar{Y})^2,$$

$$S_{xy} = k \sum_{j=1}^{n} (\bar{X}_{\cdot j} - \bar{X})(\bar{Y}_{\cdot j} - \bar{Y}), \text{ and}$$

$$S_{xx} = k \sum_{j=1}^{n} (\bar{X}_{\cdot j} - \bar{X})^2.$$

The degrees of freedom for $S_{yy(adj)}$ are (nk-k-1) - (n-1)(k-1) = n-1. The F-ratio used to test the null hypothesis of no block effects, i.e., $R_j = 0$ for all j, is:

$$F = \frac{S_{yy(adj)}/(n-1)}{E_{yy(adj)}/(N-n-k)} \qquad [46]$$

which, under the null hypothesis, has an F-distribution with n-1 and N-n-k degrees of freedom.

The analysis of covariance table for the randomized block design is presented in Table 6.

TABLE 6

Analysis of Covariance for Randomized Complete Block Design

Source of Variation	Sum of Squares and Cross Products			Adjusted Sum of Squares	Degrees of Freedom	Adjusted Mean Square	Expected Mean Square	F-Ratio
	XX	XY	YY					
Block	S_{XX}	S_{XY}	S_{YY}	$S_{YY(ADJ)}$	N-1	$\frac{S_{YY(ADJ)}}{N-1}$	$\sigma^2_{\varepsilon\|\beta} + \frac{K\Sigma R_J^2}{N-1}$	$\frac{MSB_{(ADJ)}}{MSE_{(ADJ)}}$
Treatment	B_{XX}	B_{XY}	B_{YY}	$B_{YY(ADJ)}$	K-1	$\frac{B_{YY(ADJ)}}{K-1}$	$\sigma^2_{\varepsilon\|\beta} + \frac{N\Sigma\tau_I^2}{K-1}$	$\frac{MST_{(ADJ)}}{MSE_{(ADJ)}}$
Error	E_{XX}	E_{XY}	E_{YY}	$E_{YY(ADJ)}$	(N-1)(K-1)-1	$\frac{E_{YY(ADJ)}}{N-N-K}$	$\sigma^2_{\varepsilon\|\beta}$	
Total					N-2			

$S_{xx} = k\Sigma(\overline{X}_{.j}-\overline{X})^2$

$S_{xy} = k\Sigma(\overline{X}_{.j}-\overline{X})(\overline{Y}_{.j}-\overline{Y})$

$S_{yy} = k\Sigma(\overline{Y}_{.j}-\overline{Y})^2$

$B_{xx} = n\Sigma(\overline{X}_{i.}-\overline{X})^2$

$B_{xy} = n\Sigma(\overline{X}_{i.}-\overline{X})(\overline{Y}_{i.}-\overline{Y})$

$B_{yy} = n\Sigma(\overline{Y}_{i.}-\overline{Y})^2$

$E_{xx} = \Sigma\Sigma(X_{ij} - \overline{X}_{i.} - \overline{X}_{.j} + \overline{X})^2$

$E_{xy} = \Sigma\Sigma(X_{ij}-\overline{X}_{i.} -\overline{X}_{.j}+\overline{X})(Y_{ij}-\overline{Y}_{i.}-\overline{Y}_{.j}+\overline{Y})$

$E_{yy} = \Sigma\Sigma(Y_{ij}-\overline{Y}_{i.}-\overline{Y}_{.j}+\overline{Y})^2$

$E_{yy(adj)} = E_{yy}-E^2_{xy}/E_{xx}$

$S_{yy(adj)} = (S_{yy}+E_{yy})-(S_{xy}+E_{xy})^2/(S_{xx}+E_{xx})-E_{yy(adj)}$

$B_{yy(adj)} = (B_{yy}+E_{yy})-(B_{xy}+E_{xy})^2/(B_{xx}+E_{xx})-E_{yy(adj)}$

TESTING β

For the randomized complete block analysis of covariance certain assumptions are made concerning the regression coefficient, i.e., homogeneity of regression and a nonzero regression coefficient. The test of the hypothesis that β=0 is a straightforward extention of the procedure utilized with the completely randomized design and is given by,

$$F = E_{xy}^2(N-n-k)/(E_{yy}E_{xx} - E_{xy}^2) \qquad [47]$$

where the error sum of squares terms, E_{xx}, E_{xy} and E_{yy}, have previously been defined in relation to equation 40. Under the null hypothesis, this statistic is distributed as the F-distribution with 1 and N−n−k degrees of freedom.

The test for homogeneity of regression is considerably more complex for the randomized complete block design. One would like to test the hypothesis that the regression coefficients are equal across all treatment-block combinations; but with only one observation per treatment-block combination it is impossible to conduct such a test. The most reasonable alternative is to test for homogeneity of regression across treatments under the assumptions of equal regression coefficients across blocks within treatments. In conducting this test, one would be tempted to proceed in a manner similar to that used with the completely randomized design (pages 27-28). The difficulty with this approach, i.e., using equation 14 with the error sum of squares consistent with the randomized block design, is that the computation of the error sum of squares for any single treatment uses all n block means and, therefore, utilizes information on observations from all other treatments. This results in b_{w_i}'s and associated sums of squares which are not independent over treatments, and violates an assumption necessary for the F-test. The easiest solution to this dilemma is to test for homogeneity of regression coefficients using the "added sum of squares" principle as described in the section on "Alternative Perspective of Testing and with Analysis of Covariance" (see pages 45-49).

MEAN COMPARISONS

The adjusted treatment means for the randomized complete block analysis of covariance are computed in a manner identical to that used for the completely randomized design (see equation 13), with the exception that $b_w = E_{xy}/E_{xx}$ is computed using the error sums of squares and cross products computed for the randomized block design (see Table 6). Also, the comparisons among means for the randomized complete block analysis of covariance are identical to those of the completely randomized analysis of covariance (see equations 19 through 21), except that the error term is that for the randomized complete block design and has N−n−k degrees of freedom instead of N−k−1, and the various sums of squares of X are those computed for the randomized complete block design.

NUMERIC EXAMPLE FOR RANDOMIZED COMPLETE BLOCK DESIGN

In the example accompanying the completely randomized design, researchers were concerned with the impact of the establishment of a package liquor store, alone or with a licensed restaurant, on the rate of traffic accidents in rural municipalities. Assume that illustration to have been an experimental study, and that before the experiment was conducted it was suspected that certain subcultural differences among the various geographic regions of the country might have some impact upon the dependent variable. In order to control for this possible source of variablility and, thereby, increase the precision of the experiment, one test unit (rural municipality) from each of the country's four geographical/subcultural regions was randomly assigned to each of the three treatment levels. The data resulting from this experiment are presented in Table 7.

The experimental setting, with the above described modification, represents a randomized complete block design. As with the completely randomized design, the primary purpose is to test the hypothesis that all levels of liquor licensing have equal impact on the rate of traffic accidents. This hypothesis is tested with an F-ratio (equation 44) which requires the following computations:

(1) compute the error sums of squares and cross products, E_{xx}, E_{xy} and E_{yy} (refer to Table 6 for appropriate equations for this and subsequent computations),

(2) compute the treatment sums of squares and cross products, B_{xx}, B_{xy} and B_{yy},

(3) compute the adjusted error and treatment sums of squares, $E_{yy(adj)}$ and $B_{yy(adj)}$, and

(4) compute the F-ratio.

The numeric results of these computations for the present example are presented in Table 8. The computed F-ratio is 41.20 which is significant

TABLE 7

Data for Randomized Complete Block Design: Traffic Accidents During the Test Period (Y) and Traffic Accidents During Preceding Year (X)

Geographic Regions (Blocks)	Type of Liquor Licensing (Treatment or Groups)						Block Means	
	Control (Group 1)		Store Only (Group 2)		Restaurant and Package Store (Group 3)			
	X	Y	X	Y	X	Y	$\bar{X}_J$	$\bar{Y}_J$
A	190	177	252	226	206	226	216.00	209.67
B	261	225	228	196	239	229	242.67	216.67
C	194	167	240	198	217	215	217.00	193.33
D	217	176	246	206	177	188	213.33	190.00
Treatment Means	215.50	186.25	241.50	206.50	209.75	214.50		

Sample Means $\bar{X} = 222.50$ $\bar{Y} = 202.42$

TABLE 8
Analysis of Covariance for Randomized Complete Block Design with Data From Illustrative Example

Source of Variation	Sum of Squares and Cross Products			Adjusted Sum of Squares	Degrees of Freedom	Adjusted Mean Square	F-ratio
	XX	XY	YY				
Blocks	1688.42	1212.54	1476.92	607.37	3	202.34	7.16
Treatments	2289.50	146.75	1696.17	2329.01	2	1164.51	41.20
Error	3805.83	2794.92	2193.83	141.31	5	28.26	
Total					10		

at $\alpha = .05$ ($F_{.05;2,5} = 5.79$). Therefore, the null hypothesis is rejected, implying that the treatment levels do have differential effects. The exact nature of these effects will be examined shortly.

Block effects are tested (i.e., test the hypothesis that $R_j = 0$ for all j) using the F-ratio (equation 46) of adjusted mean square for blocks to adjusted mean square error. The computations (refer to Table 6) for this test are completed as follows:

(1) compute the block sums of squares and cross products, S_{xx}, S_{xy} and S_{yy},

(2) compute the adjusted block sum of squares $S_{yy(adj)}$ (note, the error and adjusted error sums of squares have been calculated in conjunction with the test of treatment effects), and

(3) compute the F-ratio.

The numeric result of the computations outlined above are presented in Table 8, and the calculated F-ratio of 7.16 is significant at $\alpha.05$ ($F_{.05;3,5} = 5.41$). Therefore the null hypothesis of no block effects is rejected.

At this point, the assumption that the coefficient of the covariate is nonzero is considered. The null hypothesis in this case is that $\beta = 0$ and the test statistic (equation 47) is the F-ratio:

$$F = E_{xy}^2(N-n-k)/(E_{yy}E_{xx} - E_{xy}^2)$$

$$= (2794.92)^2\,(12-4-3)/[(2193.83)\,(3805.83) - (2794.92)^2]$$

$$= 72.62.$$

Given this F-value, the hypothesis that $\beta = 0$ is rejected ($F_{.05;1,5} = 6.61$), and the hypothesized model is consistent with the observed data.

The test for homogeneity of regression is easily conducted using the "added sum of squares" principle (see pp. 45-49), which results in a comparison of the standard randomized complete block covariance model (equation 39) and a similar model with three separate regression coefficients, one for each treatment level. That test gives a calculated F-ratio of 2.72, and there is no reason to reject the hypothesis of homogeneity of regression ($F_{.10;2,3} = 5.46$).

For purposes of interpretation it is useful to calculate the pooled within class regression coefficient,

$$b_w = E_{xy}/E_{xx} = 2794.92/3805.83 = 0.7344,$$

and the adjusted group means,

$$\bar{Y}_{1\cdot(adj)} = \bar{Y}_{1\cdot} - b_w(\bar{X}_{1\cdot} - \bar{X}) = 186.25 - 0.7344(215.50 - 222.25)$$
$$= 191.21,$$

$$\bar{Y}_{2\cdot(adj)} = \bar{Y}_{2\cdot} - b_w(\bar{X}_{2\cdot} - \bar{X}) = 206.50 - 0.7344(241.50 - 222.25)$$
$$= 192.36,$$

and

$$\bar{Y}_{3\cdot(adj)} = \bar{Y}_{3\cdot} - b_w(\bar{X}_{3\cdot} - \bar{X}) = 214.50 - 0.7344(209.75 - 222.25)$$
$$= 223.68.$$

The same mean comparisons that were computed in conjunction with the numeric example for the completely randomized design are now considered. The a priori comparison of group 1 and group 3, control group and treatment group with both package store and licensed restaurant respectively, is tested with the t-statistic given by equation 19 with the values of $\bar{Y}_{i(adj)}$, $MSE_{(adj)}$ and E_{xx} being those computed for the randomized complete block design. The calculated t-value is −8.56, and the null hypothesis of no difference is rejected ($t_{.05;5} = 2.57$). It is concluded that the accident rate is higher in the treatment group than in the control group. The a posteriori pairwise comparisons of all means (Tukey's HSD procedure) are computed by substituting the appropriate quantities from the randomized complete block design into equation 20. The resulting q-values are −10.71, −.43 and −10.28 for treatment 1 with 3, treatment 1 with 2 and treatment 2 with 3, respectively. Given these calculated q-values, the null hypothesis of no difference is rejected for the comparisons of treatment 1 and treatment 2 with treatment 3 ($q_{.05;5,3} = 4.60$), but cannot be rejected for the comparison of treatment 1 with treatment 2.

The reader should note that the results of the analysis for the randomized complete block design are quite similar to those for the completely randomized design. The major difference is the considerable decrease in the error sum of squares (note also the decrease in the associated degrees of freedom) for the randomized complete block design. This will occur whenever blocking is employed as long as the test unit characteristics used to define the blocks are significantly related to the dependent variable. Accompanying this decrease in the error sum of squares is an increase in the calculated F- and t-statistics.

Factorial Design

Often, interest centers on the simultaneous evaluation of two or more categorical independent variables in a single analysis. Many cases such as this exist and a variety of designs, all included under the general classification of factorial designs, are available to handle them. In these cases, the researcher is simultaneously interested in the effect of all categorical independent variables, and the test units are typically randomly assigned to the various combinations of levels of the categorical independent variables by the researcher. This differs from the randomized block design just discussed in that with that design, the test unit characteristics are not under the control of the researcher, could not be randomly assigned, and were not of primary interest to the researcher. However, the analysis procedures for the two types of designs can be similar.

Factorial designs may include more than two independent variables, and employ a number of variations in the assignment of test units. When a quantitative independent variable (covariate) is considered in addition to the categorical independent variables, the analysis procedure employed is a factorial analysis of covariance. The design considered here is the simplest of factorial designs, the two-factor balanced factorial analysis of covariance design. This design considers two categorical independent variables, the first (designated factor A) with p levels and the second (factor B) with q levels, pq treatment combinations with an equal number of test units randomly assigned to each, and one covariate. The two-factor factorial with an unequal number of test units per treatment combination is discussed at the conclusion of the factorial design section (pages 86-87). For a discussion of more complex factorial designs the reader is referred to Ostle (1963) or Kirk (1968).

Before proceeding, it should be mentioned that the two-factor balanced factorial analysis of covariance procedure is equally applicable to observational studies and experimental studies. However, the number of observational studies in which there occurs an equal number of observations for each cell (combination of levels of two categorical variables) is limited. Observational studies tend to have unequal cell sizes and should be analyzed accordingly.

COVARIANCE MODEL

The linear model for the completely randomized factorial analysis of covariance with two factors and one covariate is,

$$Y_{ijk} = u + \alpha_i + \gamma_j + (\alpha\gamma)_{ij} + \beta(X_{ijk} - \bar{X}) + e_{ijk}; \quad i=1, \ldots, p; \; j=1, \ldots, q; \; \text{and } k=1, \ldots, n; \qquad [48]$$

where Y_{ijk} is the observed value of the dependent variable for the *kth* observation within the *ith* level of factor A and the *jth* level of factor B, u is the true mean effect, α_i is the effect due to the *ith* level of factor A with $\Sigma\alpha_i = 0$, γ_j is the effect due to the *jth* level of factor B with $\Sigma\gamma_j = 0$, $(\alpha\gamma)_{ij}$ is the effect due to the interaction of the *ith* level of factor A with the *jth* level of factor B with $\Sigma_i(\alpha\gamma)_{ij} = 0$ and $\Sigma_j(\alpha\gamma)_{ij} = 0$, β is the (regression) coefficient of the covariate, X_{ijk} is the observed value of the covariate, $\bar{X}$ is the general mean of the covariate, and e_{ijk} is the random error which is normally and independently distributed with mean zero and variance σ^2.

For the completely randomized factorial design, primary interest lies in examining the differences in the effects of the various levels of the categorical independent variables (factors) and their interactions. As with the designs previously considered, the hypotheses of no effect due to factors and interaction are tested using F-ratios of adjusted mean squares. The procedures for calculating the necessary adjusted sums of squares for the two-factor factorial analysis of covariance are considered below.

The adjusted error sum of squres of Y, $E_{yy(adj)}$, for the factorial design is obtained in a manner directly analogous to that used for the completely randomized and the randomized complete block designs. The computational equation for $E_{yy(adj)}$ is;

$$E_{yy(adj)} = E_{yy} - b_w^2 E_{xx} = E_{yy} - E_{xy}^2/E_{xx} \qquad [49]$$

where;

$$E_{yy} = \sum_{i=1}^{p}\sum_{j=1}^{q}\sum_{k=1}^{n} (Y_{ijk} - \bar{Y}_{ij})^2,$$

$$E_{xy} = \sum_{i=1}^{p}\sum_{j=1}^{q}\sum_{k=1}^{n} (X_{ijk} - \bar{X}_{ij})(Y_{ijk} - \bar{Y}_{ij}),$$

$$E_{xx} = \sum_{i=1}^{p}\sum_{j=1}^{q}\sum_{k=1}^{n} (X_{ijk} - \bar{X}_{ij})^2, \text{ and}$$

$$b_w = E_{xy}/E_{xx},$$

with $\overline{Y}_{ij}$ and $\overline{X}_{ij}$ equal to the mean values of Y_{ijk} and X_{ijk}, respectively, for the *ith* level of factor A and the *jth* level of factor B. The degrees of freedom for $E_{yy(adj)}$ are N−pq−1.

The adjusted factor and interaction sums of squares of Y for the factorial analysis of covariance are computed in the same manner as the adjusted treatment sum of squares of Y in the randomized complete block design. First, consider factor A.

If it were assumed that the factor A effects are zero, i.e., $\alpha_i = 0$ for all i, then the adjusted error sum of squares of Y would be computed as:

$$E^*_{yy(adj)} = E^*_{yy} - E^{*2}_{xy}/E^*_{xx} \qquad [50]$$

where;

$$E^*_{yy} = \sum_{i=1}^{p}\sum_{j=1}^{q}\sum_{k=1}^{n}(Y_{ijk} - \overline{Y}_{\bullet j})^2,$$

$$E^*_{xy} = \sum_{i=1}^{p}\sum_{j=1}^{q}\sum_{k=1}^{n}(X_{ijk} - \overline{X}_{\bullet j})(Y_{ijk} - \overline{Y}_{\bullet j}), \text{ and}$$

$$E^*_{xx} = \sum_{i=1}^{p}\sum_{j=1}^{q}\sum_{k=1}^{n}(X_{ijk} - \overline{X}_{\bullet j})^2,$$

with $\overline{Y}_{.j}$ and $\overline{X}_{.j}$ equal to the mean values of Y_{ijk} and X_{ijk}, respectively, for the *jth* level of factor B. Now, if the assumption that factor A effects are zero is not valid, $E^*_{yy(adj)}$ consists of both factor A effects and error effects. But, by subtracting out the error effects, as computed by equation 49, the remainder would be the factor A effects. Therefore, the adjusted factor A sum of squares of Y, $A_{yy(adj)}$, is obtained by subtraction,

$$A_{yy(adj)} = E^*_{yy(adj)} - E_{yy(adj)} \qquad [51]$$

Further, it can be shown that

$$E^*_{yy} = A_{yy} + E_{yy},$$

$$E^*_{xy} = A_{xy} + E_{xy}, \text{ and}$$

$$E^*_{xx} = A_{xx} + E_{xx}$$

where;

$$A_{yy} = qn \sum_{i=1}^{p} (\bar{Y}_{i\cdot} - \bar{Y})^2,$$

$$A_{xy} = qn \sum_{i=1}^{p} (\bar{X}_{i\cdot} - \bar{X})(\bar{Y}_{i\cdot} - \bar{Y}), \text{ and}$$

$$A_{xx} = qn \sum_{i=1}^{p} (\bar{X}_{i\cdot} - \bar{X})^2,$$

with $\bar{Y}_{i\cdot}$ and $\bar{X}_{i\cdot}$ equal to the mean values of Y_{ijk} and X_{ijk}, respectively, for the *ith* level of factor A. Using these relationships, equation 51 is expressed:

$$A_{yy(adj)} = (A_{yy} + E_{yy}) - (A_{xy} + E_{xy})^2/(A_{xx} + E_{xx}) - E_{yy(adj)}. \qquad [52]$$

The degrees of freedom for $A_{yy(adj)}$ are (N−pq+p−2)−(N−pq−1) = p−1, the difference in the degrees of freedom of the terms in equation 51.

The adjusted factor B sum of squares of Y, $B_{yy(adj)}$, and the adjusted interaction sum of squares of Y, $AB_{yy(adj)}$, are obtained in a like manner. For factor B,

$$B_{yy(adj)} = (B_{yy} + E_{yy}) - (B_{xy} + E_{xy})^2/(B_{xx} + E_{xx}) - E_{yy(adj)} \qquad [53]$$

where,

$$B_{yy} = pn \sum_{j=1}^{q} (\bar{Y}_{\cdot j} - \bar{Y})^2,$$

$$B_{xy} = pn \sum_{j=1}^{q} (\bar{X}_{\cdot j} - \bar{X})(\bar{Y}_{\cdot j} - \bar{Y}), \text{ and}$$

$$B_{xx} = pn \sum_{j=1}^{q} (\bar{X}_{\cdot j} - \bar{X})^2.$$

The degrees of freedom for $B_{yy(adj)}$ are $(N-pq+q-2) - (N-pq-1) = q-1$. For the interaction,

$$AB_{yy(adj)} = (AB_{yy} + E_{yy}) - (AB_{xy} + E_{xy})^2/(AB_{xx} + E_{xx}) - E_{yy(adj)} \quad [54]$$

where,

$$AB_{yy} = n \sum_{i=1}^{p} \sum_{j=1}^{q} (\bar{Y}_{ij} - \bar{Y}_{i\cdot} - \bar{Y}_{\cdot j} + \bar{Y})^2,$$

$$AB_{xy} = n \sum_{i=1}^{p} \sum_{j=1}^{q} (\bar{X}_{ij} - \bar{X}_{i\cdot} - \bar{X}_{\cdot j} + \bar{X})(\bar{Y}_{ij} - \bar{Y}_{i\cdot} - \bar{Y}_{\cdot j} + \bar{Y}), \text{ and}$$

$$AB_{xx} = n \sum_{i=1}^{p} \sum_{j=1}^{q} (\bar{X}_{ij} - \bar{X}_{i\cdot} - \bar{X}_{\cdot j} + \bar{X})^2.$$

The degrees of freedom for $AB_{yy(adj)}$ are

$(N-p-q) - (N-pq-1) = (p-1)(q-1)$.

For this two-factor factorial design there are three major hypotheses of interest. In each case an F-ratio is the appropriate test statistic. The first hypothesis considered is the null hypothesis of no factor A effects, i.e., $\alpha_i = 0$ for all i. The test statistic is the F-ratio,

$$F_A = \frac{A_{yy(adj)}/(p-1)}{E_{yy(adj)}/(N-pq-1)} \quad [55]$$

which under the null hypothesis has an F-distribution with p-1 and N-pq-1 degrees of freedom. The next hypothesis is the null hypothesis of no factor B effects, i.e., $\gamma_j = 0$ for all j. The test statistic is the F-ratio,

$$F_B = \frac{B_{yy(adj)}/(q-1)}{E_{yy(adj)}/(N-pq-1)} \quad [56]$$

which under the null hypothesis has an F-distribution with q−1 and N−pq−1 degrees of freedom. The third hypothesis is that of no interaction effect, i.e., $(\alpha\gamma)_{ij} = 0$ for all i and j. The test statistic is the F-ratio,

$$F_{AB} = \frac{AB_{yy(adj)}/(p-1)(q-1)}{E_{yy(adj)}/(N-pq-1)} \qquad [57]$$

which under the null hypothesis has an F-distribution with (p−1)(q−1) and N−pq−1 degrees of freedom. The analysis of covariance table for the two-factor factorial design is presented in Table 9.

If there is only one test unit per treatment combination, i.e., n = 1, the interaction effects, $(\alpha\gamma)_{ij}$, are assumed to be zero, the adjusted error sum of squares is computed according to equation 40, and the computations and test associated with the interaction are deleted.

FURTHER CONSIDERATIONS

In the presence of a significant interaction effect, the interpretation of a statistically significant factor effect may become very complex. Under these circumstances, the significance of a factor indicates that significant differences in the dependent variable exist on average (averaged over levels of the other factor) across the levels of that significant factor. But, for any given level of the other factor, the differences in the dependent variable over the levels of that significant factor may, or may not, be themselves statistically significant. This suggests the usefulness of testing the significance of one factor while holding the other factor constant at given levels. Tests of this type are referred to as tests of *simple* main effects.

If a significant interaction effect is found, added insight into the nature of the experimental results can be gained through an examination of the simple main effects. Simple main effect tests for a two-factor factorial design, in the case of factor A, tests the null hypothesis that the factor A effect is zero over a specified level of factor B, i.e., $\alpha_i = 0$ for all i given j = J, and, for factor B, test the null hypothesis that the factor B effect is zero over a specified level of factor A, i.e., $\gamma_j = 0$ for all j given i = I. In order to conduct these tests it is necessary to compute adjusted factor sums of squares of Y for one factor while holding the other factor constant at the specified level. The computation of these adjusted sums of squares is discussed below.

TABLE 9

Analysis of Covariance for Two-Factor Factorial Design

Source of Variation	Sun of Squares and Cross Products XX	XY	YY	Adjusted Sum of Squares	Degrees of Freedom	Adjusted Mean Square	Expected Mean Square	F-Ratio
Treatment A	A_{XX}	A_{XY}	A_{YY}	$A_{YY(ADJ)}$	P-1	$\frac{A_{YY(ADJ)}}{P-1}$	$\sigma^2_{\varepsilon\mid\beta} + \frac{QN\Sigma\alpha^2_I}{P-1}$	$\frac{MSA(ADJ)}{MSE(ADJ)}$
Treatment B	B_{XX}	B_{XY}	B_{YY}	$B_{YY(ADJ)}$	Q-1	$\frac{B_{YY(ADJ)}}{Q-1}$	$\sigma^2_{\varepsilon\mid\beta} + \frac{PN\Sigma\gamma^2_J}{Q-1}$	$\frac{MSB(ADJ)}{MSE(ADJ)}$
Interaction	AB_{XX}	AB_{XY}	AB_{YY}	$AB_{YY(ADJ)}$	(P-1)(Q-1)	$\frac{AB_{YY(ADJ)}}{(P-1)(Q-1)}$	$\sigma^2_{\varepsilon\mid\beta} + \frac{N\Sigma\Sigma(\alpha\gamma)^2_{IJ}}{(P-1)(Q-1)}$	$\frac{MSAB(ADJ)}{MSE(ADJ)}$
Error	E_{XX}	E_{XY}	E_{YY}	$E_{YY(ADJ)}$	N-PQ-1	$\frac{E_{YY(ADJ)}}{N-PQ-1}$	$\sigma^2_{\varepsilon\mid\beta}$	
Total					N-2			

$A_{xx} = qn\Sigma(\overline{X}_{i.}-\overline{X})^2$

$A_{xy} = qn\Sigma(\overline{X}_{i.}-\overline{X})(\overline{Y}_{i.}-\overline{Y})$

$A_{yy} = qn\Sigma(\overline{Y}_{i.}-\overline{Y})^2$

$B_{xx} = pn\Sigma(\overline{X}_{.j}-\overline{X})^2$

$B_{xy} = pn\Sigma(\overline{X}_{.j}-\overline{X})(\overline{Y}_{.j}-\overline{Y})$

$B_{yy} = pn\Sigma(\overline{Y}_{.j}-\overline{Y})^2$

$AB_{xy} = n\Sigma\Sigma(\overline{X}_{ij}-\overline{X}_{i.}-\overline{X}_{.j}+\overline{X})^2$

$AB_{yy} = n\Sigma\Sigma(\overline{Y}_{ij}-\overline{Y}_{i.}-\overline{Y}_{.j}+\overline{Y})^2$

$AB_{yy} = n\Sigma\Sigma(\overline{Y}_{ij}-\overline{Y}_{i.}-\overline{Y}_{.j}+\overline{Y})^2$

$E_{xx} = \Sigma\Sigma\Sigma(X_{ijk}-\overline{X}_{ij})^2$

$E_{xy} = \Sigma\Sigma\Sigma(X_{ijk}-\overline{X}_{ij})(Y_{ijk}-\overline{Y}_{ij})$

$E_{yy} = \Sigma\Sigma\Sigma(Y_{ijk}-\overline{Y}_{ij})^2$

$E_{yy(adj)} = E_{yy}-E^2_{xy}/E_{xx}$

$A_{yy(adj)} = (A_{yy}+E_{yy})-(A_{xy}+E_{xy})^2/(A_{xx}+E_{xx})-E_{yy(adj)}$

$B_{yy(adj)} = (B_{yy}+E_{yy})-(B_{xy}+E_{xy})^2/(B_{xx}+E_{xx})-E_{yy(adj)}$

$AB_{yy(adj)} = (AB_{yy}+E_{yy})-(AB_{xy}+E_{xy})^2/(AB_{xx}+E_{xx})-E_{yy(adj)}$

The adjusted factor A sum of squares of Y at level B_j, designated $A_{yy(adj,B_j)}$, is computed as follows:

$$A_{yy(adj,B_j)} = (A_{yy(B_j)} + E_{yy}) - (A_{xy(B_j)} + E_{xy})^2/(A_{xx(B_j)} + E_{xx}) - E_{yy(adj)} \quad [58]$$

where,

$$A_{yy(B_j)} = n \sum_{i=1}^{p} (\bar{Y}_{ij} - \bar{Y}_{.j})^2,$$

$$A_{xy(B_j)} = n \sum_{i=1}^{p} (\bar{X}_{ij} - \bar{X}_{.j})(\bar{Y}_{ij} - \bar{Y}_{.j}), \text{ and}$$

$$A_{xx(B_j)} = n \sum_{i=1}^{p} (\bar{X}_{ij} - \bar{X}_{.j})^2$$

The degrees of freedom for $A_{yy(adj,B_j)}$ are p–1. The adjusted factor B sum of squares at level A_i is computed in a like manner:

$$B_{yy(adj,A_i)} = (B_{yy(A_i)} + E_{yy}) - (B_{xy(A_i)} + E_{xy})^2/(B_{xx(A_i)} + E_{xx}) - E_{yy(adj)} \quad [59]$$

where,

$$B_{yy(A_i)} = n \sum_{j=1}^{q} (\bar{Y}_{ij} - \bar{Y}_{i.})^2,$$

$$B_{xy(A_i)} = n \sum_{j=1}^{q} (\bar{X}_{ij} - \bar{X}_{i.})(\bar{Y}_{ij} - \bar{Y}_{i.}), \text{ and}$$

$$B_{xx(A_i)} = n \sum_{j=1}^{q} (\bar{X}_{ij} - \bar{X}_{i.})^2.$$

The degrees of freedom for $B_{yy(adj,A_i)}$ are q−1.

The test statistic for the factor A null hypothesis, $\alpha_i = 0$ for all i at level B_j, is the F-ratio

$$F_{A(B_j)} = \frac{A_{yy(adj,B_j)}/(p-1)}{E_{yy(adj)}/(N-pq-1)} \qquad [60]$$

which under the null hypothesis has an F-distribution with p−1 and N−pq−1 degrees of freedom. It is recommended to assign the same error rate for the *set* of simple main effects as that determined for the overall F-ratio. Thus, if the level of significance is selected to be $\alpha = .05$ for the overall test, the simple main effect ratios for treatment A should be tested at the .05/q level of significance.

To test the factor B null hypothesis, $\gamma_j = 0$ for all j at A_i, the calculated F-ratio is:

$$F_{B(A_i)} = \frac{B_{yy(adj,A_i)}/(q-1)}{E_{yy(adj)}/(N-pq-1)} \qquad [61]$$

which under the null hypothesis has an F-distribution with q−1 and N−pq−1 degrees of freedom. The recommended significance level is α/p where α is the significance level selected for the overall test.

TESTING β

The covariance model assumes the within cell regression coefficients are equal for all combinations of factors A *and* B. The hypothesis of homogeneity of regression is tested with an F-statistic, similar to that used in the completely randomized design. The test statistic is:

$$F = \frac{(E_{yy(adj)} - S_1)/(pq-1)}{S_1/(N-2pq)} \qquad [62]$$

where $E_{yy(adj)}$ is given by equation 49 and,

$$S_1 = E_{yy} - \sum_{i=1}^{p}\sum_{j=1}^{q} b_{w_{ij}}^2 E_{xx_{ij}} \qquad [63]$$

where E_{yy} is the error sum of squares of Y for the factorial design, $b_{w_{ij}} = E_{xy_{ij}}/E_{xx_{ij}}$ is the within cell regression coefficient for the *ith* level of factor A and the *jth* level of factor B, $E_{xy_{ij}} = \Sigma_k(X_{ijk} - \bar{X}_{ij})(Y_{ijk} - \bar{Y}_{ij})$ is the error sum of squares for the cross product of X and Y for the *ith* level of factor A and the *jth* level of factor B, and $E_{xx_{ij}} = \Sigma_k(X_{ijk} - \bar{X}_{ij})^2$ is the error sum of squares of X for the *ith* level of factor A and the *jth* level of factor B. Under the null hypothesis of homogeneity of within cell regression, this test statistic is distributed as the F-distribution with pq–1 and N–2pq degrees of freedom.

The test statistic for the hypothesis that $\beta = 0$ is given by,

$$F = E_{xy}^2(N-pq-1)/(E_{yy}E_{xx} - E_{xy}^2) \qquad [64]$$

where the error sums of squares have been defined in relation to equation 49. Under the null hypothesis this test statistic is distributed as the F-distribution with 1 and N–pq–1 degrees of freedom.

COMPARISONS AMONG MEANS

A significant F-ratio for a main effect (factor A or factor B) in a two-factor factorial design indicates that at least one level of that main effect is different from the others. As with the other designs discussed, further investigation into the nature of these differences requires the use of mean comparisons, and, as with the other designs, these mean comparisons utilize adjusted group means. However, for the factorial design it is sometimes useful to differentiate between two types of mean comparisons. The first is designated a main effect mean comparison and compares means for different levels of one factor where the means are averaged over all levels of the other factor. The second is referred to as a *simple* main effect mean comparison and compares means for different levels of one factor within a single level of the other factor, i.e., compares cell means while holding one of the factors constant. The reason for having these two types of comparisons is that when the interaction effect is significant, tests of differences among means for main effects are often of little interest, and, the interesting findings are sought by comparisons among *simple* main effects.

The adjusted means for these two types of comparisons are computed as follows:

$$\bar{Y}^{(k)}_{(adj)} = \bar{Y}^{(k)} - b_w(\bar{X}^{(k)} - \bar{X}) \qquad [65]$$

where $b_w = E_{xy}/E_{xx}$ is the pooled within cell regression coefficient, and $\overline{Y}^{(k)}$ and $\overline{X}^{(k)}$ are equal to $\overline{Y}_{i.}$ and $\overline{X}_{i.}$, $\overline{Y}_{.j}$ and $\overline{X}_{.j}$, and $\overline{Y}_{ij}$ and $\overline{X}_{ij}$ for main effect factor A, main effect factor B and simple main effect comparisons, respectively.

A priori orthogonal comparisons among means for both main effects and simple main effects are given by

$$t = \frac{\Sigma c_k \overline{Y}^{(k)}_{(adj)}}{\sqrt{MSE_{(adj)}\left[\Sigma(c_k^2/n_k) + [\Sigma c_k(\overline{X}^{(k)} - \overline{X})]^2/E_{xx}\right]}} \qquad [66]$$

where $\overline{Y}_{(adj)}$ and $\overline{X}^{(k)}$ are defined as above, and n_k is nq and np respectively for factor A and B main effect comparisons, and n for simple main effect comparisons. Under the hypothesis of no difference this ratio has a t-distribution with N−pq−1 degrees of freedom. (It should be kept in mind that when testing *simple* main effect comparisons the level of significance should be set a α/q and α/p for A and B, respectively.)

For unplanned, a posteriori, pairwise comparisons, Tukey's (HSD) test is computed:

$$q = \frac{c_k \overline{Y}^{(k)}_{(adj)} + c_{k'} \overline{Y}^{(k')}_{(adj)}}{\sqrt{\dfrac{MSE_{(adj)}}{n_k} \quad 1 + \left[\dfrac{K_{xx}}{[d.f.(K)]\,E_{xx}}\right]}} \qquad [67]$$

where $\overline{Y}^{(k)}_{(adj)}$ and n_k are defined as above, K_{xx} equals A_{xx}, B_{xx} and AB_{xx} respectively for factor A and B main effect comparisons and simple main effect comparisons, and d.f. (K) is the degrees of freedom associated with $K_{yy(adj)}$. The corresponding a posteriori test using Scheffe's procedure results in the following test statistic:

$$F = \frac{\Sigma c_k \overline{Y}^{(k)}_{(adj)}}{MSE_{(adj)}\left[1 + \dfrac{K_{xx}}{[d.f.(K)]\,E_{xx}}\right]\left[\Sigma(c_k^2/n_k)\right]} \cdot \frac{1}{(m_k - 1)} \qquad [68]$$

where m_k is the total number of means from which the specific comparison is formed, and the other quantities are defined above. This F-value is compared to the critical value from the F-distribution with d.f.(K) and N−pq−1 degrees of freedom. (Again it is noted that the significance levels should be adjusted for simple main effect comparisons.)

NUMERIC EXAMPLE FOR TWO-FACTOR DESIGN WITH EQUAL CELL SIZE

In the example provided for the completely randomized design, researchers were concerned with the impact of three levels of liquor licensing (no liquor sold, package store only, and both package store and licensed restaurant) on the rate of traffic accidents in rural municipalities. Now, assume that a fourth treatment level, licensed restaurant only, is added to the initial design and all treatment levels are randomly assigned to four rural municipalities. With the addition of this fourth group the study may be conceptualized as a two-by-two factorial design, where factor A is the establishment of a package store (two levels: yes or no), and factor B is the establishment of a licensed restaurant (two levels: yes or no). The data from this study are presented in Table 10.

As was the case with the previous analyses, the primary purpose is to test the impact of the various treatment combinations on the dependent variable. With the two-factor factorial design this is accomplished by testing three hypotheses; one concerning factor A, a second concerning factor B, and the third concerning the interaction of factors A and B. Each of these hypotheses is tested with an F-ratio (see equations 55-57). The F-ratios require the calculation of the adjusted sums of squares of Y, $E_{yy(adj)}$, $A_{yy(adj)}$, $B_{yy(adj)}$ and $AB_{yy(adj)}$ (see equations 49, 52-54), which in turn require the computation of twelve sums of squares and cross product terms (E_{xx}, E_{xy}, E_{yy}, A_{xx}, A_{xy}, A_{yy}, B_{xx}, B_{xy}, B_{yy}, AB_{xx}, AB_{xy} and AB_{yy}). The calculated values of the F-ratios, the adjusted sums of squares of Y, and the sums of squares and cross products are reported in Table 11. The three F-ratios are all significant at the $\alpha = .05$ level ($F_{.05;1,11} = 4.84$), therefore, all three null hypotheses are rejected.

Some researchers consider it preferable to test for interaction effects first, and if they are found to be significant proceed directly to test the simple main effect hypotheses. The merit of this approach is the simplicity of interpretation of simple main effect tests, as compared to main effect tests, in the presence of a significant interaction. For the present example there are four simple main effect hypotheses, each of which are examined, with summary results presented in Table 12.

TABLE 10
Data for Two-Factor Factorial Design: Traffice Accidents During Test Period (Y) and Traffic Accidents During Preceding Year (X)

Licensed Restaurant (Factor B)	Package Store (Factor A)				Factor B Means	
	Yes (Level 1)		No (Level 2)			
	X	Y	X	Y	X	Y
Yes (Level 1)	206	226	248	229		
	239	229	208	190		
	217	215	225	195		
	177	188	239	202		
Means	209.75	214.50	230.00	204.00	219.88	209.25
No (Level 2)	252	226	190	177		
	228	196	261	225		
	240	198	194	167		
	246	206	217	176		
Means	241.50	206.50	215.50	186.25	228.50	196.38
Factor A Means	225.63	210.50	222.75	195.13		

Sample Means X = 224.19 Y = 202.81

The first simple main effect hypothesis considered is H_o: $\alpha_i = 0$ for all i at level B_1; i.e., given a licensed restaurant is established, there is no difference in the traffic accident rate whether or not a package store is also established. The F-value (calculated using equation 60) to test this hypothesis is 12.91. $F_{.025;1,11} = 6.72$, therefore, the null hypotheses that the addition of the package store does not make any difference given a licensed restaurant is established, is rejected. The second hypothesis tested is H_o: $\alpha_i = 0$ for all i at level B_2; i.e., given a licensed restaurant is not established, there is no difference in the traffic accident rate whether or not a package store is established. The calculated F-ratio is 0.004. This ratio is far from significant and, therefore, one cannot reject the null hypothesis that the addition of the package store does *not* make any difference given a

TABLE 11
Analysis of Covariance for Factorial Design with Data From Illustrative Example

Source of Variation	Sum of Squares and Cross Products			Adjusted Sum of Squares	Degrees of Freedom	Adjusted Mean Square	F-Ratio
	XX	XY	YY				
Factor A	33.06	176.81	945.56	696.04	1	696.04	7.71
Factor B	297.56	-444.19	663.06	1427.42	1	1427.42	15.80
Interaction	2139.06	450.94	95.06	462.51	1	462.51	5.12
Error	6408.75	4792.00	4576.75	993.64	11	90.33	
Total					14		

TABLE 12
Analysis of Simple Main Effects for Factorial Design with Data From Illustrative Example

Source of Variation	Sum of Squares and Cross Products			Adjusted Sum of Squares	Degrees of Freedom	F-ratio
	XX	XY	YY			
Factor A at B_1	820.13	-425.25	220.50	1165.79	1	12.91
Factor A at B_2	1352.00	1053.00	820.13	1.08	1	0.004
Factor B at A_1	2016.13	-508.00	128.00	1532.72	1	16.97
Factor B at A_2	420.50	514.75	630.13	89.56	1	0.99
Error				993.64	11	

licensed restaurant is *not* established. The third hypothesis tested is H_o: $\gamma_j = 0$ for all j at level A_1; i.e., given a package store is established, there is no difference in the accident rate if the licensed restaurant is established or not. The F-value, calculated using equation 61, is 16.97. Since $F_{.025;1,11} = 6.72$, the null hypotheses that the addition of the licensed restaurant does not make any difference given a package store is established, is rejected. The final simple main effect hypothesis tested is H_o: $\gamma_j = 0$ for all j at level A_2; i.e., given a package store is not established, there is no difference in the accident rate if a licensed restaurant is established or not. The computed F-value of 0.99 is not significant and one cannot reject the null hypothesis that the addition of the licensed restaurant does *not* have any effect on the traffic accident rate given a package store is *not* established. In summary, establishing either package store or licensed restaurant alone did not seem to have significant impact on traffic accident rates, but if both are established in a municipality the effect is significant.

The covariance model assumes equality of within cell regression coefficients. The test of this assumption of homogeneity of regression is given by equation 62, which requires the calculation of the error sum of squares of X for each cell, $E_{xx_{ij}}$, and the within cell regresion coefficients, $b_{w_{ij}} = E_{xy_{ij}}/E_{xx_{ij}}$, where $E_{xy_{ij}}$ is the error sum of squares for the cross product of X and Y for cell ij. The computation of these quantities for cells 11, 12 and 22 has already been completed in conjunction with the numeric example for the completely randomized design (see pages 37-38; cells 11, 12 and 22 correspond to treatments 3, 2 and 1 of the completely randomized design, respectively). These quantities are similarly calculated for cell 21. The resulting values are: $E_{xy_{21}} = 785.00$, $E_{xx_{21}} = 914.00$ and $b_{w_{21}} = 0.8589$. The calculated F-value is 0.255 and the hypothesis of homogeneity of regression ($F_{.10;3,8} = 2.92$) is not rejected.

The second assumption tested is that the regression coefficient is nonzero. The test statistic (computed using equation 64) for the null hypothesis that $\beta = 0$ is 13.465. Given this F-ratio, the hypothesis that $\beta = 0$ is rejected ($F_{.05;1,11} = 4.84$), and the hypothesized model is consistent with the observed data.

In the presence of a significant interaction effect it is usually helpful to graphically present the results. In order to do this the pooled within cell regression coefficient, b_w, and the adjusted cell means, $\bar{Y}_{ij(adj)}$, must be obtained. These quantities are computed as follows:

$$b_w = E_{xy}/E_{xx} = 4792.00/6408.75 = 0.7477,$$

$$\bar{Y}_{11(adj)} = \bar{Y}_{11} - b_w(\bar{X}_{11} - \bar{X}) = 214.50 - 0.7477(209.75 - 224.19)$$

$$= 225.29,$$

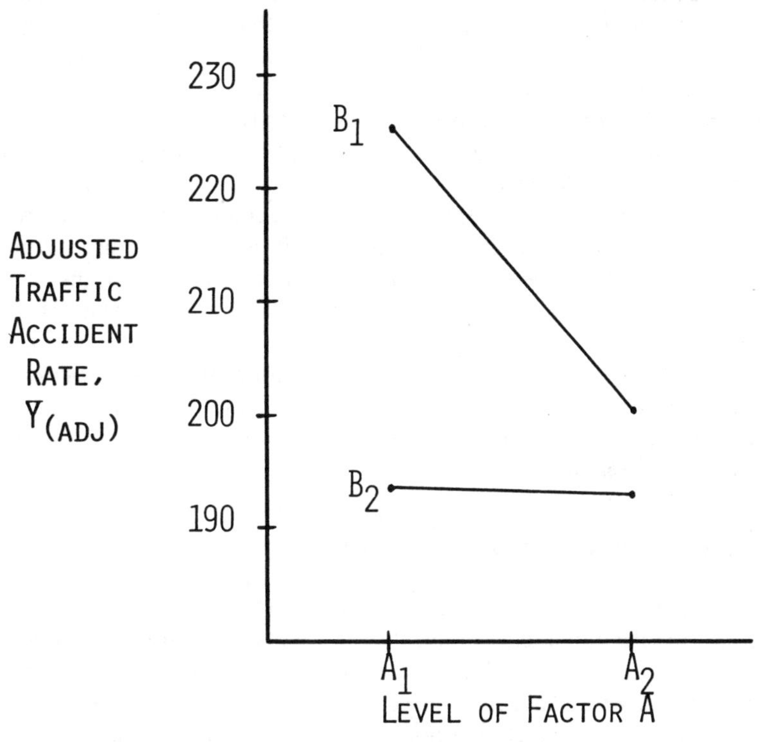

Figure 5: Adjusted Treatment Means

$$\bar{Y}_{12(adj)} = \bar{Y}_{12} - b_w(\bar{X}_{12} - \bar{X}) = 206.50 - 0.7477(241.50 - 224.19)$$

$$= 193.56,$$

$$\bar{Y}_{21(adj)} = \bar{Y}_{21} - b_w(\bar{X}_{21} - \bar{X}) = 204.00 - 0.7477(230.00 - 224.19)$$

$$= 199.65,$$

and

$$\bar{Y}_{22(adj)} = \bar{Y}_{22} - b_w(\bar{X}_{22} - \bar{X}) = 186.25 - 0.7477(215.50 - 224.19)$$

$$= 192.75.$$

The graphical presentation (Figure 5) shows clearly that the effects of a package store (factor A) and the licensed restaurant (factor B) are not independent. The fact that the two lines in the graph are not parallel demonstrates this interaction. It can be seen that the effect of establishing a package store seems very minor if no licensed restaurant is established (the B_2 line), while the package store has a significant increasing effect on the accident rate if a licensed restaurant is also established (the B_1 line). These graphical interpretations complement the results of the hypothesis tests on the simple main effects.

In many cases, the researcher may wish to conduct mean comparisons, and where significant interactions exist it would be more helpful if simple main effect mean comparisons were used. However, for the example considered here, each factor has only two levels and the tests of simple main effects have already accomplished all possible simple main effect mean comparisons. In other cases, where significant interactions exist and factors have more than two levels, it may be useful to conduct specific simple main effect mean comparisons in addition to testing the simple main effect hypotheses.

ANALYSIS WITH UNEQUAL CELL SIZES

Even in experimental studies, where the researcher has direct control over the selection and assignment of test units, there are often cases when cell sizes are unequal. There are basically three reasons why an experimental study may have unequal cell sizes. Each of these calls for a different kind of analysis (which will not be discussed in detail here).

The first case is when the researcher chooses, for convenience, to obtain a different number of observations for different levels of the factors, and then assigns the test units to the cells *proportionally*. The reason why the cell sizes differ must be assumed to be independent of the nature of the independent variables. For example, different levels of a categorical variable may require different kinds of interviewers and only a very limited number of each kind is available. The interviews may need to be conducted simultaneously, and the researcher may want to use all available interviewers even though for some factor levels there are more interviewers than for some others. The so-called conventional analysis, an analysis identical to that discussed earlier in this section but with n_i substituted for n in the appropriate places (Kirk, 1968), is appropriate for this kind of situation.

The second case is when the researcher plans to have equal cell sizes, but for reasons unrelated to the nature of the independent variables, data from some test units are not obtained. For example, because of the unavailability of some test units during the study, or because data from some test units must be discarded for various reasons unrelated to the nature of the independent variables. The so-called unweighted means analysis (Kirk, 1968), which is very similar to the analysis discussed in this section is used under these circumstances.

The third case is when the unequal cell sizes are present for reasons related to the nature of independent variables. For example, some respondents may refuse to participate *because of* their membership in a given cell. The analysis technique for this case is the least-squares method. (For a detailed discussion of the least-squares method for unequal cell sizes in factorial design for analysis of variance refer to Winer, 1971.)

Other Designs

From the preceding discussion it should be clear to the reader that covariance analysis may be conducted within the context of any type of design. While it is unrealistic to discuss all possible alternate designs for analysis of covariance, in this section we will briefly consider and provide further references for selected additional experimental designs.

The Latin square design is a somewhat more complex design than those already considered. However, the Latin square may be an effective way to experimentally minimize the effects of two extraneous, or nuisance variables when investigating the impact of alternate levels of a single treatment (categorical independent) variable. This design is somewhat restrictive in the sense that it requires an equal number of levels for each of the two extraneous variables and the treatment variable. The Latin square design results in n^2 cells, where n equals the number of treatment levels. Futhermore, if there are no replications within cells, it is not advisable to conduct a Latin square analysis with fewer than five treatment levels because this provides too few degrees of freedom for the error term. The computations for the Latin square analysis of covariance are relatively similar to those used in conjunction with the randomized complete block design. If the reader is familiar with the computations for the regular Latin square analysis of variance and the basic principles of the analysis of covariance as described in conjunction with the randomized complete block design, it should be fairly easy to understand the computations relating to the analysis of covariance for Latin square designs. For a discussion and numeric examples of the Latin square analysis of covariance the reader is referred to Federer (1955), Snedecor (1956), and Ostle (1963).

The use of blocking has been discussed within the context of the completely randomized design. However, sometimes it is useful to use blocking in conjunction with a factorial design, in which case the design is referred to as a randomized block factorial design. The analysis for this design may be viewed as an extension of analysis of covariance for either the factorial design or the randomized complete block design. This extension is straightforward and involves an increase in the number of variables. For a discussion and numeric examples for the randomized block factorial analysis of covariance the reader is referred to Steel and Torrie (1960) and Ostle (1963).

One might also find applications of analysis of covariance with respect to various repeated designs, such as the split plot design. For a discussion of analysis of covariance in conjunction with repeated designs the reader is referred to Winer (1971). Also, Zelen (1957) discusses the analysis of covariance for incomplete block designs, and Cornish (1940) discusses the analysis of covariance for various quasi-factorial designs.

REFERENCES

BLALOCK, H. M. (1972) Social Statistics. New York: McGraw-Hill.

BLAU, P. M. and O. D. DUNCAN (1967) American Occupational Structure. New York: John Wiley.

CORNISH, E. A. (1940) "The analysis of covariance in quasi-factorial designs." Annals of Eugenics 10: 269-279.

ELASHOFF, J. C. (1969) "Analysis of covariance: a delicate instrument." American Educational Research Journal 6: 383-401.

FEDERER, W. T. (1955) Experimental Design. New York: Macmillan.

FEIERABEND, I. K. and R. L. FEIERABEND (1972) "Coerciveness and change: cross-national trends." American Behavioral Scientist 15: 911-927.

GLASS, G. V., P. D. PECKHAM and J. R. SANDERS (1972) "Consequences of failure to meet assumptions underlying the fixed effects analysis of variance and covariance." Review of Educational Research 43: 237-288.

IVERSON, G. R. and H. NORPOTH (1976) Analysis of Variance. Sage University Paper on Quantitative Applications in the Social Sciences, series no. 07-001. Beverly Hills and London: Sage Publications.

KIRK, R. E. (1968) Experimental Design: Procedure for the Behavioral Sciences. Belmont, CA: Brooks/Cole.

LORD, F. M. (1967) "A paradox in the interpretation of group comparisons." Psychological Bulletin 68: 304-305.

——— (1969) "Statistical adjustments when comparing preexisting groups." Psychological Bulletin 72: 336-337.

OSTLE, B. (1963) Statistics in Research. Ames: Iowa State University Press.

PASTERNACK, B. and G. CHAREN (1969) "A simplified guide to covariance analysis using two concomitant variables illustrated on data from an experiment in education." Science Education 53: 78-88.

PECHMAN, P. D. (1968) "An investigation fo the effects of non-homogeneity of regression slopes upon the F-test of analysis of covariance." Laboratory of Educational Research, Report No. 16. Boulder: University of Colorado.

SNEDECOR, G. W. (1956) Statistical Methods Applied to Experiments in Agriculture and Biology. Ames: Iowa State University Press.

STEEL, R. G. and J. H. TORRIE (1960) Principles and Procedures of Statistics. New York: McGraw-Hill.

STOKOLS, D., T. E. SMITH, and J. J. PROSTOR (1975) "Partitioning and perceived crowding in a public space." American Behavioral Scientist 18: 792-814.

WINER, B. J. (1971) Statistical Principles in Experimental Design. New York: McGraw-Hill.

ZELEN, M. (1975) "The analysis of covariance for incomplete block designs." Biometrics 13: 309-332.

APPENDIX

Model Assumptions and Sensitivity

Statistical models for analysis of covariance in various design contexts have been stated earlier and specific assumptions relevant to those models have been noted when required by the discussion. The intent of this section is to state the model assumptions in explicit form, and to provide a discussion of the consequences of violating the assumptions. (For further reading in this area see Elashoff [1969] and Glass, Peckham and Sanders [1972].) The following discussion will explicitly consider the completely randomized design but, in general, will apply to other contexts.

The algebraic form of the statistical model for analysis of covariance in the context of a completely randomized design is given by equation (1). To use the analysis of covariance technique in a valid manner, the following assumptions are made:

(1) The scores on the dependent variable are a linear combination of four independent components: an overall mean, a treatment effect, a linear covariate effect, and an error term.

(2) The error is normally and independently distributed with mean zero and variance σ_{ϵ}^2.

(3) The (weighted) sum over all groups of the treatment/group effect is zero.

(4) The coefficient of the covariate (slope of the regression line) is the same for each treatment/group.

(5) The covariate is a fixed mathematical variable measured without error, not a stochastic variable.

The first assumption incorporates four points: additivity, linearity of regression, independence of the error component from the predictive factors included in the model, and independence of the covariate from the treatment effects. As with analyses of variance, the principal effect of employing an additive model when the underlying process is nonadditive is a loss of information. Most authors conclude that violation of this additivity assumption should not be a prime concern for researchers. In certain cases, severe departure from an additive model may be corrected by variable transformations. For example, a multiplicative model may be transformed via log transformation into an additive model. In addition to additivity, the covariance model assumes a linear relationship between the covariate and the dependent variable. If this assumption is seriously violated the mean comparisons may be biased. If the researcher is concerned about the viability of the linearity assumption there are two basic options available. The assumption may be tested statistically or scatter diagrams may be prepared for each group to determine if the relationship between the covariate and the dependent variable departs greatly from linearity. The assumption concerning the independence of the error term from the predictive (i.e., nonrandom) elements of the model is a necessary requisite for conducting the statistical analysis both in analysis of variance and analysis of covariance. Violation of this assumption may lead to serious consequences. However this does not present much of a problem to the researcher in experimental studies, since this independence can be assured by the random assignment of test units to treatment groups. The final part of this assumption, that the covariate is independent of the treatment, is a basic tenet of the analysis of covariance model. When the covariate and treatment are not independent, the regression adjustment may obscure part of the treatment effect or may produce spurious treatment effects. This difficulty can be avoided in experimental contexts by measuring the covariate prior to the administration of the treatments and assigning the treatments to test units at random. It is noted that with nonexperimental studies violation of this assumption may seriously affect the interpretation of results.

The second assumption involves three points: normality, homogeneity of variance, and independence of error. These are the assumptions upon which the F-test is based. (It should be noted that in the analysis of covariance framework, the e_{ij}'s are residuals about the within group regression line estimated via a common slope, and the common variance is the error variance of the estimate.) Most researchers indicate that the analysis of covariance model is robust with respect to violations of the assumptions of normality and homogeneity of variance, as is the analysis of variance model. However, there are some indications that the model sensitivity to these assumptions may be affected by the values of the covariates (see Glass et al., 1972: 274-275). Also, as in analysis of variance, nonindependence of errors can have serious effects on the validity of probability statements relative to the statistical tests. Although no adequate measure of the degree of independence of errors within groups exists, this problem is usually circumvented in experimental studies by the careful design of the experiment to insure that independence is preserved.

The third assumption, the summation of the weighted treatment effects is zero, is more of a restriction placed upon the model than an assumption. By specifying treatment means as the sum of two components, the overall mean and the increment for each treatment, the researcher satisfies this restriction.

The fourth assumption is the homogeneity of regression assumption. It states that the slope of the regression line (i.e., the incremental impact of the covariate) is the same for all treatment groups. In other words, there are no treatment-slope interactions. Little study has been done on the effects of violations of this assumption. The work most relevant to typical research applications (Pechman, 1968) is based on findings obtained from Monte Carlo simulations. Pechman found that the empirical sampling distribution of the F-statistic differed little from the theoretical distribution unless the departures from homogeneous slopes were extreme. His work indicates that, as the situation departs from homogeneous slopes, the analysis becomes more conservative with respect to making a type I error. These results were obtained under conditions which required the distribution of the covariate to be the same for each treatment group. A second phase of his investigation suggests that the robustness continues to hold in quasi-experimental settings in which the distributions of the covariate (or covariate means) differ by treatment group. As the reader is aware, statistical tests exist for examining the heterogeneity of regression slopes.

The analysis of covariance procedure is based on the assumption that the covariate is fixed and measured without error. Violations of this assumption occur when the covariate is either random and/or measured with error. Limited available research indicates that if the covariate is a random variable measured without error there is little effect on the F-test. And, in those situations where error in measurements are involved, the major impact appears to be a lowering of the precision of the analysis. For a more complete discussion of this matter refer to Glass et al. (1972: 279-281).

PART V

MULTIVARIATE ANALYSIS OF VARIANCE

JAMES H. BRAY

SCOTT E. MAXWELL

1. INTRODUCTION TO MULTIVARIATE ANALYSIS OF VARIANCE

The application of multivariate analysis of variance (MANOVA) in the behavioral sciences has increased dramatically, and it appears that it will be used frequently in the future for data analysis. Although the mathematical basis of MANOVA and related techniques was largely developed in the 1930s and 1940s, only in recent years have the techniques been applied in the social sciences. This increase is largely due to the availability of accessible computer programs that simplify the tedious calculations required. The result is the application of these sophisticated techniques to a wide variety of research problems.

MANOVA is a conceptually straightforward extension of the well-known univariate ANOVA techniques. The major distinction is that in ANOVA one evaluates mean differences on a single dependent criterion variable, whereas in MANOVA one evaluates mean differences on two

AUTHORS' NOTE: *The two authors contributed equally to the preparation of the work. Dr. Bray's contribution was supported by grant 1 RO1 HD18025-01 from the National Institute of Child Health and Human Development of the National Institutes of Health. Sections 3 and 4 of this work are a modified draft of J. H. Bray and S. E. Maxwell, "Analyzing and interpreting significant MANOVAs,"* Review of Education Research *52 (1982): 340-367. Copyright by the American Educational Research Association. This material is reprinted with permission of the AERA.*

or more dependent criterion variables simultaneously. Although ANOVA and MANOVA are often associated with experimental studies involving a manipulation introduced by the experimenter, both techniques are in fact appropriate whenever the research question involves a comparison of mean scores. For example, the average (i.e., mean) scores for females and males might be compared on a battery of intellectual measures, or the average political attitudes of city dwellers might be compared to those of people in rural areas. When means on single variables are to be compared, ANOVA is appropriate (if its assumptions are reasonably satisfied). However, when means on several different variables are to be compared simultaneously, MANOVA is usually necessary (again, contingent on meeting a set of assumptions to be discussed later).

Like ANOVA, MANOVA is usually conducted as a two-step process. The first step is to test the overall hypothesis of no differences in the means for the different groups (i.e., the overall or omnibus test). If this test is significant, the second step is to conduct follow-up tests to explain group differences. The mathematical basis for applying MANOVA is well known and generally accepted (see Bock, 1975; Finn, 1974; Timm, 1975). However, two broad areas are still in development: (1) issues concerning the overall test, such as choice between test statistics, power and sample size concerns, and measures of effect size, and (2) methods for further analyzing and interpreting group differences when an overall significant MANOVA is found. There is currently considerable controversy on these topics, with little consensus as to the "proper" use of the methods (Borgen and Seling, 1978; Bray and Maxwell, 1982; Gabriel, 1979; Kaplan and Litownik, 1977; Larrabbe, 1982; Leary and Altmaier, 1980; O'Grady, 1978; Spector, 1977, 1980; Stevens, 1972; Strahan, 1982; Wilkinson, 1975). In addition, there is a more recent trend to understand MANOVA and related techniques in the context of the General Linear Model and their relationship to structural models that underlie the methods (Bray and Maxwell, 1982; Kenny, 1979).

The purpose of this book is to comprehensively review and discuss the use of MANOVA and related techniques in the behavioral sciences. The book will focus on three areas: (1) developing a conceptual understanding of MANOVA, appropriate application, and issues in the use of the MANOVA method; (2) procedures for analyzing and interpreting significant MANOVAs; and (3) the causal models underlying MANOVA and their relationship to other multivariate techniques. The position we take is that there is no one "right" method but, instead, that there are advantages and disadvantages to each, which depend on what the researcher hopes to glean from the data. The approach taken will be nonmathematical and will focus on the appropriate use and interpretation of the various methods. In this regard, we will provide some decision rules to facilitate researchers choosing the appropriate techniques for their study.

Use of Multiple Criterion Variables

A reasonable question to ask is why use more than one criterion variable? In most cases researchers are not interested in a single measure of group differences. Rather, there are usually several components, constructs, or behaviors that might be affected by the treatment or that are useful to separate the groups.

For example, if we wanted to evaluate the effects of a training program to increase assertiveness, we might be interested in measuring the effects of the training program on the person's (1) assertive behavior, (2) anxiety about being assertive, and (3) self-esteem. It might reasonably be expected that there would be a non-zero correlation between these variables because they measure different aspects of assertion. In this case MANOVA provides a distinct advantage over separate ANOVAs because the MANOVA test considers the correlations between the variables. In fact, if separate ANOVA tests are performed it is implicitly assumed that either the correlations between the variables are zero or that the correlations are not of interest (more on this in Section 3). In addition, even if the major interest is in assessing the effects on only one construct, it is almost always the case that it is better to multi-operationalize a construct (i.e., have several measures of it), rather than mono-operationalize the construct (i.e., have a single measure of it; Cook and Campbell, 1979). Particularly in the social sciences, in which measurement is considerably less than perfect, multi-operationalizing constructs and using multivariate methods to assess the effects of treatments may provide a more valid assessment of treatment effects (Cole et al., 1981).

A note of caution is warranted here. First, the indiscriminant use of multiple dependent measures is never an appropriate substitute for a well-conceived study with a select number of variables. Just conducting a study and measuring everything related to one's area of interest is a poor substitute for a more controlled design in which a small number of reliable measures are employed. Although MANOVA allows the researcher to handle multiple dependent variables, these should be selected carefully to accurately measure the effects of interest. In fact, the use of too many dependent variables may hinder the chances of finding a significant result because of low statistical power or it may result in spurious findings due to chance. These last two issues will be discussed further in Sections 2 and 3.

Relationship of ANOVA to MANOVA

In an ANOVA we test the null hypothesis that the means of k groups (where k = the number of groups) are all equal to one another. In this case we are testing whether there are significant differences between the groups on a single dependent variable.

In the multivariate case we test the null hypothesis that the population means of the k groups are equal to one another for all p variables. This is a test that the k group centroids are equal. (A centroid is the p-dimensional vector of population means for that group.) With one MANOVA approach we are testing whether there are significant differences between groups on a new variate, called a centroid, that maximally separates the groups. (A *variable* refers to one of the criteria that is observed and measured in the study, whereas a *variate* is a statistical criterion resulting from a linear combination of the original observed variables.) In one sense an ANOVA is performed on the new criterion variate, the weighted linear combination of the p variables. (It is important to note that the above statement is limited to one MANOVA approach.) Unlike the univariate case, there is not just one method (i.e., the F test) to form a test statistic. Instead, there are several methods. A more complete discussion and comparison of these methods will be developed and presented in Section 2.

Why Use MANOVA?

There are several reasons to use MANOVA in studies investigating mean differences. First, researchers are typically interested in evaluating mean differences on several criterion variables, rather than a single criterion variable. Even if the researcher is only interested in these differences on each variable individually, MANOVA may still be the optimal technique. In this case, MANOVA is used to control the overall alpha level at the desired level (usually .05), but the researcher is interested only in the separate univariate analyses that may subsequently be performed. Another alternative in this situation, which will be discussed later, is to perform separate ANOVAs with a Bonferroni adjustment of the alpha level (Bird, 1975; Timm, 1975).

A second major reason to use MANOVA is because the researcher wants to look at the relationships among the variables rather than looking at each of them in isolation. That is, the researcher wants to evaluate the mean differences on all of the dependent variables simultaneously, while controlling for the intercorrelations among them. In this case there are several potential uses to consider: (1) the researcher wants to look at the relationships among the *p* variables for the group comparisons; (2) the researcher wishes to reduce the *p* variables to some smaller set of theoretical dimensions; (3) the researcher wants to select the variables that contribute most to group separation; and/or (4) the researcher is interested in the *set* of measures as they represent some underlying construct(s). In each of these cases there is the opportunity to learn more about the data by looking at the variables in some combination or pattern rather than individually. This is where MANOVA offers some unique advantages over separate ANOVAs.

To further exemplify the differences between ANOVA and MANOVA, consider the case in which we have an experiment with two groups of teachers: Group 1 subjects receive a treatment to improve their teaching and Group 2 subjects serve as controls. In this case we are interested in whether the treatment improves teaching as measured by two criterion variables: student ratings and peer ratings of teaching quality. Hypothetical data for this example are illustrated in Figure 1.1. The axes represent the frequency distributions for each variable. If we look at each variable individually, it appears that the distributions overlap sufficiently that it is unlikely that we would find significant effects on either of the ANOVAs separately. However, the MANOVA looks at the two-dimensional space simultaneously. Figure 1.2 illustrates a possible bivariate frequency distribution for the two-dimensional space. Here we notice that the groups are more separated in the two-dimensional space than in either dimension individually.

Thus, one benefit of MANOVA is that by examining both variables together, it may provide a more powerful test than doing separate ANOVAs.

Another potential benefit of MANOVA is that interpretation of results may be enhanced by considering criterion variables simultaneously. As mentioned above, one way of conceptualizing MANOVA is that it forms a new criterion for each subject, which is that linear combination of the *p* variables that maximally separates the groups. In other words, when $p = 2$ (for simplicity), MANOVA finds a criterion of the form:

$$V_{ij} = k_1 Y_1 + k_2 Y_2$$

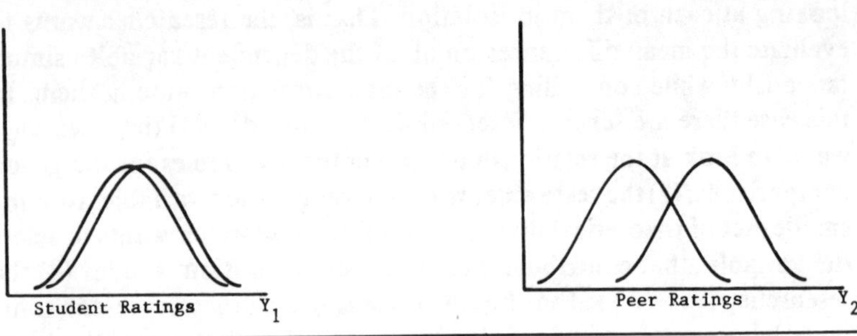

Figure 1.1

where k_1 is the weight for variable Y_1 and k_2 is the weight for variable Y_2. This new criterion has the property that mean differences are maximized relative to within-group variance on this variable. Any other linear combination of Y_1 and Y_2 would produce more overlap between the distributions. Because the linear combination found by MANOVA maximizes group differences, it is often informative to interpret MANOVA results based on the magnitude of the weights derived for each of the dependent variables (see further discussion in Sections 2 and 3).

Although MANOVA may sometimes provide a more useful and valid means of analyzing data, this is not always the case. There are some situations in which MANOVA is unnecessary. If a researcher plans to only use dependent variables that are uncorrelated, there is little advantage for using MANOVA. In fact, with uncorrelated criteria and relatively small sample size, MANOVA may be at a disadvantage to separate ANOVAs in terms of statistical power. Second, the results from an analysis using MANOVA may be more complex and difficult to interpret than those from ANOVAs. Although this complexity may accurately reflect the phenomena under study, multivariate statistics can be more difficult to understand and consequently make the interpretation more complex. The reverse situation can also be true; that is, MANOVA may sometimes simplify the data and make them more understandable. Thus, the researcher is wise to seriously consider both the advantages and the disadvantages before using MANOVA or any statistical technique *before* collecting the data.

In the following sections we will discuss the overall or omnibus MANOVA test, issues concerning the selection of the appropriate test statistic, and related considerations, such as power and measures of effect size. Section 3 will present the various methods for analyzing and interpreting a significant MANOVA, and Section 4 will describe the

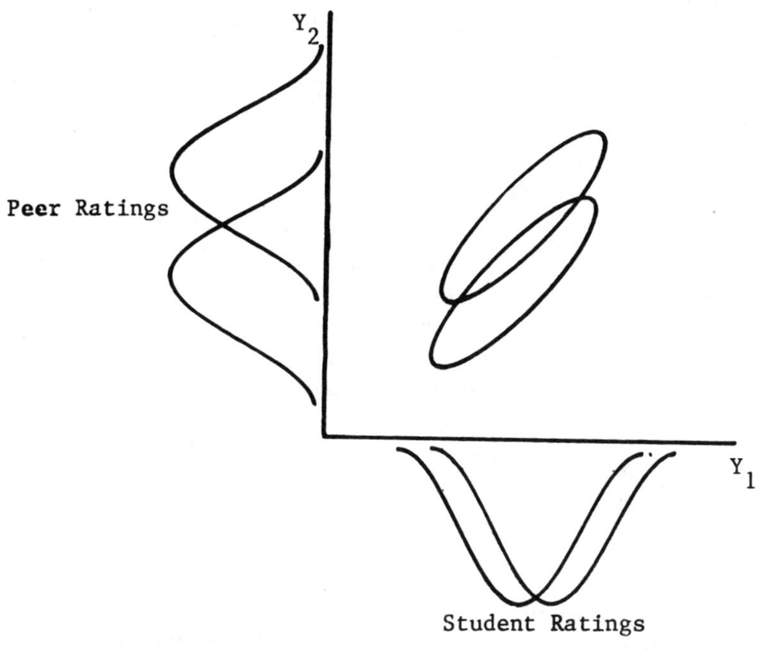

Figure 1.2

causal models underlying MANOVA analyses. Section 5 will briefly discuss the use of MANOVA in more complex designs. The last section will review the popular statistical computer packages for MANOVA.

2. OMNIBUS MANOVA TESTS

The omnibus or overall MANOVA test is the first step in the MANOVA procedure. It is analogous to the overall F test in ANOVA. In the univariate case this F test is the uniformly most powerful invariant test of the overall null hypothesis if its assumptions are met. However, in MANOVA there is no single invariant test that is uniformly most powerful, even if all assumptions have been satisfied. For this reason, in MANOVA there are several test statistics that might be used to evaluate the overall null hypothesis. Because the various test statistics are based on different mathematical criteria, the results of a study may differ depending on the test statistic chosen. In this chapter the various MANOVA test statistics will be discussed. In addition, issues related to the overall MANOVA test will be presented. Before discussing the various MANOVA test criteria, it is important to understand the multivariate null hypothesis.

Multivariate Null Hypothesis

Before considering hypothesis testing in MANOVA, we will briefly review the univariate case. For the sake of simplicity, we will only deal with a single factor design: that is, a situation in which there is no factorial structure imposed on the groupings of subjects. However, the relationships between the univariate and multivariate approaches we will develop in this special case also hold for more complex designs. In ANOVA the purpose is to compare the means of *k* groups ($k \geq 2$) on some dependent measure. In particular, the null hypothesis to be tested is

$$H_0\colon \mu_1 = \mu_2 = \ldots = \mu_k$$

where μ_j is the population mean of the *jth* group. In other words, the null hypothesis is that all *k* groups have the same population mean. The alternative hypothesis (H_A) is that at least one of the groups has a population mean different from the others. Notice that it is not necessary for every group to differ in order for H_0 to be false; instead, it is only required that one of the groups be different.

What is the relationship between the null hypothesis being tested in ANOVA and the null hypothesis being tested in MANOVA? In the multivariate case, scores have been obtained for each subject on several dependent measures. For purposes of generality, we will let *p* represent the number of dependent variables in the study. Before writing the multivariate null hypothesis, we need to develop some notation. We will let μ_{mj} represent the population mean on variable *m* for group *j*. Notice that *m* ranges from 1 to *p*, while *j* ranges from 1 to *k*. Now the multivariate null hypothesis can be written as

$$H_o\colon \begin{array}{c} \mu_{11} = \mu_{12} = \ldots = \mu_{1k} \\ \mu_{21} = \mu_{22} = \ldots = \mu_{ak} \\ \vdots \quad \vdots \quad \vdots \quad \vdots \\ \mu_{p1} = \mu_{p2} = \ldots = \mu_{pk} \end{array}$$

In words, the null hypothesis is that for each variable all k groups have the same population mean. The null hypothesis can be written much more compactly by using matrix algebra notation. Specifically, we can let $\boldsymbol{\mu}_j$ be a column vector of population means for group j: i.e.,

$$\boldsymbol{\mu}_j = \begin{bmatrix} \mu_{1j} \\ \mu_{2j} \\ \cdot \\ \cdot \\ \cdot \\ \mu_{pj} \end{bmatrix}$$

Then we can write the multivariate null hypothesis simply as an equality of vectors:

$$H_0: \boldsymbol{\mu}_1 = \boldsymbol{\mu}_2 = \ldots = \boldsymbol{\mu}_k$$

Notice that we have not changed the meaning of H_0 in any way; instead, we have just written it more compactly. The alternative hypothesis in this case is that for at least one variable, there is at least one group with a population mean different from the others. Much like the univariate case, all it takes is one inequality in the population to make the null hypothesis false.

Univariate Test of Significance

In practice, a sample of data is randomly obtained from each of the k groups in order to decide whether or not the null hypothesis should be rejected. The univariate procedure will again be reviewed in the process of developing the multivariate test. The approach that we will take is based on the principle of model comparisons (see Cramer, 1972; Neter and Wasserman, 1974). We will use the hypothetical data in Table 2.1 first to illustrate this principle in the univariate case, and then show how it can be generalized to the multivariate case. Although in practice a larger sample size than we have here is advisable, we have chosen to present a small data set so as to facilitate computations.

Table 2.1 contains data for 5 individuals on 2 variables in each of 3 groups. Let us first perform a univariate ANOVA on the first variable, completely ignoring the second variable. According to the model comparisons principle, the first step in deriving such a test is to form a "full model." For ANOVA, a full model stipulates that an individual's score

TABLE 2.1
Hypothetical Data for Three Groups and Two Dependent Variables

Raw Data

Group	*Indiv*	Y_1	Y_2
1	1	8	60
1	2	7	57
1	3	13	65
1	4	15	63
1	5	12	60
2	1	15	62
2	2	16	66
2	3	11	61
2	4	12	63
2	5	16	68
3	1	17	52
3	2	20	59
3	3	23	59
3	4	19	58
3	5	21	62

Summary Data for the Original Variables and the Discriminant Variates

Group	Y_1		Y_2		V_1		V_2	
	mean	*sd*	*mean*	*sd*	*mean*	*sd*	*mean*	*sd*
1	11.0	3.4	61.0	3.1	19.5	1.1	14.9	1.1
2	14.0	2.3	64.0	2.9	19.1	0.9	15.9	0.9
3	20.0	2.2	58.0	3.7	13.3	1.0	15.3	1.0

depends solely on the group to which he or she belongs. All other causes are considered to be error. Thus, a univariate full model is given by

$$Y_{ij} = \mu_j + \epsilon_{ij}$$

where Y_{ij} is the score for subject *i* in group j, μ_j is the population mean of group j, and ϵ_{ij} is an error term for this subject. According to the null hypothesis, however, this model is overly complex, because if H_0 is true, we know that

$$\mu_1 = \mu_2 = \ldots = \mu_k$$

In this case, an equally good model (i.e., the models are equivalent in the population) is given by

$$Y_{ij} = \mu + \epsilon_{ij}$$

where μ is the common population mean of all of the groups. This second model is referred to as a "reduced model."

The task at this point is to choose between the full and reduced models as a description of the population. The model comparisons approach proceeds by using the principle of least squares to estimate the parameters of each model. In ANOVA models, the least squares estimate of a population mean is given by the corresponding sample mean. Thus, in the full model the estimated population mean for group j simply equals the sample mean for group j. In symbols,

$$\hat{\mu}_j = \overline{Y}_j$$

where the carat (^) over μ_j indicates an estimate of the parameter. In the reduced model,

$$\hat{\mu} = \overline{Y}.$$

where $\overline{Y}.$ is the grand mean of all of the observations regardless of group. Thus, the full ANOVA model predicts that each subject's score will equal the mean score for that subject's group, while the reduced ANOVA model predicts that each subject's score will equal the grand mean.

The full and reduced models can be compared by considering the magnitudes of the errors in each model. The estimated error for subject i in group j is simply the difference between that subject's actual score and the score predicted by the model. For example, the equation for the full model can be written as

$$\epsilon_{ij} = Y_{ij} - \mu_j$$

An estimate of the error for subject i in group j is given by

$$\hat{\epsilon}_{ij}\ (F) = Y_{ij} - \hat{\mu}_j = Y_{ij} - \overline{Y}_j$$

For the reduced model,

$$\hat{\epsilon}_{ij}\ (R) = Y_{ij} - \hat{\mu} = Y_{ij} - \overline{Y}.$$

TABLE 2.2
Errors for Full and Reduced Models for Data of Table 1

		Full Model					*Reduced Model*				
Grp	*Indiv*	e_1	e_2	e_1^2	e_2^2	e_1e_2	e_1	e_2	e_1^2	e_2^2	e_1e_2
1	1	−3	−1	9	1	3	−7	−1	49	1	7
	2	−4	−4	16	16	16	−8	−4	64	16	32
	3	2	4	4	16	8	−2	4	4	16	−8
	4	4	2	16	4	8	0	2	0	4	0
	5	1	−1	1	1	−1	−3	−1	9	1	3
	Sum	0	0	46	38	34		0	126	38	34
2	1	1	−2	1	4	−2	0	1	0	1	0
	2	2	2	4	4	4	1	5	1	25	5
	3	−3	−3	9	9	9	−4	0	16	0	0
	4	−2	−1	4	1	2	−3	2	9	4	−6
	5	2	4	4	16	8	1	7	1	49	7
	Sum	0	0	22	34	21	−5	15	27	79	6
3	1	−3	−6	9	36	18	2	−9	4	81	−18
	2	0	1	0	1	0	5	−2	25	4	−10
	3	3	1	9	1	3	8	−2	64	4	−16
	4	−1	0	1	0	0	4	−3	16	9	−12
	5	1	4	1	16	4	6	1	36	1	6
	Sum	0	0	20	54	25	25	−15	145	99	−50
Grand sum		0	0	88	126	80	0	0	298	216	−10

Table 2.2 displays the errors associated with the data of Table 2.1 for both models and for both dependent variables. For each subject, e_1 represents the estimated error (ϵ_{ij}) for the first dependent variable, and e_2 represents the estimated error for the second dependent variable. Remember the goal is to compare the adequacy of the full and reduced models as descriptions of the data. Obviously, a good model should lead to "small" errors. An index of the magnitude of error for a model is given by the sum of squared errors for the model:

$$\text{SSE (full)} = \sum_j \sum_i \hat{\epsilon}_{ij}^2 (F) = \sum_j \sum_i (Y_{ij} - \bar{Y}_j)^2$$

$$\text{SSE (reduced)} = \sum_j \sum_i \hat{\epsilon}_{ij}^2 (R) = \sum_j \sum_i (Y_{ij} - \bar{Y}.)^2$$

In ANOVA terminology, SSE (full) is usually referred to as the sum of squares within groups, SS_W, because it reflects the sum of squared errors, where error is defined for each group on the basis of its individual mean. Similarly, SSE (reduced) is called the total sum of squares, SS_T. The difference $SS_T - SS_W$ is the between group sum of squares and can be shown to equal

$$SS_B = n_j (\overline{Y}_j - \overline{Y}.)^2$$

where n_j is the number of subjects in group j. An F test of the null hypothesis is then given by

$$F(k-1, N-k) = \frac{SS_B/k-1}{SS_W/N-k}$$

where $N = \Sigma n_j$ is the total sample size. The numerator degrees of freedom (df) for the F distribution equals k-1, and the denominator df equals N-k.

Inspection of Table 2.2 shows that for the data of Table 2.1

	1st variable	2nd variable
SSE(F)	46 + 22 + 20 = 88	38 + 34 + 54 = 126
SSE(R)	126 + 27 + 145 = 298	38 + 79 + 99 = 216

Thus, the univariate F values equal

1st variable

$$F = \frac{(298 - 88)/2}{88/12} = 14.32$$

2nd variable

$$F = \frac{(216 - 126)/2}{126/12} = 4.29$$

By looking in a table of the F distribution, we discover that the critical F for 2 and 12 degrees of freedom and an alpha level of .05 is 3.89. Thus, there is a statistically significant difference at the .05 level between the groups for each variable considered separately.

However, for reasons discussed earlier, it might be preferable to employ a multivariate test, in order to consider the two dependent variables simultaneously. The multivariate approach accomplishes the simultaneous consideration of the variables through the use of matrix algebra. Only a brief, nonmathematical coverage will be provided here.

For further details, such textbooks as Bock (1975), Finn (1974), Harris (1975), Marascuilo and Levin (1983), Morrison (1976), Tatsuoka (1971), and Timm (1975) may be consulted.

Multivariate Test of Significance

As we have seen, the univariate test is based on a comparison of SS_B and SS_W for the particular variable. The multivariate test considers not just SS_B and SS_W for the two dependent variables (or, in general, *p* variables), but also the relationship between the variables. This relationship is captured in the product of e_1 times e_2 for each model (see Table 2.2). Whereas the univariate approach compares $\sum_j \sum_i e_1$ (F) versus $\sum_j \sum_i e_1$ (R) for variable 1 (and a similar comparison for variable 2), the multivariate approach also compares $\sum_j \sum_i e_1 e_2$ (F) versus $\sum_j \sum_i e_1 e_2$ (R).

Two points merit further consideration. First, what meaning can be attached to $\sum_j \sum_i e_1 e_2$, which is called a sum of cross-products? Recall that an error is just a deviation from a mean; specifically, for the full model, the error is a deviation from the group mean, whereas for the reduced model, the error is a deviation from the grand mean. The $\sum_j \sum_i e_1 e_2$ term for a model is closely related to the correlation between the 2 variables. In particular,

$$r_{Y_1 Y_2} \text{ (within groups)} = \sum_j \sum_i e_1 e_2 (F) / \left(\Sigma \Sigma\, e_1^2 (F) \sum_j \sum_i e_2^2 (F)\right)^{1/2}$$

and

$$r_{Y_1 Y_2} \text{ (total sample)} = \sum_j \sum_i e_1 e_2 (R) / \left(\sum_j \sum_i e_1^2 (R) \sum_j \sum_i e_2^2 (R)\right)^{1/2}$$

where the first correlation is a pooled (i.e., average) within-groups correlation between the two variables, and the second correlation is a measure of relationship ignoring group membership. In general, these two correlations are different, as can be seen by examining Figure 2.1, which depicts the data of Table 2.1 graphically using the horizontal axis to represent the first variable and the vertical axis to represent the second. Each ♦ in the figure represents a member of Group 1, and so forth. From inspecting the figure, it is obvious that within each group the two variables are strongly positively correlated. This is verified numerically, because

$$r_{Y_1Y_2}\text{ (within)} = 80/((88)(126))^{1/2} = 0.76$$

However, if the figure is conceptualized as a representation of 15 data points irrespective of group, visual inspection suggests little or no relationship. Once again this is verified numerically, because

$$r_{Y_1Y_2}\text{ (total)} = -10/((298)(216))^{1/2} = -0.04$$

Second, now that we realize the meaning of the sum of cross-products, how can this quantity be incorporated into a test statistic? Whereas in univariate ANOVA we compare the relative magnitudes of two numbers, namely SS_B and SS_W, in MANOVA the comparison is based on two matrices. To see how this is done, consider first the errors of the full model. We can represent $\sum_j\sum_i e_1^2(F)$, $\sum_j\sum_i e_1^2(F)$, and $\sum_j\sum_i e_1e_2(F)$ in matrix form as

$$E = \begin{bmatrix} \sum_j\sum_i e_1^2(F) & \sum_j\sum_i e_1e_2(F) \\ \sum_j\sum_i e_1e_2(F) & \sum_j\sum_i e_2^2(F) \end{bmatrix}$$

This matrix is referred to as a sum of squares and cross-products (SSCP) matrix, and is closely related to a covariance matrix and a correlation matrix. (Dividing each element of E by N-k would yield a covariance matrix. Corresponding correlations could be found by dividing each covariance by the product of the square roots of the variances of the two variables.) Similarly, for the reduced model information regarding the errors can be written in matrix form as

$$T = \begin{bmatrix} \sum_j\sum_i e_1^2(R) & \sum_j\sum_i e_1e_2(R) \\ \sum_j\sum_i e_1e_2(R) & \sum_j\sum_i e_2^2(R) \end{bmatrix}$$

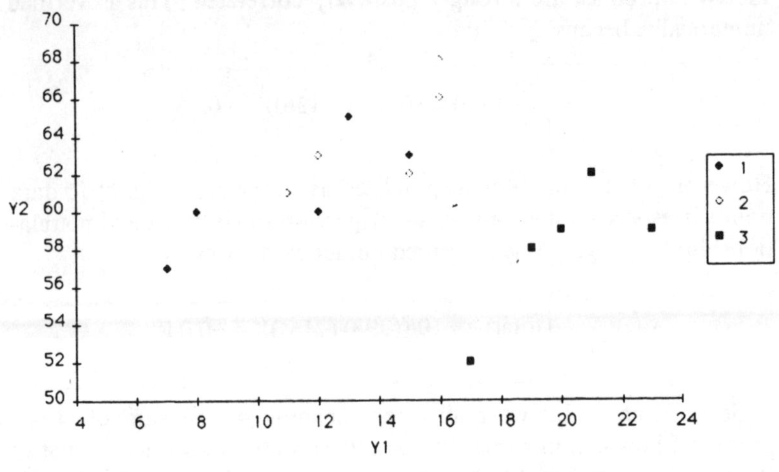

Figure 2.1

The difference between the two models can be represented as the difference between the T and E matrices. The resulting matrix, usually represented H for hypothesis sum of squares and cross-product matrix (or sometimes B for between matrix), is thus given by

$$H = T - E$$

It can be shown that in the general case of k groups and $p = 2$ variables, H equals

$$H = \begin{bmatrix} \sum_j n_j(\bar{Y}_{1j} - \bar{Y}_{1\cdot})^2 & \sum_j n_j(\bar{Y}_{1j} - \bar{Y}_{1\cdot})(\bar{Y}_{2j} - \bar{Y}_{2\cdot}) \\ \sum_j n_j(\bar{Y}_{1j} - \bar{Y}_{1\cdot})(\bar{Y}_{2j} - \bar{Y}_{2\cdot}) & \sum_j n_j(\bar{Y}_{2j} - \bar{Y}_{2\cdot})^2 \end{bmatrix}$$

The elements on the main diagonal are just the between-group sum of squares for each variable, while the off-diagonal element represents the between-group relationship between the two variables.

How can these matrices be used to test the multivariate null hypothesis of group equality? In the univariate case it was possible to divide SS_B

by SS_W, and with proper adjustment for degrees of freedom, arrive at an exact F value. Not surprisingly, in the multivariate case things are more complicated. The matrix analog to division of numbers is to multiply one matrix by the inverse of the other matrix. Here, then, it is necessary to multiply H by the inverse of the E matrix. This product is written as HE^{-1}, where E^{-1} denotes the inverse of E. In the special case of $p = 1$ (i.e., 1 dependent variable), this is simply SS_B/SS_W. In general, however, the result is a $p \times p$ matrix.

Before proceeding, it may be helpful to illustrate these concepts with the data of Table 2.1. The E, T, and H matrices for these data are given by:

$$E = \begin{bmatrix} 88 & 80 \\ 80 & 126 \end{bmatrix}$$

$$T = \begin{bmatrix} 298 & -10 \\ -10 & 216 \end{bmatrix}$$

and

$$H = \begin{bmatrix} 210 & -90 \\ -90 & 90 \end{bmatrix}$$

Multiplying H by the inverse of E yields

$$HE^{-1} = \begin{bmatrix} 7.18 & -5.27 \\ -3.95 & 3.23 \end{bmatrix}$$

Role of Discriminant Function Variates

Unlike the univariate situation, where a single ratio (i.e., SS_B/SS_W adjusted for degrees of freedom) can be used to test the null hypothesis, in the multivariate case the test of statistical significance is based on the entire HE^{-1} matrix. We are obviously facing a complex situation here, because the HE^{-1} matrix consists of p^2 elements. Even when p is only 2, it is not at all clear how we might interpret this many numbers to arrive at a judgment of statistical significance. It turns out, however, that we can simplify the problem through an alternate conceptualization involving certain linear combinations of the variables. Specifically, as mentioned in Section 1, the MANOVA test of significance can be viewed in terms of a set of variates often called discriminant function variates, each of which represents a linear combination of the original variables. The first such variate, which we will label V_1, is that linear combination of the original variables that has the property that SS_B/SS_W is maximized on V_1. In other words, SS_B/SS_W is less for any other linear combination of the original variables. The formation of this linear combination is equivalent to the creation of a new reference axis in Figure 2.1. That is, a new dimension is defined in the original p – dimensional space in such a way that group differences are maximized on this dimension (see Tatsuoka, 1980, for more details). Whenever $k \geq 3$ and $p \geq 2$, it is possible to find a second variate (i.e., dimension) that accounts for some between-group variation left unexplained by the first variate. (As will be discussed later, the magnitude of variation accounted for by this second variate may or may not be statistically significant.) The second such variate, V_2, maximizes SS_B/SS_W subject to the constraint that scores on V_2 be uncorrelated with scores on V_1. In general, for k groups and p variables, the total number of such variates that may be formed equals the smaller of k-1 and p. This number of variates, which we will represent by s, completely accounts for all of the between-group variation in the sample.

When p = 2 as in our numerical example, the general form of V_1 is given by

$$V_1 = a_{11}Y_1 + a_{21}Y_2$$

where Y_1 and Y_2 are the original variables, and a_{11} and a_{21} are the coefficients defining V_1 in terms of the original Y variables. Similarly, V_2 is defined as

$$V_2 = a_{12}Y_1 + a_{22}Y_2$$

The values of the coefficients are found from the eigenvectors of the HE^{-1} matrix. Readers interested in the methods for calculating eigenvectors should consult such sources as Green and Carroll (1976) or

Namboodiri (1984). For our purposes, we will simply state that the two eigenvectors of HE^{-1} for our numerical example are

$$\begin{bmatrix} -.5538 \\ .4200 \end{bmatrix} \quad \text{and} \quad \begin{bmatrix} .1258 \\ .2211 \end{bmatrix}$$

(In fact, these vectors are only determined up to a constant of proportionality, but this is unimportant for our purposes.) This tells us that for our data V_1 and V_2 are defined as

$$V_1 = -.5538Y_1 + .4200Y_2$$

and

$$V_2 = .1258Y_1 + .2211Y_2$$

Thus, the largest difference among the 3 groups occurs on a variate that is essentially the difference between the Y_2 and Y_1 variables.

Suppose we were to calculate V_1 and V_2 for each subject, and then form E, T, and H matrices for these variables, using the same formulas we previously used for the Ys. If we were to do this for our data, we would find (the interested reader is urged to verify these results)

$$E = \begin{bmatrix} 12 & 0 \\ 0 & 12 \end{bmatrix}$$

$$T = \begin{bmatrix} 134.148 & 0.000 \\ 0.000 & 14.716 \end{bmatrix}$$

and

$$H = \begin{bmatrix} 122.148 & 0.000 \\ 0.000 & 2.716 \end{bmatrix}$$

Several points need to be made here. First, notice that E, T, and H are all diagonal matrices (this means that all of the elements off the main diagonal equal zero). These zero off-diagonal elements reflect the fact that V_1 and V_2 are uncorrelated, within groups, between groups, and in the total sample. This fact, which is true regardless of p and k (Bock, 1975: 405) simplifies our interpretation considerably. Second, notice that each diagonal element of H equals SS_B for a given variate, while each diagonal element of E equals SS_W for that same variate. Thus, in our numerical example, the ratio of SS_B to SS_W equals 122.148/12 = 10.179 for V_1 and 2.716/12 = 0.226 for V_2. Third, by forming the Vs, we no longer have to consider all p^2 elements of HE^{-1}, because the off-diagonal elements of HE^{-1} for the Vs are necessarily zero. Thus, for the variates, only the diagonal elements of HE^{-1} are nonzero, and each diagonal value equals the ratio of SS_B to SS_W for that variate, as shown by HE^{-1} for our data:

$$HE^{-1} = \begin{bmatrix} 10.179 & 0.000 \\ 0.000 & 0.226 \end{bmatrix}$$

In addition, it is clear that the larger these s different ratios are, the stronger is the evidence that the population means of the groups differ. Thus, we have reduced a complicated problem involving p^2 elements of a matrix to a question of how large s different ratios are. In our data, then, the question to be answered is whether the values of 10.179 and .226 are large enough that the null hypothesis should be rejected.

Before answering this question, we first need to examine the two values of 10.179 and .226 more closely. It turns out that these numbers are the eigenvalues associated with the eigenvectors of the HE^{-1} matrix for the original Y variables. We mention this for two reasons: First, individuals studying multivariate statistics will repeatedly encounter eigenvalues. In MANOVA an eigenvalue of HE^{-1} is simply a ratio of SS_B to SS_W for a particular discriminant function variate. Thus, larger eigenvalues indicate larger group differences on that variate. (Readers should be cautioned that some books present eigenvalues of HT^{-1}, which reflects SS_B/SS_T for a variate.) Second, we found each ratio (eigenvalue) by first calculating each subject's score on the discriminant variate and then taking the ratio of SS_B to SS_W for that variate. However, in fact, it is possible to find the eigenvalues directly from the HE^{-1} matrix of the original variables. Readers interested in computations of eigenvalues should consult such references as Green and Carroll (1976) or Namboodiri (1984).

Multivariate Test Statistics

The next step in testing the multivariate null hypothesis is to ascertain how large the *s* eigenvalues are. In other words, we must compare their values to what we would expect to occur if the null hypothesis is true. It turns out that there are 4 reasonable ways of combining the information in the *s* eigenvalues, and each of these ways leads to a unique test statistic. We will present the formula for all 4 test statistics together with a brief intuitive rationale for its meaning. We will follow standard notation by letting λ_i represent the *i*th eigenvalue of HE^{-1}. Notice then that λ_1 refers to the ratio of SS_B to SS_W for V_1, which is the variate for which this ratio is a maximum.

The four multivariate test statistics are Wilks' lambda, the Pillai-Bartlett trace, Roy's greatest characteristic root, and the Hotelling-Lawley trace. The formula for Wilks' lambda is

$$U = \prod_{i=1}^{s} \frac{1}{1 + \lambda_i}$$

For readers unfamiliar with the Π notation, this is a shorthand notation for multiplication in exactly the same way that Σ is an abbreviation for addition. Recalling that λ_i is SS_B/SS_W for V_i, it follows that $1/(1 + \lambda_i)$ equals SS_W/SS_T for V_i. Thus, Wilks' lambda is the product of the unexplained variances on each of the discriminant variates. As we will see shortly, small values of U lead to statistical significance. The formula for the Pillai-Bartlett trace is given by

$$V = \sum_{i=1}^{s} \frac{\lambda_i}{1 + \lambda_i}$$

It can be shown that $\lambda_i/(1 + \lambda_i)$ equals SS_B/SS_T (i.e., the proportion of explained variance) for V_i. Thus, the Pillai-Bartlett trace is the sum of explained variances on the discriminant variates. The formula for Roy's greatest characteristic root is

$$GCR = \frac{\lambda_1}{1 + \lambda_1}$$

which is SS_B/SS_T for V_1 alone. Thus, Roy's test is based only on the first discriminant variate. Finally, the formula for the Hotelling-Lawley trace is

$$T = \sum_{i=1}^{s} \lambda_i$$

which is the sum of SS_B/SS_W for each of the discriminant variates.

Any of these 4 statistics might be used to test the multivariate null hypothesis. Only in the special case of $s = 1$ (i.e., either $k = 2$ or $p = 1$) do the 4 approaches necessarily agree with one another.

Whenever $s > 1$, it is possible that the 4 approaches will disagree as to whether the null hypothesis should be rejected at a specified alpha level. Choosing which test to employ involves a complex consideration of robustness and statistical power. Olson (1976, 1979) and Stevens (1979) have provided an enlightening discussion of the relevant issues.

We will only present the tests of significance based on U (Wilks' lambda) and V (Pillai-Bartlett trace), because the former is historically the most widely used of the 4 approaches and the latter was found to be the most robust by Olson (1976). For further information on R and T, the reader is referred to Harris (1975) and Olson (1976).

Recalling that for the data in Table 2.1 the eigenvalues of HE^{-1} were $\lambda_1 = 10.179$ and $\lambda_2 = 0.226$, it easily follows that $U = 0.0729$ and $V = 1.0951$. Based on either statistic, should the null hypothesis be rejected? To answer this question, the observed value of the test statistic must be compared to the sampling distribution of the statistic under the null hypothesis. The sampling distributions of both U and V are exceedingly complex. For this reason, approximations to the sampling distribution are usually employed. For Wilks' lambda, Rao (1951) showed that a complicated transformation of the U statistic results in a variable with an approximate F distribution. The specific transformation, which is performed by most computer programs alleviating the need for hand calculation, is given by

$$R = \frac{(1 - U^{1/q})(mq - \frac{1}{2}p(k-1) + 1)}{U^{1/q}\ p^{(k-1)}}$$

where

$$m = N - 1 - 1/2(p + k)$$

and

$$q = \frac{p^2 (k-1)^2 - 4^{1/2}}{p^2 + (k-1)^2 - 5}$$

The R statistic (not to be confused with Roy's greatest characteristic root) is distributed approximately as an F variable with $p(k-1)$ and mq $-1/2p(k-1)+1$ degrees of freedom. Whenever $k = 2$ or $k = 3$ (regardless of p) or $p = 1$ or $p = 2$ (regardless of k), R is distributed exactly as an F variable (assuming that the required statistical assumptions to be discussed later are met). A simpler transformation is necessary for the V statistic:

$$F \approx \frac{(N-k-p+s)\,V}{b(s-V)}$$

where $b = \max(k-1, p)$. Pillai (1960) showed that this transformation of V has an approximate F distribution with sb and $s(N-k-p+s)$ degrees of freedom. For the data in Table 2.1, then, tests are obtained by substituting U and V into the corresponding formulas. For Wilks' lambda, this yields R = 14.864, which implies a p-value of .00003 in an F distribution with 4 and 22 degrees of freedom. For the Pillai-Bartlett trace, the observed F equals 7.261, which corresponds to a p-value of .00079 with 4 and 24 degrees of freedom. Thus, with either test statistic, the null hypothesis is rejected at the .05 level.

Comparison of MANOVA and ANOVA

Now that we have presented the omnibus significance tests in ANOVA and MANOVA, let us consider the following examples to further compare the univariate and multivariate approaches. Figures 2.2a and 2.2b present graphical representations of hypothetical data, similar to Figure 2.1, which represented the data of Table 2.1. However, instead of representing each individual subject in the figure as was done in Figure 2.1, ellipses are used in Figures 2.2a and 2.2b to represent the central 95% of subjects in each group. Figure 2.2a represents data comparing a treatment group designed to alleviate hypertension with a control group, where the two dependent variables are systolic and

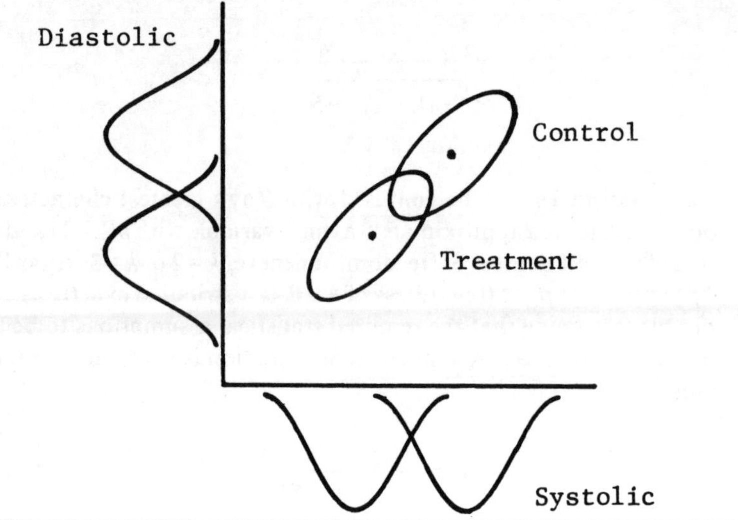

Figure 2.2a

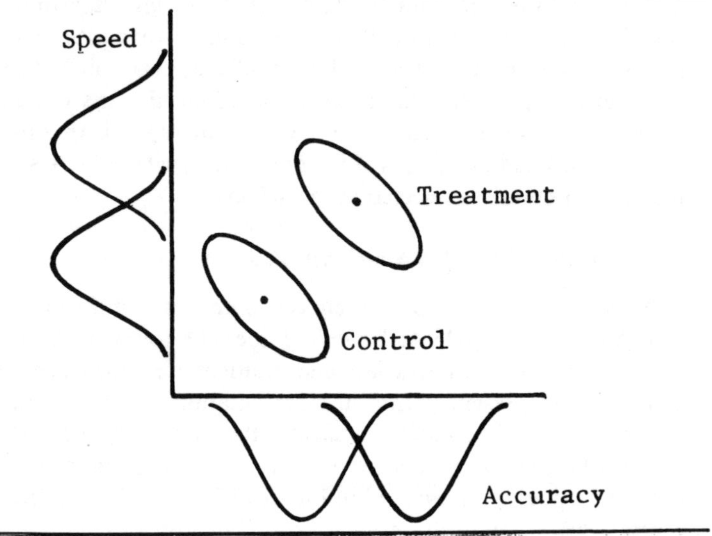

Figure 2.2b

diastolic blood pressure. Figure 2.2b represents data comparing a treatment group to a control group on a choice reaction time task in cognitive psychology, where the dependent variables are accuracy and speed of response. These two figures are drawn in such a way that the univariate statistics are the same in both situations. This can be seen from the figures by examining the distributions projected onto the axes representing the two variables. However, when the variables are considered jointly, the groups in Figure 2.2b are more separable than the groups in Figure 2.2a. This distinction arises because in the first figure the two dependent variables are positively correlated within groups, while in the second figure the correlation is negative. As previously illustrated, a basic difference between the multivariate test and separate univariate tests is that only the multivariate test is sensitive to the direction and magnitude of the correlations among the dependent variables. Thus, although univariate tests of data from Figure 2.2a would yield identical results to univariate tests for 2.2b (because the means are the same on both variables in both cases), the multivariate test would be different. As might be expected, the multivariate test would judge the groups to be more different from one another in Figure 2.2b than in Figure 2.2a.

Although it is obvious geometrically from the figures that the groups overlap less in Figure 2.2b than in 22.2a when the variables are considered simultaneously, it may be less obvious why the correlation between the variables is so important. To consider this issue, suppose for simplicity that in each experiment subjects have been randomly assigned to groups. In spite of random assignment, the samples will inevitably differ to some degree because of sampling error. For example, the most severe hypertensives might have been assigned to the control group. If, in fact, this occurred and the null hypothesis is true, we would expect the control group to have a higher mean than the experimental group on both dependent variables, because the two variables are positively correlated. The situation in the second experiment (Figure 2.2b) is very different. Suppose here that by chance more accurate subjects were assigned to the treatment group. If, in fact, this occurred and the null hypothesis is true, we would expect the treatment group to have a higher mean than the control group on accuracy but a lower mean than the control group on speed, because the two variables are negatively correlated within a group. According to the figure, however, the experimental group has the higher mean on both variables. Such an occurrence is extremely unlikely due to sampling error alone, because sampling error here would make one group higher on one variable but lower on the other. The fact that the experimental group has a higher mean for both variables is strong evidence for a nonzero treatment effect. Thus, the group differences depicted in Figure 2.2b are less likely to arise from sampling error than are the differences depicted in Figure 2.2a.

There are two important points to note from this example. First, correlations between variables are important in judging the magnitude of group differences. MANOVA has a distinct advantage over ANOVA in this regard. Second, although statistically significant effects can be obtained when the data resemble Figure 2.2a, the multivariate test is less powerful than it would be for the data depicted in Figure 2.2b.

When the multivariate omnibus null hypothesis is rejected, all that can be said is that it is not true that

$$\mu_1 = \mu_2 \ldots = \mu_k$$

Obviously, more work is necessary to interpret the meaning of group differences on the set of variables. A variety of procedures exist for further probing the meaning of a statistically significant MANOVA result. The majority of this monograph will be devoted to precisely this topic. Before considering interpretational issues, however, we will touch briefly on four other topics regarding the omnibus test: assumptions, robustness, power, and measures of effect size.

Assumptions of MANOVA

As with any inferential statistical technique, the mathematics of MANOVA is based on a set of assumptions. In particular, the assumptions needed for MANOVA closely parallel those for ANOVA. The MANOVA assumptions are

(1) Units (e.g., persons, families, countries) are randomly sampled from the population of interest.

(2) Observations are statistically independent of one another.

(3) The dependent variables have a multivariate normal distribution within each group. In practice, this can usually be thought of as a requirement that each separate variable follow a normal distribution. In theory, however, univariate normality is necessary but not sufficient for multivariate normality (Carroll, 1961).

(4) The k groups have a common within-group population covariance matrix. This assumption is twofold: (1) The ANOVA homogeneity of variance assumption must be met for each dependent variable; (2) the correlation between any two dependent variables must be the same in all k groups.

Robustness of MANOVA

Although the aforementioned assumptions are mathematical requirements for MANOVA, in practice it is unlikely that all of the assumptions will be met precisely. Fortunately, as in ANOVA, at least under many conditions, violating the assumptions does not necessarily invalidate the results. In other words, both ANOVA and MANOVA are relatively robust to violations of the assumptions in many circumstances. Although less is known about robustness for MANOVA than for ANOVA, the general pattern of results is very similar. In particular, MANOVA is not robust to violations of either of the first two assumptions.

A number of Monte Carlo studies (e.g., Ito, 1969; Mardia, 1971; Olson, 1974) have been conducted to investigate the extent to which MANOVA is robust to violations of multivariate normality and equality of covariance matrices. It is important to realize here that "MANOVA" can actually be any of four things, because of the four different test statistics. Indeed, the relative robustness and power of each test statistic (to be discussed next) are the relevant criteria for choosing which statistic to use.

Departures from multivariate normality generally have only very slight effects on the Type I error rates of the four statistics. The sole known exception to this rule is that Roy's greatest characteristic root test may lead to too many Type I errors when only one of several groups has a distribution with high positive Kurtosis (Olson, 1976). As in ANOVA departures from normality may reduce statistical power. One possible solution to this problem is to employ transformations of the data to achieve normality (or at least approximate it more closely), in much the same manner as ANOVA. At the time of this writing, none of the three most popular statistical packages (BMDP, SAS, SPSS-X) contains procedures for assessing degree of departure from multivariate normality. The most promising approach at this time is a graphical test described by Johnson and Wichern (1982) and Stevens (1984), who provides an example of how the test can be conducted easily using BMDP.

The effects of failing to meet the equality of covariance matrices assumption are more complicated. When sample sizes are unequal, none of the four test statistics is robust (Hakstian et al., 1979; Ito, 1980). Depending on the relationship between the sample sizes and the covariance matrices, either too many or too few Type I errors will result. Several statisticians have developed test statistics for the situation in which covariance matrices are unequal. Timm (1975) has recommended Yao's (1965) procedure, which is a generalization of Welch's method for the univariate Behrens-Fisher problem. When sample sizes are equal, all of the test statistics tend to be robust unless sample sizes are small, or the number of variables is large, and the difference in matrices is quite large. However, Olson (1974, 1976) has found that the Pillai-Bartlett trace is much more robust across a wide range of population configurations than any of the other three statistics. Olson (1979) and Stevens (1979) have argued the practical implication of this finding for choosing an optimal test statistic. In general, with equal sample sizes, the Pillai-Bartlett trace seems to be the best of the 4 multivariate test statistics in terms of Type I error, because it is most robust to violations of assumptions. However, it should be realized that even the Pillai-Bartlett trace is not robust to violation of equality of covariance matrices when sample sizes are unequal. Although a test of homogeneity of covariance matrices is widely available (Box's M), this test is generally not useful, because the test itself is extremely sensitive to departures from normality (Olson, 1974).

Statistical Power

Issues of statistical power (the probability of rejecting the null hypothesis when it is false) are just as relevant for MANOVA as for ANOVA. However, a priori estimation of power when planning a MANOVA study is difficult, because so many unknown parameters must be estimated. Instead of attempting to cover this complex topic in detail, we will provide a brief overview and refer the reader to the references we cite for additional detail.

Stevens (1980) has written a useful article on MANOVA power aimed at social science researchers. Several general findings emerge from Stevens's work. First, as p (the number of dependent variables) increases, it is necessary to increase sample size to maintain a given level of power for a specified effect size. Thus, it is wise to limit the number of dependent variables to a reasonably small number (e.g., 10 or fewer) unless sample sizes are quite large. Second, "the power of the multivariate tests with small-to-moderate group and effect sizes is poor, as is true in univariate ANOVA" (Stevens, 1980: 736). Third, "the magnitude of within-group intercorrelations definitely has an effect on power" (1980: 736). Indeed, researchers often do not realize that depending on these intercorrelations, the MANOVA test can be either much more powerful or much less powerful than the separate ANOVA tests on individual variables. This differential power explains the seemingly anomalous situation in which the MANOVA test is significant but none of the ANOVAs is, or the opposite situation, in which the MANOVA is nonsignificant but some or even all of the ANOVAs are significant. Ramsey (1982) has thoroughly compared the relative powers of MANOVA and separate ANOVAs in the two-group case.

Stevens (1980) provides tables for calculating power in both the two-group and the *k*-group case. However, the tables for the *k*-group case leave many gaps, as Stevens admits. Muller and Peterson (1984) describe a procedure whereby a linear models program can be used to calculate multivariate power even in the *k*-group case. Olson (1976, 1979) and Stevens (1979) discuss conditions that favor the 4 different multivariate test statistics in terms of power. When the noncentrality structure is "concentrated" (i.e., groups differ along a single dimension), the power ordering (from most to least powerful) of the 4 test statistics is R, T, W, and V. However, when the noncentrality structure is "diffuse" (the groups differ along several dimensions), the power ordering is V, W, T, and R. Thus, no multivariate test statistic is uniformly most powerful. Finally, Pruzek has offered a useful recommendation for one way to increase power regardless of which test statistic is used. Pruzek (1971: 187) argues that often it is advisable "to combine (usually add) highly similar response measures in MANOVA studies, particularly when basic measurements tend individually to be quite unreliable. . . . When the correlations among the set of dependent variables differ widely, principles and methodology of factor analysis seem likely to offer hope of facilitating interpretations of data." We will discuss this further in Section 3.

Measures of Effect Size

Suppose a researcher has obtained a statistically significant multivariate result in testing an omnibus null hypothesis. As in ANOVA, a statistically significant result is not necessarily an important result, because trivial differences may be statistically significant with huge sample sizes. On the other hand, meaningful sample differences may go undetected when sample sizes are small. A number of multivariate strength of association measures that are independent of sample size have been proposed in the literature. Cramer and Nicewander (1979) provide a review of these measures.

In univariate ANOVA, one measure of strength of association between group membership and a dependent variable is the correlation ratio, usually represented by $\hat{\eta}^2$. Eta squared ($\hat{\eta}^2$) is defined to be

$$\hat{\eta}^2 = SS_B/(SS_B + SS_W)$$

It can be shown that eta squared is equal to the squared multiple correlation between the dependent variable and $k - 1$ dummy variables coded to represent group membership. In MANOVA the analog to a multiple correlation is a canonical correlation (see Knapp, 1978; Thompson, forthcoming). In a k-group, p-variable MANOVA there are s canonical correlations (where, again, $s = \min(k = 1, p)$). It can be shown that the following relationship holds relating a canonical correlation (r_i) to an eigenvalue of $HE^{-1}(\lambda_i)$:

$$r_i = \frac{\lambda_i}{1 + \lambda_i}$$

Cramer and Nicewander (1979) proposed as a measure of multivariate association the average of the s canonical correlations,

$$\hat{\eta}^2_{mult} = \sum_{i=1}^{s} r_{1/s}$$

However, recall that

$$V = \sum_{i=1}^{s} \frac{\lambda_i}{1 + \lambda_i} = \sum_{i=1}^{s} r_i/S$$

so that

$$\hat{\eta}^2_{mult} = V/s$$

which is just the value of the Pillai-Bartlett trace divided by s. This value is a measure of the degree of association in the sample, not the degree of association to be expected in the population (see Maxwell et al., 1981). Serlin (1982) has derived an adjusted measure that may be used to estimate the strength of association in the population:

$$\hat{\eta}^2_{\text{mult}}\,(\text{adj}) = 1 - (1 - \hat{\eta}^2_{\text{mult}})\left(\frac{N-1}{N-b-1}\right)$$

where N is total sample size and b is the larger of p and $k - 1$. Applying these formulas to the data of Table 2.1 yields

$$\hat{\eta}^2_{\text{mult}} = 1.0951/2 = 0.5476$$

$$\hat{\eta}^2_{\text{mult}} = 0.4722$$

Thus, it is estimated that in the population 47.22% of the variance in the two dependent measures can be attributed to group membership.

Numerical Example

The following example is provided to demonstrate the different results and interpretations gained from the various procedures we have covered thus far. The example will be used throughout the monograph to illustrate the various methods of analysis. The data come from a longitudinal study of the developmental changes in neuropsychological correlates of reading achievements (Fletcher and Satz, 1980). Given the purposes of this monograph, no attempt will be made to build a theory for the data.

The data are from 571 second-grade children in Florida schools. The classification variable consisted of a test-based assessment of word recognition skills. Four groups were formed based on standard deviation cutoffs: (1) severely disabled readers (N = 93); (2) mildly disabled readers (N = 113); (3) average readers (N = 274); and (4) superior readers (N = 91). The criterion variables for the ANOVA analyses consisted of the Peabody Picture Vocabulary Test (PPVT), Verbal Fluency Test (VF), Similarities subtest of the Wechsler Preschool and Primary Scale of Intelligence (SIM), Beery Visual Motor Integration Test (VMI),

TABLE 2.3
Means, Standard Deviations, and Within-Cells Correlations for Real Data Example

Variable		*Group*				
		Overall Means	*Severe N = 93*	*Mild N = 113*	*Average N = 274*	*Superior N = 91*
PPVT	M	107.44	97.18	103.19	107.88	121.87
	SD	20.85	11.19	12.88	14.70	37.69
RD	M	13.30	11.97	13.17	13.54	14.12
	SD	1.73	1.96	1.32	1.41	2.03
LI	M	12.26	9.37	11.84	12.76	14.21
	SD	2.94	2.95	2.31	2.32	3.10
VI	M	33.73	28.39	31.85	34.31	39.74
	SD	8.73	6.97	8.03	7.69	10.12
VMI	M	86.78	74.25	83.04	89.42	96.32
	SD	18.57	11.20	17.63	17.71	20.59
SIM	M	17.48	15.55	16.97	17.79	19.18
	SD	2.41	2.94	2.29	1.97	1.50

Pooled within-cells correlations

Variable	*PPVT*	*RD*	*EF*	*VF*	*VMI*	*SIM*
PPVT	1.00					
RD	0.42	1.00				
EI	0.42	0.52	1.00			
VI	0.08	0.07	0.15	1.00		
VMI	0.04	0.22	0.32	0.09	1.00	
SIM	0.17	0.15	0.19	0.22	0.08	1.00

Recognition-Discrimination Test (RD), and the Embedded Figures Test (EF). The PPVT is a general verbal measure of IQ, whereas the VF and SIM tests are verbal criteria. The EF taps higher-order nonverbal abilities, whereas the VMI and RD are general nonverbal measures.

Table 2.3 presents the means, standard deviations, and pooled within-cell correlations for the data. In Table 2.4 are the eigenvalues and canonical correlations for the data. Notice that most of the between-group variance (93.14%) is explained by the first root. Calculating the overall MANOVA tests of significance from the eigenvalues shows that there is a statistically significant association between the classification variable and criterion variables at the .001 level for all 4 multivariate test statistics (see Table 2.4). The sample value of multivariate association equals 0.14 for these data. The corresponding adjusted population estimate equals 0.13.

TABLE 2.4
Eigenvalues and Omnibus MANOVA Tests
for Real Data Numerical Example
Eigenvalues and Canonical Correlations

Root No.	*Eigenvalue*	*% of Variance*	*Canonical Correlations*
1	0.61	93.14	0.61
2	0.04	6.52	0.20
3	0.00	0.34	0.05

Test Name	*Value*	*Approx. F*	*Hyp df*	*Err df*	*p*
Pillais *V*	.41997	15.30	18	1692.00	.001
Hotellings	.64997	20.25	18	1682.00	.001
Wilks' lambda	.59626	17.72	18	1590.06	.001
Roy's GCR	.37709		18		.001

Given that the omnibus tests are significant, the next step is to probe the data further to interpret the nature of the differences. There is a whole array of techniques for analyzing and interpreting significant MANOVAs. These techniques will be discussed in detail in the next two sections.

3. ANALYZING AND INTERPRETING SIGNIFICANT MANOVAS

Once a significant overall MANOVA has been found, the next step is to investigate the specific differences between groups. As in ANOVA, this involves determining which groups are responsible for the significant omnibus test. In addition, the follow-up analyses are used to evaluate which variables are important for group separation. Investigating these differences requires further analysis of both the criterion and classification variables. There are a number of techniques available and they will be discussed in detail in this section. We will also present several examples of how to apply these techniques with actual data. It is important to note that there is no one "right" method for these follow-up analyses; rather, the type of analyses performed will be determined by the research questions and type of data collected.

Analyzing Criterion Variables

UNIVARIATE F TESTS

Historically, following a significant MANOVA with ANOVAs on each of the *p* variables was one of the first methods recommended for interpreting group differences (Cramer and Bock, 1966). Many researchers still advocate this method, which is often referred to as the Least Significant Difference (LSD) test or the protected F or *t* procedure (Bock, 1975; Cooley and Lohnes, 1971; Finn, 1974; Hummel and Sligo, 1971; Spector, 1977; Wilkinson, 1975). The term "protected" comes from the idea that the overall multivariate test provides protection from an inflated alpha level on the *p* univariate tests. Assuming that the null hypothesis of no differences between groups is true, the overall alpha level for the *p* univariate tests is held near the specified nominal alpha. Hummel and Sligo (1971) demonstrated in a Monte Carlo study that investigated various numbers of criteria, sample sizes, and within-groups correlations that this protected F approach adequately controls the experimentwise error rate near the nominal alpha level. They therefore recommend this procedure as the method of choice. If *only* the univariate F tests are interpreted it is implicitly assumed that the *p* variables do not represent some smaller set of dimensions or factors.

Each univariate F ratio that reaches the specified alpha level is considered to be statistically significant and available for interpretation (Bock, 1975). The F tests are invariant under permutation of the other criterion measures. In other words, each F test is exactly the test that would have been obtained if it were the only dependent variable under study. Thus, the *p* univariate tests are insensitive to the correlations among the variables. Although the univariate F tests are insensitive to the correlations among the variables, the F tests are not statistically independent, because of the correlations. This situation is analogous to the test of nonorthogonal between-group contrasts in ANOVA. The largest single F ratio occurs for the variable that has the largest between-group difference relative to within-group variation. Likewise, the smallest F ratio represents the variable with the smallest group differences. However, correlated criterion variables do not represent independent sources of variation and should not be viewed as partial tests of the overall MANOVA test (Finn, 1974).

The protected F approach has a flaw in regard to controlling Type I error. As Miller (1966: 93) concludes, "the preliminary *F* test guards against falsely rejecting the null hypothesis when the null hypothesis is true. However, when, in fact, the null hypothesis is false and likely to be rejected, the second stage of the LSD gives no increased protection to that part (if any) of the null hypothesis which still remains true." In many cases the null hypothesis of no group differences is in fact false for one or more but not all variables. Hence, the multivariate test will produce significant results with a high probability if power is sufficient. However, univariate tests will then be performed for those variables for which there is no true difference as well as for those variables for which there is a difference. Because the individual alpha levels are not adjusted despite performing multiple significance tests, the overall multivariate test does not provide "protection" for each of the *p* univariate tests. Consequently in such cases the experimentwise error rate for the set of *p* univariate F ratios may be inflated above the nominal alpha level, even if the initial MANOVA test was significant. It is precisely for this reason that the protected F or LSD approach is usually considered an unacceptable method for performing post hoc comparisons in univariate ANOVA. Thus, the actual degree of alpha protection afforded by the approach is often misunderstood (Bray and Maxwell, 1982; Strahan, 1982).

An alternative to employing MANOVA to control the experimentwise alpha is to use a Bonferroni procedure (Harris, 1975). This involves dividing the nominal alpha by the number of variables in the study and comparing each individual F ratio to the critical F for this adjusted alpha level. One important question is whether this procedure is more or less powerful than the MANOVA method. There is no simple answer to this question. As mentioned in Section 2, Ramsey (1982) showed that even in the special case of two groups, the relative power is a complex function of three factors: (1) sample size, (2) the treatment effects for each of the *p* variables, and (3) the within-groups correlation between the variables.

In general, use of separate univariate F tests or the Bonferroni procedure ignores any relationships among the *p* variables. Therefore, many potentially useful sources of information, such as suppressor effects or redundancies, are left unknown. Bock (1975: 417-420) provides some excellent examples of the effects of various correlation patterns among the criteria on the univariate F tests and discriminant analysis results. However, if the purpose of the analysis is to control the Type I error rate for a set of *p* univariate ANOVAs, then these methods are generally appropriate. Additionally, the separate ANOVAs can provide information concerning the contribution of individual variables

TABLE 3.1
Analyses and Statistics for Hypothetical Data Set

		Dimension Reduction Analysis				
Roots	*Eigen Value*	*Wilks' lambda*	*F*	*HDF*	*EDF*	*Sig of F*
1 to 2	10.18	.073	14.86	4.00	22.00	.001
2 to 2	0.23	.815	2.60	1.00	11.50	.143

	Variables	
Statistic	Y_1	Y_2
Univariate F_S	14.32 $p < .001$	4.29 $p < .039$
SDWs		
Function 1	−1.50	1.36
Function 2	.34	.72
CVCs		
Function 1	−.47	.22
Function 2	.88	.98
u statistic	2.96	2.43
Fs-to-remove	8.48 $p < .001$	16.77 $p < .001$
Step-down Fs with Y_1 entered first	14.32 $p < .001$	16.77 $p < .001$

NOTE: SDW = standardized discriminant weight; CVC = canonical variate correlation.

when used in combination with other techniques such as discriminant analysis (Finn, 1974; Borgen and Seling, 1978).

Throughout this section we will exemplify the use of the various follow-up methods with the hypothetical data set from Section 2. We will also present a complete example at the end of this section based on the real Fletcher and Satz data.

Recall that the overall multivariate test for the hypothetical data was significant, so follow-up analyses are necessary to further explain the group differences. Each of the univariate ANOVAs is significant at the .05 level (see Table 3.1). Using the Bonferroni method for determining the significance level, alpha of $\alpha/p = .05/2 = .025$, only Y_1 is significant. Y_2 is not significant using this more conservative approach.

DISCRIMINANT ANALYSIS

Discriminant analysis finds the linear combination of the *p* variables that best separates the *k* groups by maximizing the between-group variance of the linear combination relative to the within-group variance. The procedure produces $s = \min(p, k - 1)$ discriminant functions, some or all of which may be significant at the specified alpha level. Each of the discriminant functions is a linear composite of the p variables that maximizes group separation with the restriction that scores on each of the functions are uncorrelated with scores on each of the preceding functions. In the special case of $k = 2$, the discriminant analysis is formally equivalent to a multiple regression problem (Tatsuoka, 1971).

In general, Huberty (1975) indicates that discriminant analysis is appropriate for four purposes: (1) separation between the k groups; (2) discrimination with respect to dimensions and variates; (3) estimation of the relationship between the p variables and k group membership variables; and (4) classifying individuals to specific populations. The first three uses are most relevant in the follow-up analysis of MANOVA.

In the context of interpreting a significant MANOVA, discriminant analysis can provide information concerning (1) the minimum number of dimensions that underlie the group differences on the p variables, (2) how the individual variables relate to the underlying dimensions and the other variables, (3) which variables are most important for group separation, and (4) how the groups can be represented geometrically in this reduced discriminant space (Borgen and Seling, 1978; Cooley and Lohnes, 1971; Fletcher et al., 1978; Huberty, 1975, 1984; Overall and Klett, 1972; Tatsuoka, 1971).

Within discriminant analysis there are several alternatives that address the above points and facilitate interpretation of the discriminant functions either separately or together. Of the s discriminant functions that result from the analysis, only those that are statistically significant are interpreted. In many cases, only a single function exists. However, in some cases several significant functions will be obtained, indicating that there are several constructs or dimensions underlying the data. Although this more accurately reflects the complexity of the data, it can also present problems in interpretation of the results.

One of the most common methods of interpreting the discriminant function is to use the discriminant function standardized weights or coefficients (Darlington et al., 1973; Huberty, 1975; Stevens, 1972; Tatsuoka, 1971). The weights are the coefficients of the linear combinations derived to maximize group separation. The coefficients represent the *relative* contribution of the variable to the discriminant function; however, the weights are highly influenced by the intercorrelations among the other variables (Bock, 1975; Finn, 1974; Timm, 1975). The standardized discriminant weights are analogous to standardized regression weights. Thus, the effects of the variables' interdependencies dramatically affect the interpretation and are not easily controlled. Just as in the interpretation of beta weights in multiple regression (Darlington, 1968), problems due to suppressor effects, multicolinearity, and variable redundancies must all be considered in the interpretation of the discriminant coefficients (Finn, 1974; Huberty, 1984; Timm, 1975; Wilkinson, 1975). Discriminant coefficients can change drastically with the addition or deletion of one or more variables.

In addition, if two variables are highly correlated with each other, the relative importance of the variables may be split between the two variables, or one variable may receive a large weight and the other a small weight (see Bock, 1975: 417-420, for examples). However, each variable may discriminate equally well when used singularly (Wilkinson, 1975). This has led several writers to caution against employing discriminant coefficients for interpretation when the *p* variables are highly correlated (Borgen and Selig, 1978; Finn, 1974; Huberty, 1984; Spector, 1977). Huberty (1975) also points out that discriminant coefficients have been erroneously interpreted as if they are factor loadings. In fact, the coefficients do not represent the common parts of discrimination, rather the discriminant coefficients are only *partial* coefficients. The relationship between the magnitude of a coefficient for a given variable and the univariate F ratio for the same variable may be very different (see Bock, 1975; Wilkinson, 1975), particularly when the variables are correlated. The difference is because the F ratio is calculated without regard to the other variables, while the discriminant coefficient considers the intercorrelations among the *p* variables (Bock, 1975).

Huberty (1984) proposes a transformation of the standardized discriminant weights as a means of controlling for multicolinearity between variables. This index is referred to as a *u* statistic and is given by

$$u_{ji} = (b^*_{ji})^2 / r^{ii}$$

where u_{ji} is the index of importance for variable i and function j, b^*_{ji} is the standardized discriminant weight for variable i and function j, and r^{ii} is the *i*th diagonal element of the inverse of the within-groups correlations matrix. Dividing by r^{ii} takes into consideration the colinearity of the variable with the other dependent variables. (See Huberty, 1984, for details of how to calculate the index.)

An alternative to interpreting the standardized discriminant coefficients is to employ a canonical structure matrix (Meredith, 1964;

Porebski, 1966a, 1966b). This procedure involves calculating the correlation of each individual variable with each discriminant function (referred to as canonical variate correlations). More specifically, the discriminant variates determined through the linear composite of the p variables are correlated with each of the original p variables. (For the mathematics, see Porebski, 1966b; Stevens, 1972; or Timm, 1975). This method provides a measure of how each of the p variables independently relates to each of the s discriminant functions. Bargmann (1970) contends that in cases in which some variables have large correlations with the discriminant function and others have small correlations, the ones with the larger correlations contribute most to group separation. This method is useful for ordering the variables as to their relative contributions to group separation. However, as in multiple regression the variables operate as a set and changing that set can have dramatic effects (Darlington, 1968; Huberty, 1975).

Some researchers recommend using the canonical variate correlations rather than using the discriminant coefficients for interpretation (Bargmann, 1970; Borgen & Seling, 1978; Cooley and Lohnes, 1971; Darlington et al., 1973; Timm, 1975). The reason given for this decision is that the correlations are supposedly more stable than the weights in cross-validation. Three separate studies investigating the stability of discriminant coefficients and canonical variate correlations found mixed results (Barcikowski and Stevens, 1975; Huberty, 1975b; Thorndike and Weiss, 1973). Thus, the alleged superiority attributed to the canonical variate correlation method (see Borgen and Selig, 1978; Cooley and Lohnes, 1971; Spector, 1977) does not hold up under empirical testing.

What many researchers do not realize is that these two approaches answer different questions. The discriminant weights, as previously stated, are analogous to regression weights, and represent the unique contribution of a variable to the composite variate. The canonical variate correlations, on the other hand, are analogous to factor loadings and, hence, represent how much variance a given variable shares with the underlying composite. For this reason, the canonical variate correlations are more useful than the discriminant weights for interpreting the *substantive* nature of the discriminant function. In contrast, the discriminant weights provide information concerning the degree of necessity of retaining a variable in the complete set of discriminators. Again it should be noted, however, that the variables operate as a set and changing that set (by adding or deleting a variable) will affect the weights of all the variables in that set.

An additional method of determining the importance of individual variables for group separation is the F-to-remove index (Huberty, 1984). This index considers all p variables simultaneously and across all of the discriminant dimensions. The F-to-remove index tests the hypothesis that the k group means are equal on a given variable when the other variables are partialled out. A large F value for a given variable indicates that deleting that variable decreases group separation substantially. The advantage of this index is that in a two-group case the F-to-remove is proportional to estimates of the decrease in the intergroup distances if that variable is deleted and it also takes into consideration the colinearity among the variables (Huberty, 1984; Huberty and Smith, 1982).

A major advantage of discriminant analysis over the protected F approach is that discriminant analysis reduces and explains the p variables in terms of s underlying dimensions. In essence, the number of significant discriminant functions denotes the underlying psychological or theoretical dimensions of the criterion variables. Investigating the dimensionality of the data is impossible with the univariate F approach because the univariate approach does not address this issue at all. With one significant function, inspection of the group means along the significant dimension for each variable characterizes group differences. If more than one discriminant function is significant, the group centroids can be plotted (geometrically) in discriminant space to facilitate interpretation (Cooley and Lohnes, 1971; Borgen and Selig, 1978; Kaplan and Litrownik, 1977; Tatsuoka, 1971). Kaplan and Litrownik (1977) provide an excellent and readable discussion of employing centroid maps to interpret MANOVAs. Using either or both the standardized coefficients or the canonical variate correlations, the dimensions may be interpreted in terms of some theoretically meaningful construct. If there are more than two significant functions, pairwise two-dimensional plots may be employed. Excellent and detailed discussions of further graphing techniques in multivariate analysis can be found in Everitt (1978) and Gnanadesikan (1977).

Although plotting the group centroids in discriminant space provides a graphical representation of the group differences, simple centroid plotting does not provide information on how the groups differ on the original p variables. Overall and Klett (1972) suggest that inserting the original measurement vectors into the reduced discriminant space more clearly illustrates how the groups differ with respect to the original p variables. Measurement vectors are determined by calculating the product-moment correlation of group means on each variable with the group means on the derived discriminant variates. The length of the vector is calculated by multiplying the between-groups correlations by the univariate F value for a given variable. The vectors are then plotted in two-dimensional discriminant space. The beginning of each vector is the grand centroid, that is the mean of all of the group means for each of the variables. Interpretation is facilitated by observing how a particular variable relates to one group centroid versus the other group centroids, while the length of the vector indicates the relative importance of each variable for group separation. Overall and Klett (1972: 292-295) discuss how to calculate and plot the measurement vectors, in addition to providing an example of their use.

Discriminant analysis provides more sophisticated and complex analyses of the data than does the univariate approach. However, this complexity can be a drawback to the use of discriminant analysis, particularly when there are multiple significant discriminant functions. The underlying dimensionality of the variables, the relationship of the variables to the underlying dimensions, and the interrelationships among the variables are all considered in discriminant analysis. In contrast, the univariate approach simply provides the individual effects of each variable, ignoring all other variables. Inspecting the univariate F ratios along with the discriminant coefficients and canonical variate correlations will often provide useful information for interpreting the unique and common contribution of each variable. It should again be noted that these methods will also produce different types of information, particularly when the variables are correlated (see Spector, 1977; Wilkinson, 1975).

The discriminant function analyses for the hypothetical data set are presented in Table 3.1. First notice that only one significant function is significant using the partitioned *U* method (see dimension reduction analysis in Table 3.1). This indicates that group differences on the two dependent variables can be explained by one underlying dimension. The remaining analyses indicate how to interpret this dimension. The standardized discriminant weights (SDWs) and canonical variate correlations (CVCs) both show that the first dimension is represented by the difference between the two variables. Both of these approaches, as well as the *u* statistics and the Fs-to-remove, also support the univariate F values by implying that both Y_1 and Y_2 are important for group separation, although Y_1 is somewhat more important according to all the indices. Notice that the Fs-to-remove are substantially higher than the

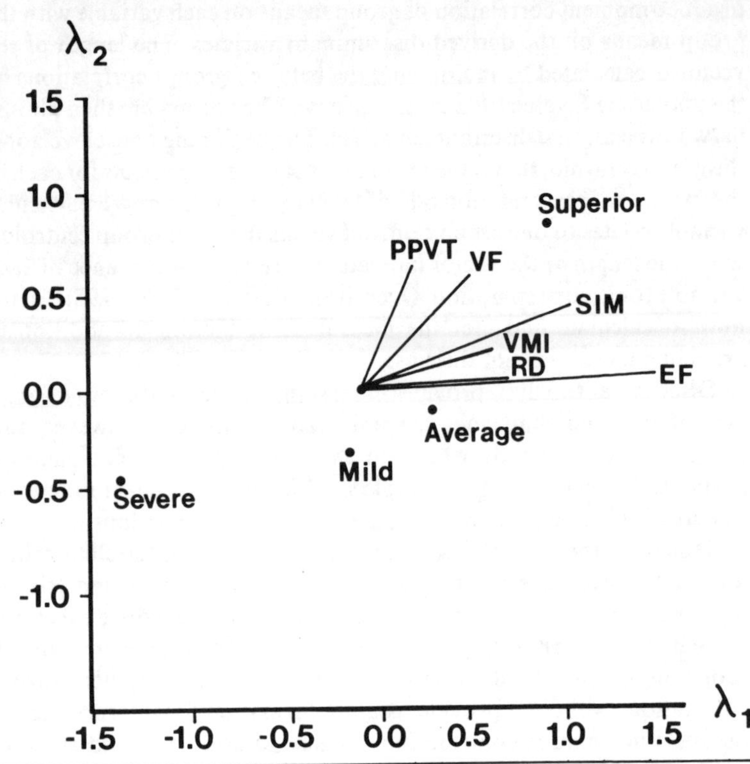

Figure 3.1

univariate Fs for both variables. This indicates that because of the correlation between the variables, each variable is more significant in the context of the other than it is by itself. The plot of the group centroids (see Figure 2.1) graphically demonstrates the differences between these groups in the discriminant space. Note that all of the analyses, including the univariate Fs, indicate that both variables are important for group separation. However, the univariate Fs, CVCs, and F-to-remove statistics all suggest that Y_1 is more important than Y_2.

STEP-DOWN ANALYSIS

Step-down analysis (Roy, 1958) is a form of analysis of covariance in which the criterion variables are entered in a specified order to test the relative contribution of successive measures (Bock, 1975; Bock and Haggard, 1968; Stevens, 1972, 1973). This technique is particularly useful when there is an a priori theoretical ordering of the *p* variables (Bock, 1975; Finn, 1974; Stevens, 1973). Roy and Bargman (1958) demonstrated that each of the successive F tests are statistically independent under the null hypothesis. The first step-down F and the univariate F ratio for that variable are identical. However, successive steps are not equivalent. The second step is the effect on the second criterion with the first criterion covaried out or removed. The third step is the effect with the first two variables' effects removed, and so on.

The appropriate technique for interpreting the step-down statistics is to begin with all *p* variables in the model ordered according to a priori hypotheses. The last variable is then tested with the remaining criterion variables covaried out. If this test is not significant, the next criterion variable is tested with the remaining j–1 (where j = number of variables still in the step-down model) variables covaried out. Testing continues in this backward selection process until a significant F for a variable is encountered. If a significant F test is found for a variable, then the variable being tested is related significantly to the classification variables over and above the j–1 criterion variables which are covaried out. When a significant F for a variable is encounterd, testing stops and the null hypothesis of group differences is rejected. The j–1 preceding variables cannot be tested separately because they are confounded with significant variation due to the jth variable. Redundancies among the variables are easily detectable with this method. It should be noted that the order of testing the variables is extremely important in this method, as the effects of the variables are considered with the preceding variables eliminated.

Some researchers might note that the step-down analysis appears similar to stepwise discriminant analysis included in many popular statistical packages. Mathematically, the two procedures can be identical (depending on the criteria for inclusion in the function); however, conceptually they are different. In general, stepwise discriminant analysis adds or deletes variables from the discriminant function based on some predetermined mathematical criteria (e.g., Wilks' lambda, Mahalanobis distance) and seeks to find the group of j variables that maximally discriminates between groups. Thus, decisions made at each step are entirely empirical. Step-down analysis requires an a priori conceptual ordering of the variables to test how a specific variable contributes to group separation given the preceding $j - 1$ variables in the function. The important difference between the techniques is whether the variables are ordered conceptually as in step-down analysis or selected empirically as in stepwise procedures (see Huberty, 1975a, 1984, for further discussion of backward and forward stepwise discriminant analysis).

Issues of Type I error must be confronted with step-down tests, since there are p significance tests that may be performed. For this reason, a Bonferroni approach is often recommended (Bock, 1975; Bock and Haggard, 1968). Increased power can be obtained for some tests by taking advantage of the fact that the overall alpha level need not be split into p equal parts; instead, the only requirement is that the p significance levels must sum to the overall level. Thus, variables that a priori are considered to contribute to group separation can be given a less stringent alpha, whereas variables that are considered to add little to group discrimination can be given more stringent alphas. Through these procedures a more parsimonious explanation of the group discrimination can be developed in which more important and perhaps simpler variables are retained instead of more dubious or complex variables.

The step-down Fs for the hypothetical data are also presented in Table 3.1. These statistics are for the model in which Y, is entered first followed by Y_2. Thus, the test of Y_2 is with the effects of Y_1 partialled out. Notice that this F test is the same as the F-to-remove and that the F test for Y_1 is the same as its univariate F. This is because it is exactly the test of Y_1 ignoring Y_2. Remember also that because the test of Y_2 is significant that testing stops at this point.

Analyzing Classification Variables

Once the multivariate null hypothesis is rejected, differences among the k groups need to be investigated. This section focuses on techniques for exploring the relationships between the k groups. The discussion of contrasts in this section assumes that (1) all p variables are tested simultaneously (i.e., a subset of the variables is not used) or (2) a contrast is coded for each variable separately (univariate contrasts). Consideration of a more general procedure in which double linear combinations of both classification and criterion variables are investigated will be discussed later.

Specific contrasts on the classification variables can be coded through dummy or contrast coding to determine how a specific group differs from another group or a linear combination of several groups

(Stevens, 1972). Depending on how the coding is performed, the contrasts may be *orthogonal*, in which the total between-groups variance is divided among $k - 1$ contrasts, or *nonorthogonal*, in which there is some overlap or correlation among the contrasts. Contrasts may also be nonorthogonal because of unequal *n*s in the *k* groups. If specific group differences are found, then use of the methods discussed in the previous section may be employed to further investigate the differences on the criterion variables. For example, inspection of the univariate F ratios or discriminant function coefficients may help clarify how the contrasting groups differ.

MULTIVARIATE CONTRASTS

If the contrasts of interest are comparisons of two groups, or more generally, any single degree of freedom contrasts, on the vector of *p* variables, several multivariate statistics are available to evaluate the group differences (Green, 1978; Porebski, 1966a; Stevens, 1972). The most common statistic is Hotelling's T^2. Hotelling's T^2 statistic is the multivariate generalization of the *t*-test, which in the more general case of $k > 2$ is equivalent to Wilks' lambda ratio when $s = \min(\gamma, p) = 1$, where γ = the degrees of freedom for the multivariate hypothesis. T^2 for two groups represents the difference between the groups on the centroids along the same direction (Porebski, 1966a). For the mathematics and a general discussion of test statistics in discriminant analysis, see Porebski (1966a).

Controlling Type I Error Rates. Just as in univariate ANOVA some steps must be taken to control the experimentwise alpha level for a set of *g* (where *g* = number of contrasts) a priori or post hoc contrasts. Very little discussion of this topic has occurred in the literature and few of the univariate post hoc procedures have been generalized to the multivariate case (Harris, 1975).

The Bonferroni technique (Bird, 1975; Miller, 1966) provides a powerful method of controlling the experimentwise error rate for any set of *g* contrasts. However, if the contrasts are chosen on a post hoc basis, rather than a priori, the experimentwise error rate for the Bonferroni procedure may exceed the nominal (Rodger, 1973). Thus, for any set of a priori contrasts (pairwise or other), to control the experimentwise error rate to the nominal alpha, a per comparison alpha level of α / g can be used. Harris (1975: 103-105) provides a good discussion on the use of contrasts. He suggests a set of decision rules to determine the critical F value depending on whether the linear combinations of the criterion and classification variables are a priori or post hoc.

The three multivariate pairwise contrasts for our hypothetical data indicate that Group 3 is significantly different from Group 1, $F = 44.93$, $p < .001$, and from Group 2, $F = 39.49$, $p < .001$, while Groups 1 and 2 are not significantly different from one another, $F = 1.43$, $p < .28$. This is also the case if one uses the more conservative Bonferroni alpha level of $.05/3 = .017$. These significant differences can be further explored on each individual variable using univariate contrasts.

UNIVARIATE CONTRASTS

If the researcher wants to investigate group differences among the p variables individually for each variable, the usual ANOVA comparison techniques (Scheffe, Tukey, etc.) are applicable. The principal choice that must be made in this case is whether to control the experimentwise error rate separately for each variable or for all p variables simultaneously. The former approach seems appropriate when Type II error is considered relatively important, because the procedure allows the experimentwise alpha for the collection of p variables to exceed the alpha level that is set by the researcher for a single variable (see Ramsey, 1980). With this approach, the first step is to perform a univariate protected F test for each variable to determine which variables display significant group differences. The second step is to search for specific group differences for those variables with significant univariate F ratios. Type I error can be controlled per variable using the usual procedures for a priori or post hoc tests (e.g., Bonferroni, Tukey, Scheffe).

A more conservative approach developed by Bird (1975) is to control alpha for either all or a subset of the contrasts and variables. Bird (1975) generalized the Bonferroni, Scheffe, and Tukey procedures to cases in which there is more than one criterion. For a set of completely a priori contrasts Bird recommends using a Bonferroni procedure in which each contrast is tested using a per comparison alpha level of α/gp. If the contrasts are partially planned and partially post hoc, then a Scheffe-Bonferroni decision rule is applied. Finally, if all of the contrasts are two group comparisons, then a Tukey-Bonferroni procedure is recommended. Bird (1975) demonstrated that these procedures can be much more powerful (the differences in power among the techniques depend on the number of groups involved) than the use of simultaneous confidence intervals, while adequately controlling the nominal alpha level. Ramsey's (1980) findings support Bird's conclusions that Bonferroni approaches are usually optimal here, because of their reasonable power and ease of application.

Analyzing Criterion and Classification Variables Simultaneously

The most general method of analyzing a significant MANOVA is to use Roy-Bose simultaneous confidence intervals (SCI; Morrison, 1976; Stevens, 1973). This is a completely multivariate approach in which any linear combination of the classification or criterion variables can be investigated. In this manner double linear combinations of classification and criterion variables can be formed. The experimentwise alpha is controlled to the nominal alpha for any number of contrasts among the k groups and p variables. The extreme generality of the method is also one of the major drawbacks. Hummel and Sligo (1971) demonstrated in a Monte Carlo study that use of SCIs is an extremely conservative method. In fact, the conservativeness increases as N, p, and the proportion of variance in common among the p variables increase. For this reason Stevens (1973) recommends using a more liberal alpha level of .10 to increase the power of the test. Mathematically the technique is ideal because of its generality; however, in practical applications it is often not very useful.

The Roy-Bose SCI is based on Roy's greatest characteristic root (GCR) test statistic described in Section 2 for the overall MANOVA test. As Bird and Hadzi-Pavlovic (1983) point out, there are other simultaneous test procedures (STPs) based on the other overall MANOVA test statistics (e.g., the Pillai-Bartlett trace, Wilks' lambda). Because the Pillai-Bartlett V test statistic has certain advantages for the overall MANOVA test (see the earlier discussion in Section 2), it might seem that follow-up tests should also be based on the Pillai-Bartlett trace. However, Bird and Hadzi-Pavlovic (1983) present Monte Carlo data showing that the STP based on V can be extremely conservative compared to the STP based on Roy's GCR. Their data also show that the Roy-Bose approach tends to be relatively robust to violations of assumptions as long as tests are restricted to interpretable constrasts on linear combinations of variables of theoretical interest as opposed to data-determined contrasts.

An example of the above simultaneous test procedure recommended by Bird and Hadzi-Pavlovic (1983) is illustrated by a comparison conducted on the hypothetical data. Recall from Section 2 that group differences were maximized on V_1, which was found to be $-.55Y_1 + .42Y_2$. Group means on V_1 were 19.5, 19.1, and 13.3 for groups 1, 2, and 3, respectively. To facilitate interpretation, we might want to test whether the average of groups 1 and 2 differ from group 3 on the unweighted difference between Y_1 and Y_2. To test this double contrast we would need the following information: SS(contrast)/SS(contrast) + SS(within) for this new transformed variable. For these data this equals: $480/(480 + 54) = 0.899$. To find the critical value we could use Harris's (1975) table of Roy's GCR. We need to know the values of $s = 2$, $m = -.5$, and $n = 4.5$, which implies a critical value for alpha = .05 of 0.533 (using interpolation of the tabled values). As the observed value is greater than the critical value, we reject the null hypothesis.

Numerical Example

We will continue with the Fletcher and Satz example from Section 2 to further demonstrate with real data the use of the techniques discussed in this section. Recall that the omnibus test was significant. Also remember that there are s possible roots that can be significant for the multivariate test. The Wilks' lambda criterion indicates that there is a second significant discriminant function, multivariate $F(10, 1125) = 2.49$, $p < .006$ (see Dimension Reduction Analysis, Table 3.2). In contrast, when the characteristic roots are tested individually using the GCR criterion, the second root barely misses significance at the .05 level. This discrepancy between the likelihood ratio approach and the GCR approach is not entirely surprising, as pointed out by Harris (1975, 1976). We will further illustrate the use of the various analytic methods for both roots to interpret the overall differences.

The univariate F tests (see Table 3.2) for each criterion are statistically significant. The standardized discriminant weights (SDW) indicate that the variables EF, VF, and SIM are most important for group separation on Function 1. On Function 2 the PPVT has the largest SDW with RD, EF, and VF contributing highly as well. Inspection of the canonical variate correlations (CVC) indicates that all the dependent variables correlate highly with Function 1, with the tests EF and SIM having the highest correlations. The PPVT has the highest correlation with Function 2, followed by RD, EF, and VF. VMI and SIM correlate very little with Function 2. The F-to-remove statistics indicate that the variables SIM, EF, and VF are most important for group separation, while the variable RD is least important for group separation. Also

TABLE 3.2
Analyses and Statistics for Fletcher and Satz Real Data Numerical Example

Dimension Reduction Analysis

Function	*Wilks' lambda*	*Approx. F*	*Hyp df*	*Err df*	*p* <
1 to 3	.59626	17.72	18	1590.06	.001
2 to 3	.95721	2.49	10	1125.00	.006
3 to 3	.99777	0.32	4	563.00	.868

	Variable					
Statistic	*PPVT*	*RD*	*EF*	*VF*	*VMI*	*SIM*
Univariate F (3,567)	26.85	31.43	61.25	32.74	29.31	47.47
F-to-remove (3,567)	6.49	1.86	8.61	8.38	5.66	13.37
SDW						
Function 1	.15	.10	.39	.33	.29	.44
Function 2	.95	−.51	−.58	.37	.12	−.02
CVC						
Function 1	.46	.52	.73	.53	.50	.64
Function 2	.52	−.37	−.36	.33	−.10	.04

NOTE: SDW = standardized discriminant weight; CVC = canonical variate correlation.

notice how these statistics differ from the univariate F tests. This is because the correlations among the variables are considered in the F-to-remove statistics.

Figure 3.1 presents a plot of the group centroids in two dimensional discriminant space. The plot of the centroids illustrates that the first discriminant function primarily separates each of the groups, while the second discriminant function primarily separates the superior readers from the other three groups. The measurement vectors for the original variables are also displayed in Figure 3.1 (see Overall and Klett, 1972). The vectors originate from the grand mean of the group centroids. The direction of the vectors indicates as expected that the superior readers scored highest and the severely disabled readers scored lowest on all six criteria. Recall that the length of each vector is proportional to the univariate F value for that variable. The vectors reveal the additional information that the PPVT mostly discriminates the superior readers from the other three groups, whereas the EF tends to discriminate among all the groups, especially the severely disabled from the others.

If only the univariate Fs are used to interpret the data, all the dependent variables appear important for determining differences between the groups. However, only by using the discriminant analysis is it clear that there are two underlying dimensions. Using both the SDWs and the CVCs, it appears that the first dimension represents differences on higher-order verbal and nonverbal abilities, whereas the second dimension is primarily an overall verbal intelligence dimension.

It should be noted that there are differences between the pattern of results for the univariate Fs, Fs-to-remove, SDWs, and CVCs. This is due to the different questions answered by the various approaches. The univariate Fs indicate the magnitude of group differences on each variable individually without consideration of the other variables. The SDWs reflect the unique contribution of each variable in the context of the other variates for a specific discriminant function, whereas the F-to-remove index indicates the unique contribution of each variable considering the other variables across *all* of the dimensions. The CVCs measure the correlation of each variate with scores on each discriminant function. Given the intercorrelations among these variables, it is not surprising that the unique contribution of a variable (i.e., the SDW) tends to be less than the corresponding CVC.

With more than two groups, just as in a univariate ANOVA, the next step in the analysis is to determine which groups are responsible for the significant difference obtained in the overall test. The remaining examples analyze one possible contrast chosen for purposes of demonstration.

A pairwise contrast between the superior and severely disabled readers indicates that the groups are significantly different, multivariate $F(6, 562) = 51.84, p < .001$. If all six pairwise contrasts among the four groups are carried out, the appropriate alpha level is $\alpha/g = .05/6 = .008$ for each contrast. If further contrasts on all the univariate variables are conducted, the appropriate alpha for each of these comparisons is $\alpha/gp = .05/(6 \times 6) = .0014$ (Bird, 1975).

Other contrasts could be conducted in a similar manner to further understand the differences between the groups. The type of analyses performed would depend on the research questions to be answered and the nature of the differences found in the data. We will further exemplify these techniques in the next section.

4. CAUSAL MODELS UNDERLYING MANOVA ANALYSES

Purpose of Path-Analytic Representations

Path-analytic representations are developed in this section for the various techniques used in MANOVA analyses. Recognition of the causal models implicitly underlying the various methods clarifies the relationships among the strategies. The primary purpose of this section is pedagogical, in that the path diagrams to be presented for different methods often enhance understanding of the questions addressed by these methods. However, it is generally preferable to perform the actual data analysis using MANOVA computational formulas such as those presented in Section 2, rather than directly through a path-analytic representation. Bagozzi et al. (1981) provide details on how to obtain MANOVA results from the path-analytic approach using LISREL (Joreskog and Sorbom, 1983). Our purpose here, however, is primarily conceptual.

Several authors (Bentler and Huba, 1982; Blalock, 1969; Dwyer, 1983; Kenny, 1979; Van de Geer, 1971) have used path analysis to relate different multivariate techniques such as factor analysis, discriminant analysis, regression analysis, and canonical correlation analysis. Kenny (1979: 203-205) discusses several models for analysis of variance with more than one dependent measure. We will discuss such models in the context of alternative strategies to follow-up a significant omnibus MANOVA test. However, at the outset it should be emphasized that causal inferences are possible when using causal models only if a set of restrictive assumptions is satisfied (see Kenny, 1979: 51). In particular, conceptualizing MANOVA in path-analytic terms has no effect on the appropriateness of making a causal inference concerning group differences.

Overview of Path-Analytic Representation of MANOVA

We will introduce the basic ideas of path analysis in the specific context of the overall MANOVA test. Readers interested in more general introductions to path analysis should consult such references as Asher (1976), Bentler (1980), Duncan (1975), Dwyer (1983), or Kenny (1979). Figure 4.1 presents a path diagram for a two-group, three-

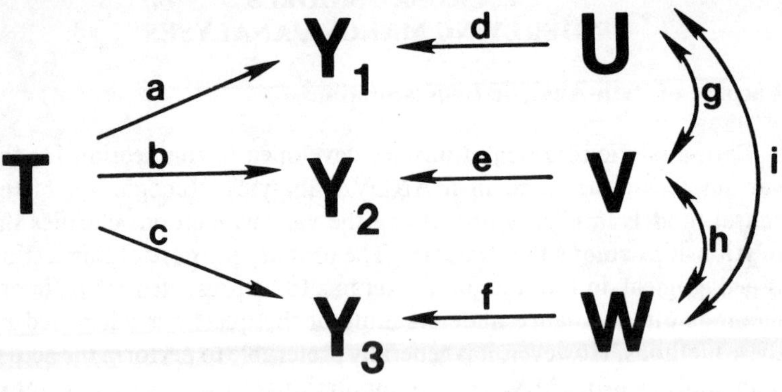

Figure 4.1

variable design. Each of the 7 capital letters in the diagram represents a variable thought to be either a cause or an effect in the system.

For example, *T* is a dummy variable that represents group membership; such a variable is typically coded 0 for subjects in one group and 1 for subjects in the other group. Y_1, Y_2, and Y_3 represent the three dependent variables. The letters *U, V,* and *W* represent disturbance terms (i.e., error terms). In general, disturbance terms represent sources of influence on the dependent variables not otherwise accounted for in the diagram. In the case of our diagram, then, *U* represents all causes of Y_1 other than *T* (that is, other than group membership). You may recall from Section 2 that this is precisely the meaning of "error" in analysis of variance models. The 6 single-sided arrows represent causal effects from one variable to another. Thus, for example, the diagram stipulates that Y is caused by *T* and *U*. The disturbances are connected to each other by two-sided arrows because they are assumed to be correlated, but without a specification of which disturbance is a cause and which is an effect of the others. An arrow, whether one-sided or two-sided, is often referred to as a "path," leading to the name "path diagram" for the picture as a whole. The lower-case letter associated with each path is called a path coefficient (or, more generally, a structural coefficient) and represents the strength of that path. It can be shown that in this model the path coefficients a, b, and c equal the correlations of *T* with Y_1, Y_2, and Y_3, respectively. (Readers interested in further details are referred to Kenny's [1979] discussion of the "tracing rule".)

A primary purpose of path analysis is typically to compare different models for a given set of data. For example, a researcher might believe that the two groups represented by the dummy variable in Figure 4.1 do not differ on the Y_1 variable. In this case, T and Y_1 would be uncorrelated, so that a = 0, implying that the path from T to Y_1 is unnecessary. Whether such a parsimonious model provided an adequate explanation of a set of data could be tested by performing a significance test of the correlation between T and Y_1. In general, it is possible to test the adequacy of parsimonious models with one or more omitted paths, because such models imply that certain correlational patterns should occur. We will now consider this idea in more detail for the specific model depicted in Figure 4.1.

Omnibus MANOVA Test

The omnibus MANOVA null hypothesis states that all groups have the same population means on all dependent variables. In terms of Figure 4.1, the null hypothesis states that the dummy variable T correlates zero with Y_1, Y_2, and Y_3 in the population. As previously stated, these three correlations equal the population values of the a, b, and c path coefficients, respectively. Thus, in terms of the path diagram, the omnibus MANOVA null hypothesis is that a, b, and c all equal zero, in which case the paths from T to Y_1, Y_2, and Y_3 can be omitted. In other words, the overall MANOVA test can be conceptualized as a comparison of the model depicted in Figure 4.1 versus an alternate model in which the paths from T to Y_1, Y_2, and Y_3 have all been omitted. In the terminology of Section 2, the model shown in Figure 4.1 is the "full" model, whereas the alternate model, in which the a, b, and c paths are omitted, is the "reduced" model.

Univariate Tests

Suppose the overall MANOVA null hypothesis is rejected. As discussed in Section 3, one follow-up procedure is to conduct univariate F tests. The path diagram depicted in Figure 4.1 can also be used to conceptualize univariate tests. Whereas the multivariate test considered a, b, and c simultaneously, the univariate approach considers each coefficient separately. The test of statistical significance for each coefficient individually is simply a test that the correlation between the dummy variable and the particular dependent variable is zero. However, this test is equivalent to the t-test of group mean differences on the

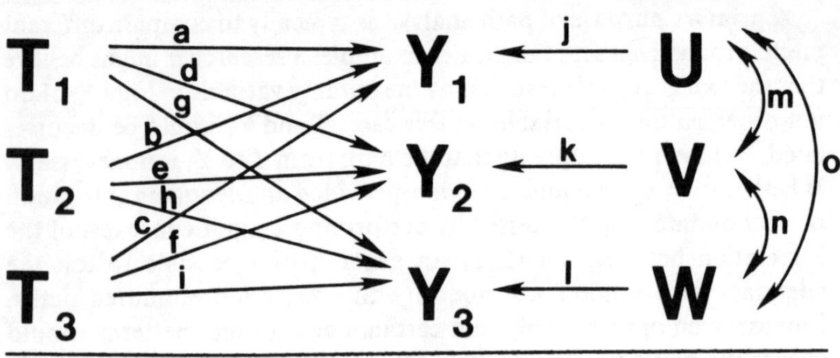

Figure 4.2

dependent variable. This path-analytic representation shows clearly that the univariate follow-up tests represent an attempt to achieve a parsimonious model by omitting unnecessary paths. We will see later that the other follow-up procedures also strive for parsimony, but consider different ways of omitting paths.

Figure 4.2 shows a path model for a more complex study involving four treatment groups and three criterion variables. For simplicity, it is assumed that orthogonal coding has been used to represent group membership ("orthogonality" simply means that no arrows between the three *T* variables are needed), although this is not necessary. It can easily be shown that the principles developed for the simpler model in Figure 4.1 also hold for the model in Figure 4.2. For example, the omnibus MANOVA test hypothesizes that the 9 path coefficients a through i are all equal to zero. Similarly, a simultaneous test of the a, b, and c coefficients in Figure 4.2 is equivalent to the univariate F test for Y_1.

In the general case of k groups and p dependent variables, there are $k - 1$ dummy variables. Each of these variables may have a path to each dependent variable, implying a total of $p\ (k - 1)$ possible paths. The multivariate null hypothesis is false if and only if at least one of the $p\ (k - 1)$ paths is nonzero in the population. Notice that this explains why the tests of significance for Wilks' lambda and the Pillai-Bartlett trace have $p\ (k - 1)$ numerator degrees of freedom in the F distribution. The goal of the univariate F follow-up approach is to achieve parsimony by examining p collections of $k - 1$ paths to discover which sets of $k - 1$ paths are nonzero and, hence, need to be retained in the model. It should be noted that analysis of classification variables is often the next step,

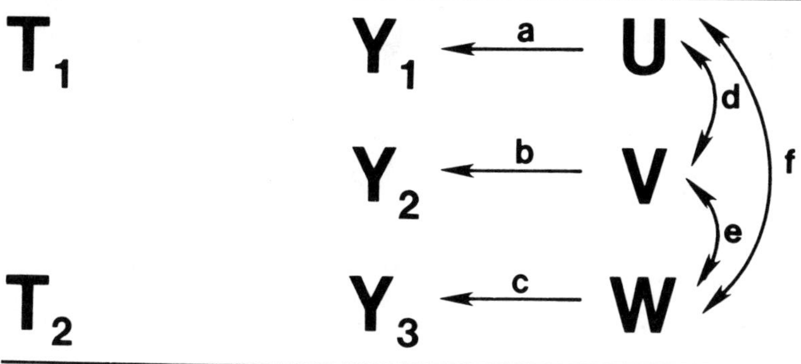

Figure 4.3

whereby individual paths in the different sets of $k - 1$ paths are tested for significance.

Discriminant Analysis Model

The model for discriminant analysis is very different from the path model for individual univariate tests. To consider the discriminant analysis approach, it is necessary to consider a sequence of several path diagrams. Figures 4.3, 4.4, and 4.5 illustrate models for a 3-group, 3-variable design, where T_1 and T_2 are dummy variables that represent group membership (orthogonal coding is again assumed for simplicity), the *Y*s represent the dependent variables, and *U, V,* and *W* are disturbance terms. Three groups are used here, because with only two groups there can be only one discriminant function by mathematical necessity.

These models include a new type of variable, represented by y (Figures 4.4 and 4.5) and y* (Figure 4.5), which are unobserved variables. These unobserved variables can be conceptualized as latent variables that are assumed to be exact linear functions of the *T* variables. In this type of model, called a MIMIC model (Joreskog and Goldberger, 1975), there are no disturbance terms associated with y and y+ because there are no unknown causes of these variables.

The models represented in Figures 4.3, 4.4, and 4.5 differ in the number of factors hypothesized to exist. Discriminant analysis significance tests can best be understood by comparing the three models. The model that assumes no underlying factors (Figure 4.3) allows no population correlation between the *T* variables and Y_1, Y_2, and Y_3. This zero

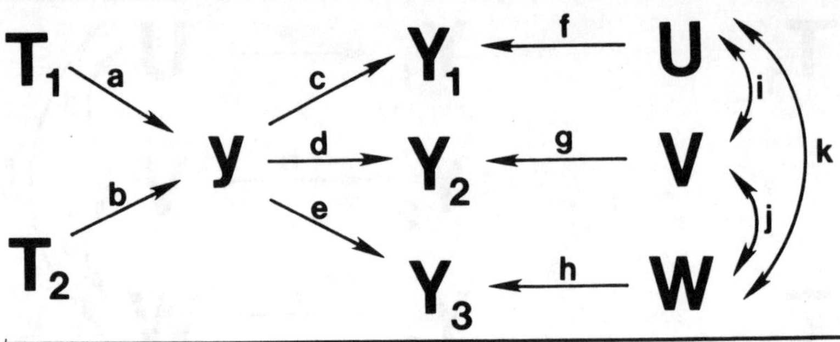

Figure 4.4

correlation implies that the largest population canonical correlation between the T set and the Y set is zero. This is the hypothesis tested by the greatest characteristic root approach (Harris, 1975; Morrison, 1976). Of course, if the largest canonical R is zero, so are the remaining $s - 1$ values. In contrast, the other 3 overall MANOVA test statistics test the hypothesis that all s values are simultaneously zero. Although both approaches test the overall multivariate null hypothesis, a significant result with the Pillai-Bartlett, Wilks' lambda, or Hotelling-Lawley approaches implies that one of the $p(k - 1)$ paths of Figure 4.1 is nonzero, whereas a significant GCR result implies that at least one factor is necessary to explain the relationship of the T variables to the criterion measures. If the GCR test yields a significant result, the model of Figure 4.3 is insufficient. In this case, a model at least as complex as that in Figure 4.4 is required, because at least one factor is necessary. Discriminant analysis then proceeds to test whether another factor is necessary to explain treatment effects; that is, whether a second discriminant function discriminates between the groups. Hauser and Goldberger (1971) and Kenny (1979) demonstrate that if the model represented in Figure 4.4 is correct, the second largest population canonical correlation is zero. The null hypothesis that this canonical R is zero can be tested by examining the second largest characteristic root of the appropriate matrix (see Harris, 1975: 108, 134). If the second largest population canonical R is zero, then so are the remaining $s - 2$ values. Many authors (Cooley and Lohnes, 1971; Overall and Klett, 1972; Tatsuoka, 1971) recommend a simultaneous test of roots 2 through s rather than simply a test of the second root. Harris (1975, 1976) argues that the use of such a procedure, called partitioned-U tests, is invalid for

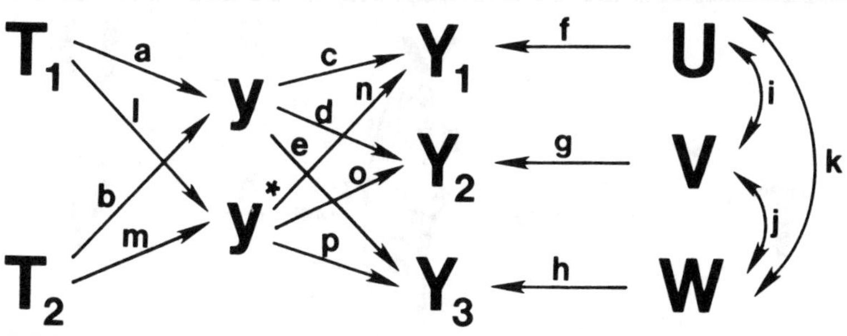

Figure 4.5

several reasons. The reader is referred to Harris (1976), Mendoza et al. (1978), and Chou and Muirhead (1979) for further discussion of this controversy.

The models in Figures 4.3, 4.4, and 4.5 illustrate how discriminant analysis determines the number of factors needed to relate treatment effects to criterion measures. Obviously, if Figure 4.3 represents the correct model, no factors are needed, because there are no treatment effects. With a single factor, as depicted in Figure 4.4, there is homogeneity of the T variables with the Y variables. The geometric meaning of homogeneity is that a single dimension (the linear discriminant function) is sufficient to explain group differences. Examination of the path coefficients of Figure 4.4 indicates that the algebraic equivalent of the geometric statement is that the correlation between any treatment dummy variable and any dependent measure equals the product of the two corresponding paths. This implies that the treatment effect can be accounted for by assuming that the p criterion measures are indicators of a single construct. The p measures differ only in the amount by which they are affected, as represented by path coefficients for the measures.

Comparison of Figures 4.3, 4.4, and 4.5 with the diagrams for the univariate approach (Figures 4.1 and 4.2) illustrates how the two strategies differ. Both techniques strive to achieve parsimony by reducing the number of path coefficients needed in the diagram, but they do so in very different ways.

Model for the Step-Down Tests

The use of step-down tests can also be represented by a path analysis diagram. Figure 4.6 is such a diagram for a 2-group, 3-variable design,

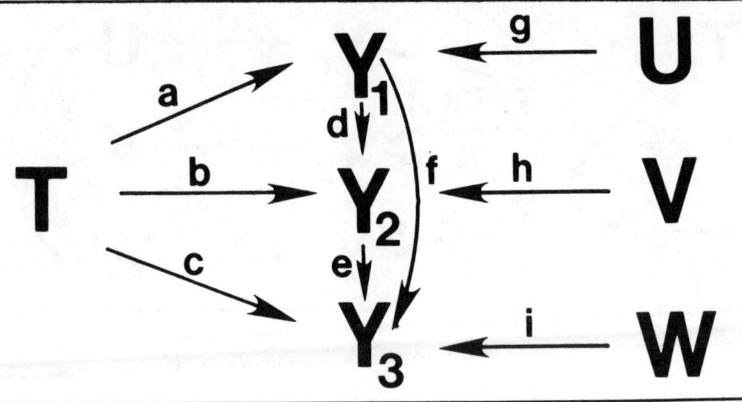

Figure 4.6

where T is again a dummy variable for group membership, the Ys represent the dependent variables, and U, V, and W are disturbance terms. This path diagram corresponds to the following set of structural equations:

$$Y_1 = aT + gU$$

$$Y_2 = dY_1 + bT + hV$$

$$Y_3 = fY_1 + eY_2 + cT + iW$$

This set of equations is a recursive set; therefore, estimates of the path coefficients and significance tests can be performed with ordinary least squares. Specifically, the Y on the left-hand side of an equation is regressed on the variables on the right-hand side of the equation. Thus Y_1 is regressed on T, while Y_2 is regressed on Y_1 and T, and Y_3 is regressed on Y_1, Y_2, and T. The significance test of T in each case corresponds to an ANCOVA test, in which all prior Y variables are included as covariates. However, as previously discussed, this is precisely the way in which step-down tests are conducted.

The meaning of the step-down approach can best be understood by contrasting Figure 4.6 with the figures for the univariate approach (Figures 4.1 and 4.2) and the discriminant analysis approach (Figures 4.3, 4.4, and 4.5). Comparison of the six diagrams shows that the step-down approach is unique in assuming a causal ordering rather than

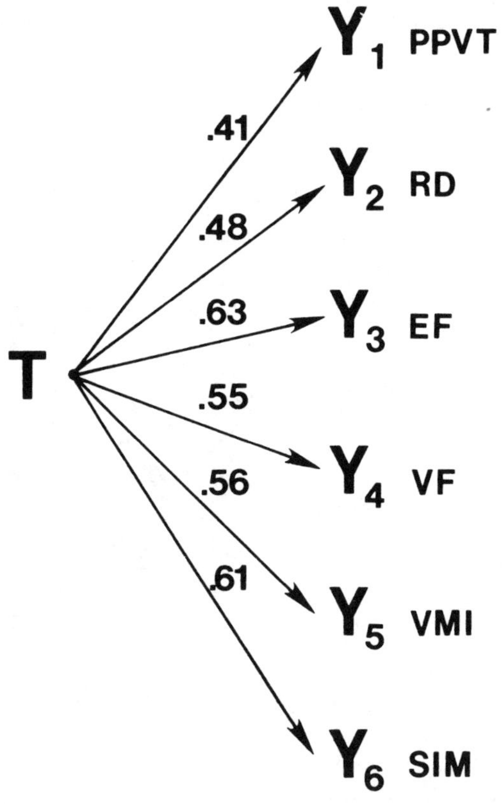

Figure 4.7

simply a correlation among the criterion variables. With this approach, it is possible to separate direct and indirect effects of the treatment on each dependent variable.

Extension of these models to the remaining techniques is straightforward. Investigation of the classification variables is accomplished by coding the *T* variables to represent specific contrasts. Simultaneous tests of various paths are conducted depending on whether the researcher is interested in univariate or multivariate comparisons. However, many of the issues in analyzing the classification variables (e.g., experimentwise error rate) do not affect the underlying structural model.

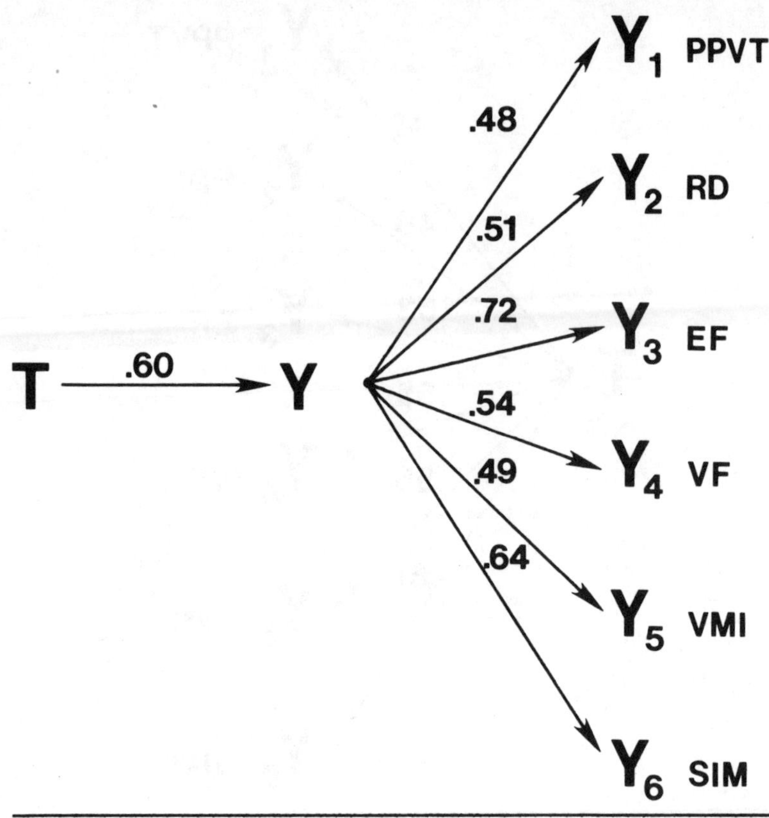

Figure 4.8

MANOVA and LISREL

Readers who are familiar with LISREL may realize that LISREL can be used to analyze group differences in factor means (Sorbom, 1974). It should be emphasized that testing for differences in factor means answers a different question than MANOVA addresses, even if a path-analytic representation of MANOVA is considered. The ways in which LISREL and MANOVA differ can be considered at a conceptual level by referring back to Figure 4.4. Recall that in the discriminant analysis model there is no disturbance for *y*, and the *U, V,* and *W* disturbance terms are allowed to correlate. In the LISREL approach there would be a disturbance term associated with *y*, because *y* would be conceptualized

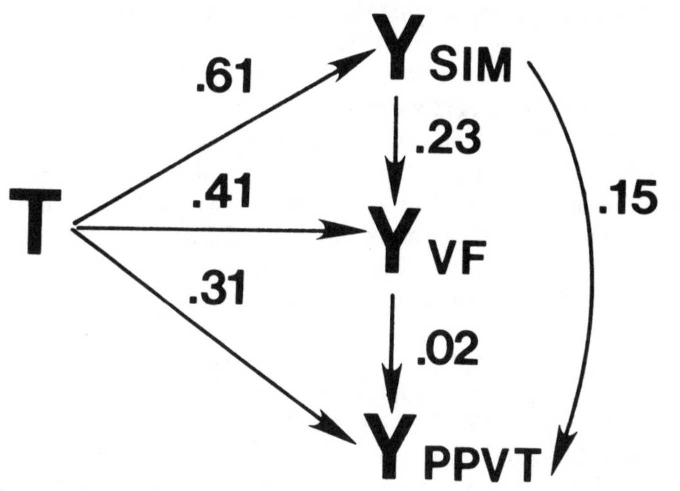

Figure 4.9

as a latent variable with multiple causes in addition to T_1 and T_2. Also, the latent variable *y* would be viewed as the sole common cause of Y_1, Y_2, and Y_3, so that the *U, V,* and *W* disturbance terms would not be allowed to correlate with one another. As a consequence of these changes from the discriminant analysis model, the LISREL test of factor means addresses a hypothesis that is different from the MANOVA hypothesis. Specifically, in the LISREL test of factor means the model stipulates that those observed variables with the largest factor loadings should display the largest group differences, because the underlying factor is the sole common cause of the *Y*s. For further details, the reader is referred to Sorbom (1974).

Numerical Example

Figures 4.7, 4.8, and 4.9 present the contrast between superior and severely disabled readers in the Fletcher and Satz (1980) study from the perspective of causal models. *T* is a dummy variable coded 0 for severely disabled readers and coded 1 for superior readers. In all cases, disturbance terms as well as any correlations among the disturbances have been omitted from the figures for simplicity.

Figure 4.7 presents the diagram corresponding to the overall MANOVA test (see Figure 4.1). The positive values of the paths from *T* to each *Y* variable indicate that the superior readers score higher on the average than the severely disabled readers on all six variables. All six paths are needed, because the overall MANOVA test and all six univariate tests are statistically significant.

Figure 4.8 presents the path representation for a discriminant analysis model with one factor (the maximum number for contrasting two groups). The path from *T* to *Y* is needed because there is a significant correlation between the dummy variable and discriminant variate. The paths from Y to each variable represent the respective CVCs. The figure shows that EF and SIM correlate most highly with the discriminant variate.

It might be expected that the group differences on specific verbal skills tests SIM and VF would subsume any differences on the general verbal IQ measure, PPVT. Figure 4.9 displays this step-down model for these data. The paths from *T* to PPVT and VF are both relatively large (0.31 and 0.41, respectively), and are statistically significant at the .05 level. They are also significant at the .025 level, if a Bonferroni adjustment is applied (Bock, 1975). Thus, group differences on the PPVT cannot be explained simply in terms of SIM and VF.

5. COMPLEX DESIGNS

In this section we will briefly discuss the use of MANOVA techniques in more complex research designs. Factorial MANOVAs, repeated measure designs, profile analysis, and multivariate analysis of covariance will be reviewed. Special issues for each of these topics will be discussed.

Higher-Order MANOVA

The extension of the techniques covered thus far to factorial design MANOVAs is generally straightforward. As with factorial designs in ANOVA, each main effect and interaction is tested separately. If the multivariate test of interaction is significant, multivariate tests of simple effects are typically conducted. In MANOVA this consists of performing a separate multivariate test for each effect. If a given effect is significant, it is further analyzed and interpreted using the techniques described in Section 3. If a specific effect is not significant, no further analyses are conducted.

For example, in a 3-way factorial design the first step is to test the 3-way interaction, then test the 3 2-way interactions, and finally test the 3 main effects. If any of the interactions are significant, the remaining lower-order effects are usually analyzed and interpreted in the context of the interactive effects of the factors (Kirk, 1982).

If all cells have equal sample sizes, the effects are orthogonal and can be tested individually. However, if the cell sizes are unequal, then the effects are nonorthogonal and the correlations between the effects must be considered in the analysis. See Appelbaum and Cramer (1974) for further discussion of these issues.

Repeated Measures Designs

In repeated measures designs or *within-subject designs*, multiple measures on each subject for different trials or times are collected using the same criterion variable at each trial or time. These criteria can be viewed as separate variables statistically and tested using MANOVA. A primary advantage of this design is that it controls for individual differences and often produces a more powerful test of the hypothesis than would a between-subject design. The traditional way to analyze this type of data is to use a mixed-model ANOVA (McCall and Appelbaum, 1973). However, there is a restrictive assumption that must be met or the mixed-model test will have an inflated alpha level (see Harris, 1975; Kirk, 1982; McCall and Appelbaum, 1973, for a discussion of these issues). The major assumption required by the mixed-model approach is that the variance-covariance matrix exhibit compound symmetry (Kirk, 1982), which most matrices resulting from social sciences data do not exhibit. This assumption is not required by the multivariate approach to repeated measures. In factorial designs there may be multiple within-subject factors and/or between-subject factors. Again, each effect is tested separately and further analyses are used to interpret the differences.

Profile Analysis

When a design consists of one or more between-subject factors and a within-subject factor, an alternate name sometimes given to the analysis is profile analysis (Morrison, 1976). The within-subject factor might be time, different scales on a test, or scores on a criterion measure under different conditions. In order for a profile analysis to be meaningful, the levels of the within-subject factor (i.e., the response variables) should be "commensurate," which means that they are measured in comparable units. When this condition is not met, the response variables should be thought of as conceptually distinct and a between-subject MANOVA should be performed on the set of dependent variables.

If the design is conceptualized as a 2-factor design, with one within-subject and one between-subject factor, 3 tests can be performed. The same 3 tests are conducted in a profile analysis. First is the test of the parallelism hypothesis, which asks whether the group profiles show the same pattern or shape across the different variables. This is equivalent to the test of the interaction between the classification and criterion variables. This question can be answered by forming p – 1 new variables (represented here by W), each of which represents the difference between two "adjacent" dependent variables, $W_i = Y_i - Y_{i+1}$. Parallelism is tested by performing a MANOVA on these $p - 1$ new variables. Notice that a significant result here implies that the difference between the variables are not the same for all groups, which in turn implies that the group profiles are not parallel.

The second test is of the levels hypothesis, which asks whether the profiles for the group means are at the same level. This is a univariate test, in which the dependent variable is the average of the *p* variables for each subject.

The third test is of the flatness hypothesis, which asks whether the "pooled" profile, ignoring group differences, is flat. In other words, this tests whether the *p* grand means (averaging over groups) on the criterion variables are identical to one another. If the parallelism hypothesis is rejected, then the other tests must be interpreted in light of the interaction between the within and between factors. Again, it should be noted that in order to perform a profile analysis, the criterion variables must all be on the same scale and must provide some meaningful conception of the subjects.

Doubly Multivariate Designs

An additional complexity that sometimes arises in repeated measures designs is that more than one qualitatively distinct variable is measured on more than one occasion. This type of design is often referred to as "doubly multivariate," because it is multivariate for two reasons. First, there are two or more conceptually distinct dependent variables. Second, each variable is measured more than once in a repeated measures fashion. Bock (1975: 502-505) discusses the analysis for this design.

It might be helpful at this point to give an example of an actual study that employed this design. Albright et al. (1984) were interested in comparing the physiological reactions of Type A and Type B coronary-prone behavior type individuals in stresssful situations. Their design consisted of two between-subject factors (behavior type and level of stress induced by the experimentor) and one within-subject factor (time). Two dependent measures (systolic blood pressure and heart rate) were obtained for each subject at each time, leading to a doubly multivariate design. A number of statistically significant results were obtained, the most interesting of which was a multivariate main effect for behavior type. Follow-up univariate tests failed to produce significance at the .05 level for either blood pressure or heart rate. As discussed in Sections 2 and 3, such a result is entirely possible, because there are situations in which the multivariate test is more powerful than the univariate tests.

Multivariate Analysis of Covariance

If one or more variables are collected to statistically control for sources of variation with multiple criterion variables, then multivariate analysis of covariance (MANCOVA) is the appropriate method of analysis. Although MANCOVA is a simple conceptual extension of ANCOVA, mathematically and practically it is much more complicated. In addition, there has been relatively little work investigating its use and properties.

Probably the most common design in which MANCOVA would be used is in a multiple-group pretest-posttest design, in which a set of variables has been measured both at the posttest and at the pretest. The reader is referred to Barcikowski (1983), Bock (1975), or Timm (1975) for further details of MANCOVA.

6. OVERVIEW OF COMPUTER PROGRAMS FOR MANOVA

Most of the overall and follow-up procedures we have described can be performed rather easily on a computer with widely available statistical packages. The purpose of this section is to provide a brief overview of capabilities of MANOVA programs. A caveat must be offered at the

TABLE 6.1
Capabilities of BMDP, SAS, and SPSS-X MANOVA Programs

	BMDP		SAS			SPSS-X
Capability	*P4V*	*P7M*	*GLM*	*ANOVA*	*CANDISC*	*MANOVA*
I. Omnibus Tests						
4 test statistics			✓[a]	✓[a]	✓	✓[a]
automatic processing of balanced (equal n) factorial design	✓		✓	✓		✓
unbalanced factorial design	✓		✓			✓
automatic processing of repeated measures designs	✓					✓
inspection of multivariate outliers		✓				
eigenvalues of He^{-1} matrix	✓	✓	✓	✓		✓
canonical correlations		✓			✓	✓
II. Analysis of Criterion Variables						
univariate F tests	✓	✓[b]	✓	✓	✓	✓
standardized discriminant weights	✓[f]	✓[f]			✓	✓
rotated discriminant weights						✓
canonical structure correlations					✓	✓
number of significant functions					✓[c]	✓[c]
plot of group centroids		✓				
insert measurement vectors						
step-down tests	✓[d]	✓	✓[d]			✓
F-to-remove		✓			✓[g]	✓[h]
III. Analysis of Classification Variables						
multivariate contrasts	✓	✓	✓			✓
univariate contrasts	✓	✓	✓	✓[e]		✓
IV. Analysis of Criterion and Classification Variables						
simultaneous confidence intervals						

NOTE: a = no p-value for GCR test; b = no p-values; c = partitioned-U test; d = requires successive ANCOVAs; e = pairwise comparisons only; f = raw coefficients only; g = available in PROC STEPDISC of SAS; h = available in SPSS-X DISCRIMINANT.

beginning, because major distributors of software packages constantly add enhancements to their programs. Thus, specific comparisons among programs may become dated rapidly. Nevertheless, it may be informative to consider the software options available for MANOVA as of this writing.

Although several special-purpose MANOVA packages are available, our review will cover only those MANOVA procedures available in BMDP, SAS, and SPSS-X, because these are the three most widely used statistical packages. Each of these packages has at least two procedures for performing MANOVA analyses. Table 6.1 shows some of the capabilities of two BMDP programs, three SAS programs, and one SPSS-X program. In addition to the general caveat mentioned above about changes in programs, we should also state that the capabilities in Table 6.1 are by no means the sole criteria for evaluating MANOVA software. Some obvious additional criteria are ease of use, quality and quantity of documentation, and accuracy of computational algorithms. Our much more limited purpose in Table 6.1 is simply to indicate whether specific techniques we have discussed are available in each of the programs. It should also be noted that other programs performing some special cases of MANOVA are BMDP3D in BMDP, STEPDISC in SAS, and DISCRIMINANT in SPSS-X. Also, additional comparisons of analysis of variance programs appear in Hosking and Hamer (1979) and Tabachnick and Fidell (1983). One other useful reference is Barcikowski (1983), which is a 3-volume collection of annotated input and output of analysis of variance programs. One volume is devoted to BMDP, a second to SAS, and a third to SPSS-X.

Finally, programs have recently become available for performing MANOVA analyses on microcomputers. Although the list of available programs is certain to grow, two programs available as of this writing that are quite impressive are GANOVA and SYSTAT. GANOVA is described in the February 1984 issue of *The American Statistician.* SYSTAT is one of 24 microcomputer statistical packages reviewed in the April 1984 issue of *BYTE* magazine. Further information on these programs is available from the authors of these reviews, whose addresses are given in the aforementioned publications. Also of significance is that BMDP recently announced that its entire set of programs will be available for the IBM personal computer and compatibles.

REFERENCES

ALBRIGHT, C., R. I. EVANS, S. E. MAXWELL, and R. DEMBROSKI (1984) "Relationship between Type A coronary prone behavior and physiological reactivity during an anxiety-provoking verbal task." (unpublished manuscript)

ANDERSON, T. W. (1958) An Introduction to Multivariate Statistical Analysis. New York: John Wiley.

APPELBAUM, M. I. and E. M. CRAMER (1974) "Some problems in the nonorthogonal analysis of variance." Psychological Bulletin 81: 335-343.

ASHER, H. B. (1976) Causal Modeling. Beverly Hills, CA: Sage.

BAGOZZI, R. P., C. FORNELL, and D. F. LARCKER (1981) "Canonical correlation analysis as a special case of a structural relations model." Multivariate Behavioral Research 16: 437-454.

BARCIKOWSKI, R. S. [ed.] (1983) Computer Packages and Research Design with Annotations of Input and Output from the BMDP, SAS, SPSS, and SPSSX Statistical Packages. Washington, DC: University Press of America.

———and J. P. STEVENS (1975) "A Monte Carlo study of the stability of canonical correlations, canonical weights, and canonical variate variable correlations." Multivariate Behavioral Research 10: 353-364.

BARGMAN, R. E. (1970) "Interpretation and use of a generalized discriminant function," in R. C. Bose et al. (eds.) Essays in Probability and Statistics. Chapel Hill: University of North Carolina Press.

BARTLETT, M. S. (1947) "Multivariate analysis." Journal of the Royal Statistical Society Supplement, Series B 9: 176-197.

BENTLER, P. M. (1980) "Multivariate analysis with latent variables: causal modeling." Annual Review of Psychology 31: 419-456.

BIRD, K. D. (1975) "Simultaneous contrast testing procedures for multivariate experiments." Multivariate Behavioral Research 10: 343-351.

———and D. HADZI-PAVLOVIC (1983) "Simultaneous test procedures and the choice of a test statistic in MANOVA." Psychological Bulletin 93: 167-178.

BLALOCK, H. M. (1969) Theory Construction. Englewood Cliffs, NJ: Prentice-Hall.

BOCK, R. D. (1975) Multivariate Statistical Methods in Behavioral Research. New York: McGraw-Hill.

———and E. A. HAGGARD (1968) "The use of multivariate analysis of variance in behavioral research," in D. Whitla (ed.) Handbook of Measurement and Assessment Sciences. Reading, MA: Addison-Wesley.

BORGAN, F. H. and M. J. SELIG (1978) "Uses of discriminate analysis following MANOVA: multivariate statistics for multivariate purposes." Journal of Applied Psychology 63: 689-697.

BRAY, J. H. and S. E. MAXWELL (1982) "Analyzing and interpreting significant MANOVAs." Review of Educational Research 52: 340-367.

CARROLL, J. B. (1961) "The nature of the data, or how to choose a correlation coefficient." Psychometrika 26: 347-372.

CHOU, K. J. and R. J. MUIRHEAD (1979) "On some distribution problems in MANOVA and discriminant analysis." Journal of Multivariate Analysis 9: 410-419.

COLE, D. A., G. S. HOWARD, and S. E. MAXWELL (1981) "Effects of mono- versus multiple-operationalization in construct validation efforts." Journal of Consulting and Clinical Psychology 49: 395.

COOLEY, W. W. and P. R. LOHNES (1971) Multivariate Data Analysis. New York: John Wiley.

CRAMER, E. M. and R. D. BOCK (1966) "Multivariate analysis." Review of Educational Research 36: 604-617.

CRAMER, E. M. and W. A. NICEWANDER (1979) "Some symmetric, invariant measures of multivariate association." Psychometrika 44: 43-54.

DARLINGTON, R. B. (1968) "Multiple regression in psychological research and practice." Psychological Bulletin 69: 161-182.

———S. L. WEINBERG, and H. J. WALBERG (1973) "Canonical variate analysis and related techniques." Review of Educational Research 43: 443-454.

DUNCAN, O. D. (1975) Introduction to Structural Equation Models. New York: Academic.

DWYER, J. H. (1983) Statistical Models for the Social and Behavioral Sciences. New York: Oxford University Press.

EVERITT, B. S. (1978) Graphical Techniques for Multivariate Data. London: Heineman Educational Books.

FINN, J. D. (1974) A General Model for Multivariate Analysis. New York: Holt, Rinehart & Winston.

FLETCHER, J. M., W. J. RICE, and R. M. RAY (1978) "Linear discriminant function analysis in neuropsychological research: some uses and abuses." Cortex 14: 564-577.

GABRIEL, R. M. (1979) "Post-MANOVA data analysis: six alternatives and criteria for selection." Presented at the American Psychological Association, New York.

GNANADESIKAN, R. (1977) Methods for Statistical Data of Multivariate Observations. New York: John Wiley.

GREEN, P. E. (1978) Analyzing Multivariate Data. Hinsdale, IL: Dryden Press.

———and J. D. CARROLL (1976) Mathematical Tools for Applied Multivariate Analysis. New York: Academic.

HAKSTIAN, A. R., J. C. ROED, and J. C. LIND (1979) "Two-sample T2 procedure and the assumption of homogeneous covariance matrices." Psychological Bulletin 86: 1255-1263.

HARRIS, R. J. (1976) "The invalidity of partitioned-U tests in canonical correlation and multivariate analysis of variance." Multivariate Behavioral Research 11: 353-365.

———(1975) A Primer of Multivariate Statistics. New York: Academic.

HAUSER, R. M. and A. S. GOLDBERGER (1977) "The treatment of unobservable variables in path analysis," in H. L. Costner (ed.) Sociological Methodology, 1977. San Francisco: Jossey-Bass.

HOSKING, J. D. and R. M. HAMER (1979) "Nonorthogonal analysis of variance programs: an evaluation." Journal of Educational Statistics 4: 161-188.

HUBERTY, C. J. (1984) "Issues in the use and interpretation of discriminant analysis." Psychological Bulletin 95: 156-171.

———(1976) "The stability of three indices of variable contribution in discriminant analysis." Journal of Experimental Education 45.

———(1975) "Discriminant analysis." Review of Educational Research 45: 543-598.

———and J. D. SMITH (1982) "The study of MANOVA effects." Multivariate Behavioral Research 17: 417-432.

ITO, P. K. (1980) "Robustness of ANOVA and MANOVA test procedures," in P. R. Krishnaiah (ed.) Handbook of Statistics, Volume 1: Analysis of Variance. New York: Elsevier North Holland.

———(1969) "On the effect of heteroscedasticity and nonnormality upon some multivariate test procedures," in P. R. Krishnaiah (ed.) Multivariate Analysis, Volume 2. New York: Academic.

HUMMEL, T. J. and J. R. SLIGO (1971) "Empirical comparison of univariate and multivariate analyses of variance procedures." Psychological Bulletin 75: 49-57.

JOHNSON, R. and D. WICHERN (1982) Applied Multivariate Statistical Analysis. Englewood Cliffs, NJ: Prentice-Hall.

JONES, L. V. (1966) "Analysis of variance in its multivariate developments," in R. B. Cattell (ed.) Handbook of Multivariate Experimental Psychology. Chicago: Rand McNally.

JORESKOG, K. G., (1978) "Structural analysis of covariance and correlation matrices." Psychometrika 43: 443-477.

———and A. S. GOLDBERGER (1975) "Estimation of a model with multiple indicators and multiple causes of a single latent variable." Journal of the American Statistical Association 70: 631-639.

JORESKOG, K. G. and D. SORBOM (1983) LISREL VI. Chicago: National Educational Resources.

KAPLAN, R. M. and A. J. LITROWNIK (1717) "Some statistical methods for the assessment of multiple outcome criteria in behavioral research." Behavior Therapy 8: 383-392.

KENNY, D. A. (1979) Correlation and Causality. New York: John Wiley.

KIRK, R. E. (1982) Experimental Design. Belmont, CA: Brooks/Cole.

KNAPP, T. R. (1978) "Canonical correlation analysis: a general parametric significance-testing system." Psychological Bulletin 85: 410-416.

LARRABEE, M. J. (1982) "Reexamination of a plea for multivariate analyses." Journal of Counseling Psychology 29: 180-188.

LARZELERE, R. E. and S. A. MULAIK (1977) "Single-sample tests for many correlations." Psychological Bulletin 84: 557-569.

LEARY, M. R. and E. M. ALTMAIER (1980) "Type I error in counseling research: a plea for multivariate analyses." Journal of Counseling Psychology 27: 611-615.

MARASCUILO, L. A. and J. R. LEVIN (1983) Multivariate Statistics in the Social Sciences: A Researcher's Guide. Belmont, CA: Brooks/Cole.

MARDIA, K. V. (1971) "The effects of nonnormality on some multivariate tests and robustness to nonnormality in the linear model." Biometrika 58: 105-121.

MAXWELL, S. E., R. D. ARVEY, and C. J. CAMP (1981) "Measures of strength of association: a comparative examination." Journal of Applied Psychology 66: 525-534.

McCALL, R. B. and M. E. APPELBAUM (1973) "Bias in the analysis of repeated-measures designs: some alternative approaches." Child Development 44: 401-415.

MENDOZA, J. L., V. H. MARKOS, and R. GONTER (1978) "A new perspective on sequential testing procedures in canonical analysis: a Monte Carlo evaluation." Multivariate Behavioral Research 13: 371-382.

MEREDITH, W. (1964) "Canonical correlation with fallible data." Psychometrika 29: 55-65.

MILLER, R. P. (1966) Simultaneous Statistical Inferences. New York: McGraw-Hill.

MORRISON, D. F. (1976) Multivariate Statistical Methods. New York: McGraw-Hill.

MULAIK, S. A. (1975) "Confirmatory factory analysis," in D. J. Amick and H. J. Walberg (eds.) Introductory Multivariate Analysis for Educational, Psychological, and Social Research. Berkeley, CA: McCutchan.

MULLER, K. E. and B. L. PETERSON (1984) "Power analysis for multivariate linear models: new results and SAS makes it practical," in 1984 SUGI Proceedings. Cary, NC: SAS Institute.

NAMBOODIRI, K. (1984) Matrix Algebra: An Introduction. Beverly Hills, CA: Sage.

O'GRADY, K. E. (1978) "Comments on 'some statistical methods for the assessment of multiple outcome criteria in behavioral research.' " Behavior Therapy 9: 471-473.

OLSON, C. L. (1979) "Practical considerations in choosing a MANOVA test statistic: a rejoinder to Stevens." Psychological Bulletin 86: 1350-1352.

———(1976) "On choosing a test statistic in multivariate analysis of variance." Psychological Bulletin 83: 579-586.

———(1974) "Comparative robustness of six tests in multivariate analysis of variance." Journal of the American Statistical Association 69: 894-908.

OVERALL, J. E. and C. J. KLETT (1972) Applied Multivariate Analysis. New York: McGraw-Hill.

PILLAI, K.C.S. (1960) Statistical Tables for Tests of Multivariate Hypotheses. Manila: University of the Philippines, Statistical Center.

POREBSKI, O. R. (1966a) "On the interrelated nature of the multivariate statistics used in discriminatory analysis." British Journal of Mathematical and Statistical Psychology 19: 197-214.

———(1966b) "Discriminatory and canonical analysis of technical college data." British Journal of Mathematical and Statistical Psychology 19: 215-236.

PRUZEK, R. M. (1971) "Methods and problems in the analysis of multivariate data." Review of Educational Research 41: 163-190.

RAMSEY, P. H. (1982) "Empirical power of procedures for comparing two groups on *p* variables." Journal of Educational Statistics 7: 139-156.

———(1980) "Choosing the most powerful pairwise multiple comparison procedure in multivariate analysis of variance." Journal of Applied Psychology 65: 317-326.

RAO, C. R. (1951) "An asymptotic expansion of the distribution of Wilks' criterion." Bulletin of the International Statistics Institute 33: 177-180.

RODGER, R. S. (1973) "Confidence intervals for multiple comparisons and the misuse of the Bonferroni inequality." British Journal of Mathematical and Statistical Psychology 26: 58-60.

ROY, J. (1958) "Step-down procedure in multivariate analysis." Annuals of Mathematical Statistics 29: 1177-1187.

———and R. E. BARGMANN (1958) "Test of multiple independence and the associated confidence bounds." Annuals of Mathematical Statistics 29: 491-503.

SERLIN, R. C. (1982) "A multivariate measure of association based on the Pillai-Bartlett procedure." Psychological Bulletin 91: 413-417.

SPECTOR, P. E. (1980) "Redundancy and dimensionality as determinants of data analytic strategies in multivariate analysis of variance." Journal of Applied Psychology 65: 237-239.

———(1977) "What to do with significant multivariate effects in multivariate analyses of variance." Journal of Applied Psychology 62: 158-163.

STEVENS, J. P. (1984) "An easily implemented graphical test for multivariate normality." (unpublished manuscript)

——(1980) "Power of the multivariate analysis of variance tests." Psychological Bulletin 88: 728-737.

———(1979) "Comment on Olson: on choosing a test statistic in multivariate analysis of variance." Psychological Bulletin 86: 355-360.

———(1973) "Step-down analyses and simultaneous confidence intervals in MANOVA." Multivariate Behavioral Research 8: 391-402.

———(1972) "Four methods of analyzing between variation for the K-Group MANOVA problem." Multivariate Behavioral Research 7: 499-522.

STRAHAN, R. I. (1982) "Multivariate analysis and the problem of Type I error." Journal of Counseling Psychology 29: 175-179.

TATSUOKA, M. M. (1977) "Review of Multivariate Statistical Methods in Behavioral Research by R. D. Bock." Applied Psychological Measurement 1: 457-461.

———(1973) "Multivariate analysis in educational research," in F. N. Kerlinger (ed.) Review of Research in Education. Itasca, IL: Peacock.

———(1971) Multivariate Analysis: Techniques for Educational and Psychological Research. New York: John Wiley.

———(1970) Discriminant Analysis: The Study of Group Differences. Champaign, IL: IPAT.

———(1969) "Multivariate analysis." Review of Educational Research 39: 739-743.

THOMPSON, B. (forthcoming) Canonical Correlation. Beverly Hills, CA: Sage.

THORNDIKE, R. M. and D. J. WEISS (1973) "A study of the stability of canonical correlations and canonical components." Educational and Psychological Measurements 33: 123-134.

TIMM, N. H. (1975) Multivariate Analysis: With Applications in Education and Psychology. Belmont, CA: Brooks/Cole.

VAN DE GEER, J. P. (1971) Introduction to Multivariate Analysis for the Social Sciences. San Francisco: Freeman.

WILKINSON, L. (1975) "Response variable hypothesis in the multivariate analysis of variance." Psychological Bulletin 82: 408-412.

YAO, Y. (1965) "An approximate degrees of freedom solution to the multivariate Behrens-Fisher problem." Biometrika 52: 139-147.

INDEX

ABOUT THE EDITOR

MICHAEL S. LEWIS-BECK, Professor of Political Science at the University of Iowa, received his Ph.D. from the University of Michigan. Currently, in addition to editing the Sage monograph series *Quantitative Applications in the Social Sciences (QASS),* he is editor of the *American Journal of Political Science*. He has authored or coauthored numerous books and articles, including *Applied Regression: An Introduction*, *New Tools for Social Scientists: Advances and Applications in Research Methods*, *Economics and Elections: The Major Western Democracies*, and *Forecasting Elections*. In addition to his work at the University of Iowa, he has taught quantitative methods courses at the Inter-University Consortium for Political and Social Research (ICPSR) Summer Program at the University of Michigan and The European Consortium for Political Research (ECPR) Summer Program at the University of Essex. Also, he has held visiting appointments at the Catholic University in Lima, Peru and the University of Paris I (Sorbonne) in France.

ABOUT THE AUTHORS

OLLI T. AHTOLA was Assistant Professor of Marketing at the University of Florida. He is a member of the editorial board of the *Journal of Marketing.* His articles have appeared in such professional publications as *Journal of Marketing Research, Journal of Consumer Research,* and *Journal of Population.* His interests include the development of models to predict and understand consumer attitudes, intentions, and purchase behavior.

JAMES H. BRAY is Associate Professor of Psychology at Texas Woman's University, Houston Center. His doctorate is in clinical psychology, with a minor in research methodology. His research interests include applied statistics, clinical research methodology, and family studies and development. He is the author of several articles appearing in publications such as *Review of Educational Research, Journal of Educational Psychology,* and *Journal of Marital and Family Therapy.*

STEVEN R. BROWN is Professor of Political Science at Kent State University. He received his Ph.D. from the University of Missouri-Columbia, where he studied experimentation under Gary Krause and the late William Stephenson. He is currently involved in research in political psychology, the policy sciences, literary criticism, and the emerging field of human subjectivity.

GUDMUND R. IVERSEN, Professor of Statistics and a statistician at the Center for Social and Policy Studies, Swarthmore College, received his Ph.D. in statistics from Harvard University. His articles have appeared in several scholarly journals, including *Public Opinion Quarterly, Psychometrika, World Politics, American Journal of Sociology,* and *American*

Statistician. He is the author of an introductory statistics text for sociology and a coauthor of a book on statistical analysis of individual and group data in addition to the text on Bayesian statistical inference in this series.

SCOTT E. MAXWELL is Associate Professor of Psychology at the University of Notre Dame. He has also taught at the University of Houston, University of North Carolina, and Duke University. His research interests include applied statistics and research methodology. He is the author of numerous articles appearing in publications such as *Review of Educational Research, Annual Review of Psychology,* and *Psychological Bulletin.*

LAWRENCE E. MELAMED is a Professor in the Department of Psychology at Kent State University. He received his Ph.D. from the University of Wisconsin where he studied experimental design under the late David A. Grant. His current research interests focus on the analysis of large data sets in longitudinal research in clinical neuropsychology and in the development of diagnostic instruments in this same field.

HELMUT NORPOTH, Professor of Political Science at the State University of New York at Stony Brook, received his Ph.D. in political science from the University of Michigan. His articles have appeared in several scholarly journals, including *American Political Science Review, American Journal of Political Science Review,* and *Political Behavior.* His work deals largely with public opinion and electoral behavior.

PAUL E. SPECTOR is currently Research Associate at the Florida Mental Health Institute in Tampa and holds a faculty appointment at the University of South Florida. He has taught both psychology and business administration and has been a mental center program evaluator. He has published in the areas of statistics, psychological measurement, organizational psychology, social psychology, and program evaluation.

ALBERT R. WILDT was Associate Professor of Marketing at the University of Georgia, on leave of absence from the University of Florida. He is a member of the editorial boards of the *Journal of Marketing* and the *Journal of Marketing Research.* His articles have appeared in several scholarly journals, including the *Journal of Marketing Research, Management Science,* and the *Journal of Consumer Research.*

*These biographical statements include updated information whenever possible. Otherwise they are as originally published.